ZAGATSURVEY®

1998

BOSTON
RESTAURANTS

**Edited by Al Stankus
and Jane Heald Lavine**

Published and distributed by
ZAGAT SURVEY, LLC
4 Columbus Circle
New York, New York 10019
Tel: 212 977 6000
E-mail: zagat@zagatsurvey.com

Acknowledgments

We gratefully acknowledge the assistance of the following people and organizations: Rebecca Alssid, American Institute of Wine & Food (Boston Chapter Board), Robert Birnbaum/Stuff Magazine, Boston Sports Club, Brookline Animal Care Center, Kurt Cassidy, Brenda Davies, Nona Dreyer, Fahey & Formaggio, Jerry Finegold, Michele Fishel, Susan Flynn, Formaggio Kitchen, Julie Waters Fox, Karen Golov/Eye of the Needle, Ihsan Gurdal, Christopher Hilton, Kitchen Arts, Charles Lavine/NPC Computer Corp., Bob Levey, Karen Levine, Karen Marshall, Mirtha Mateo, Lisa and Michael Mindick, Robert Montague/Personal Investments, Merry Morse, Nantucket Gourmet, Louise Natenshon, Party Favors, Rosemarie Peele/Williams Sonoma, Stephanie Pfeffer, Matthew Rovner, Ron Sarni/Sarni Dry Cleaners, Sally Saunders, Terry Schubach, Seattle's Best Coffee, Melissa Silk, Joan R. Stankus, Paul Stankus, Martha Stark, Debra Stark/Natural Gourmet, Carol Stearns, Linda Wartow, Leni Webber, Barry Weisman, Wellesley Cheese Shop, Laura Wernick, WGBH/Channel 2 Auction, Wulf's Fish Market; without your help, this *Survey* would not have been possible.

Contents

Introduction 5

Foreword 6

Key to Ratings/Symbols 8

Map 10

Boston's Favorite Restaurants 11

Top Ratings
- Food and by Cuisine.................... 12
- Decor, Outdoor, Romantic,
  Views, Service......................... 16

Best Buys................................. 18

**ALPHABETICAL DIRECTORY,
RATINGS AND REVIEWS**
- **Boston** 21
- **Cape Cod** 126
- **Martha's Vineyard**................. 129
- **Nantucket** 130
- **Rhode Island**...................... 132
- **New Hampshire and Maine** 135

INDEXES
- **Types of Cuisine** 140
- **Neighborhood Locations** 149
- Breakfast 157
- Brunch 157
- Buffet Served 157
- Business Dining 158
- BYO 158
- Caters............................... 158
- Dancing/Entertainment 159
- Delivers/Takeout..................... 160
- Dessert/Ice Cream.................... 162
- Dining Alone 162
- Fireplaces........................... 162
- Game in Season 163
- Health/Spa Menus 163
- Historic Interest..................... 164
- Hotel Dining......................... 164
- "In" Places.......................... 165
- Jacket Required 165
- Late Late – After 12:30 165
- Noteworthy Newcomers/Closings 166
- Offbeat.............................. 166
- Outdoor Dining....................... 167
- Outstanding Views 168
- Parking/Valet........................ 168

- Parties & Private Rooms. 171
- People-Watching/Power Scenes 173
- Pre-Theater Dining 173
- Post-Theater Dining 173
- Prix Fixe Menus. 174
- Pubs/Bars/Microbreweries 174
- Quiet Conversation 174
- Reservations Essential 175
- Romantic Spots. 175
- Saturday/Sunday Best Bets 176
- Senior Appeal 181
- Singles Scenes 181
- Sleepers/Teflons 181
- Smoking Prohibited 182
- Teenagers & Other Youthful Spirits 184
- Visitors on Expense Accounts 184
- Wheelchair Access 184
- Wine/Beer Only 184
- Winning Wine Lists. 186
- Worth a Trip. 186
- Young Children 186

Wine Chart. 188

Introduction

Here are the results of our *1998 Boston Restaurant Survey* covering some 821 restaurants in the Boston area, including Cape Cod, Martha's Vineyard, Nantucket, Rhode Island, New Hampshire and Maine.

By regularly surveying large numbers of local restaurant-goers, we think we have achieved a uniquely current and reliable guide. We hope you agree. Nearly 2,300 people participated. Since the participants dined out an average of 3.2 times per week, this *Survey* is based on about 1,000 meals per day.

We want to thank each of our participants. They are a widely diverse group in all respects but one – they are food lovers all. This book is really "theirs."

Of the surveyors, 57% are women, 43% are men; the breakdown by age is 18% in their 20s, 30% in their 30s, 23% in their 40s, 20% in their 50s and 9% in their 60s or above.

To help guide our readers to Boston's best meals and best buys, we have prepared a number of lists. See, for example, Boston's Favorite Restaurants (page 11), Top Ratings (pages 12–17) and Best Buys (pages 18–19). On the assumption that most people want a quick fix on the places at which they are considering eating, we have tried to be concise and to provide handy indexes.

We are particularly grateful to our editors, Al Stankus, restaurant critic and wine writer for *Boston Tab*, food contributor to the *Boston Herald* and cookbook author, and Jane Heald Lavine, food and restaurant consultant, member of the National Board of Directors of the American Institute of Wine & Food and a partner of Abracadabra, a Boston-based corporate and private event planning concern.

We invite you to be a reviewer in our next *Survey*. To do so, simply send a stamped, self-addressed, business-size envelope to ZAGAT SURVEY, 4 Columbus Circle, New York, NY 10019, so that we will be able to contact you. Each participant will receive a free copy of the next *Boston Restaurant Survey* when it is published.

Your comments, suggestions and even criticisms of this *Survey* are also solicited. There is always room for improvement with your help.

New York, New York   Nina and Tim Zagat
December 17, 1997

Foreword

Burgeoning is the word we used to describe the local restaurant scene in the foreword to our last *Boston Survey*. Today, terms like white hot, steaming, booming and any other synonyms are more fitting.

The economy is hot and dining out is in. Bostonians have made restaurant-going one of the city's most talked-about activities. When a newcomer like La Bettola, Mistral, Restaurant Clio or Restaurant Zinc opens, word spreads so quickly that reservations for the next three weekends are gobbled up. But this is not a city of fair weather diners who simply follow the prevailing winds – just try booking a Saturday reservation at venerable favorites like Biba, Hamersley's Bistro or Il Capriccio.

Along with the renewed interest in restaurants has come a shift in focus. For the past few years, many new ventures were designed to serve as good value neighborhood restaurants – places like Antico Forno, Chez Henri, Flora and Metropolis Cafe. While they still earn high ratings from our voters, the *1998 Survey* reveals that dining as theater, à la mid-'80s, has made a comeback. A prime example is Mistral; before the local food press had even reviewed its cuisine, a fashion writer at the *Boston Globe* wrote a two-page story on the scene at this sizzling, upscale spot. The atmosphere is equally happening at Restaurant Zinc, where singles especially like to eat at the handsome bar.

Of course, the renaissance of glamour and sophistication doesn't mean Bostonians have lost their taste for simpler dining. Indeed, diversity is one of the strengths of Boston's restaurant scene, which offers options that reflect the city's demographics and suit a wide range of spending patterns and lifestyles. Thus, for example, the growth and popularity of Irish pubs show no signs of slowing down. High scores for Matt Murphy's Pub in Brookline belie the simplicity of the operation, while places like The Burren in Somerville provide good grub to go with the good Guinness.

In the same vein, Asian restaurants are packed within days of opening, drawing curious diners eager to explore new tastes. In Chinatown, Chau Chow City fills three floors with diners ready to chow down on dim sum, seafood and more. Nearby, Jae Chung of Jae's Cafe & Grill has added a new Theater District branch to his Pan-Asian empire. Further afield, Ducky Wok, with its big fish tanks and Hong Kong–trained chef, offers a real Chinatown feeling in hardscrabble Allston. In Brookline, Pandan Leaf brings Malaysian tastes into the former Zuxuz, while in Brookline Village, Bok Choy strikes a refined chord with its menu of New Wave Pan-Asian fare.

The explosion in Asian restaurants, many of which offer a range of vegetarian options and emphasize fish, soups and other lighter fare, means we've never seen more healthy choices on menus. On the flip side, those who want a martini and a big steak followed by a cigar and cognac can find it at a growing number of places, including the luxurious new Plaza III – The Kansas City Steakhouse in Faneuil Hall. The sophisticated Oak Room in the Fairmont Copley Plaza hotel is another red meat mecca, as are the Capital Grille, Grill 23 & Bar, Morton's of Chicago and The Palm. And speaking of cigars, they're everywhere, to the delight of stogie fans and the chagrin of those who complain of "too much smoke." The market will ultimately determine which side wins.

Not surprisingly, many of the aforementioned steakhouses carry a rather hefty tab, as do some of the city's posher newcomers. Yet the average per-meal cost reported by surveyors actually dropped slightly to $21.76 (down from $21.83 in our last *Survey*), making Boston a relative bargain compared to East Coast neighbors like New York ($30.69), Philadelphia ($24.81) and Washington, D.C. ($24.49). The same holds true when you look at the average cost of the city's 20 most expensive restaurants: $46.78, comfortably lower than the corresponding figure in New York ($69.33), Philadelphia ($51.98) and Washington, D.C. ($50.67).

Unfortunately, all this good news is tempered with some sad developments. Harvest, one of the linchpins in the Boston restaurant resurgence and the starting ground for numerous chefs, is shuttered. Likewise, Amigos del Norte, Azita, Bentonwood Bakery Cafe, Cornucopia, Felucca, Grill & Cue, The Noodle Bar, Pampas, St. Botolph, Wild Ginger and Zuxuz are also gone from the scene. However, over half of these spaces have welcomed or are in the process of welcoming new restaurant tenants who feel the stove is still hot enough to support their concept. And different concepts are what dining is really all about these days.

In sum, this *Survey* shows that the energy level and quality of the Boston restaurant scene have never been greater. It also shows that after years of being shrouded in a dowdy wardrobe, Boston dining is quite fashionable. We hope this guide will lead you to some of its most appetizing aspects.

Boston, MA
December 17, 1997

Al Stankus
Jane Heald Lavine

Key to Ratings/Symbols

This sample entry identifies the various types of information contained in your Zagat Survey.

(1) Restaurant Name, Address & Phone Number

(2) Hours & Credit Cards

(3) ZAGAT Ratings

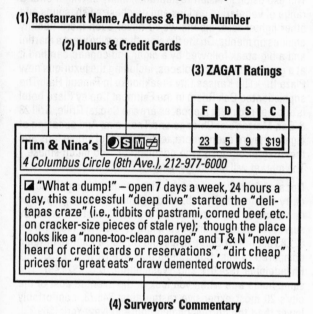

F	D	S	C
23	5	9	$19

Tim & Nina's ◗ⓈⓂ⊅

4 Columbus Circle (8th Ave.), 212-977-6000

◪ "What a dump!" – open 7 days a week, 24 hours a day, this successful "deep dive" started the "deli-tapas craze" (i.e., tidbits of pastrami, corned beef, etc. on cracker-size pieces of stale rye); though the place looks like a "none-too-clean garage" and T & N "never heard of credit cards or reservations", "dirt cheap" prices for "great eats" draw demented crowds.

(4) Surveyors' Commentary

The names of restaurants with the highest overall ratings, greatest popularity and importance are printed in **CAPITAL LETTERS**. Address and phone numbers are printed in *italics*.

(2) Hours & Credit Cards

After each restaurant name you will find the following courtesy information:

◗ .... *serving after 11 PM*

Ⓢ .... *open on Sunday*

Ⓜ .... *open on Monday*

⊅ .... *no credit cards accepted*

(3) ZAGAT Ratings

Food, **Decor** and **Service** are each rated on a scale of **0** to **30**:

F	D	S	C

F .... *Food*
D .... *Decor*
S .... *Service*
C .... *Cost*

23	5	9	$19

0 - 9	.... *poor to fair*
10 - 15	.... *fair to good*
16 - 19	.... *good to very good*
20 - 25	.... *very good to excellent*
26 - 30	.... *extraordinary to perfection*

▽ 23	5	9	$19

▽ .... *Low number of votes/less reliable*

The **Cost (C)** column reflects the estimated price of a dinner with one drink and tip. Lunch usually costs 25% less.

A restaurant listed without ratings is either an important **newcomer** or a popular **write-in**. The estimated cost, with one drink and tip, is indicated by the following symbols.

–	–	–	VE

I .... *$15 and below*
M .... *$16 to $30*
E .... *$31 to $50*
VE .... *$51 or more*

(4) Surveyors' Commentary

Surveyors' comments are summarized, with literal comments shown in quotation marks. The following symbols indicate whether responses were mixed or uniform.

◨ .... *mixed*
◼ .... *uniform*

9

Boston's Favorites

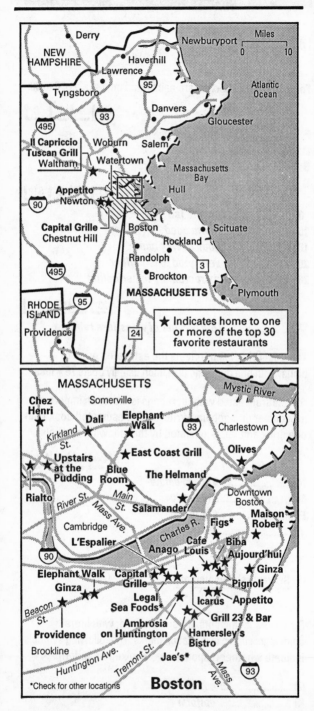

Map 1 (Greater Boston region)

NEW HAMPSHIRE

Derry
Newburyport
Haverhill
Lawrence
95
Tyngsboro
93
Danvers
495
Woburn
Salem
Gloucester
Il Capriccio
Tuscan Grill
Waltham
Watertown
★
Massachusetts
Bay
Appetito
Newton ★★
90
Hull
Capital Grille
Chestnut Hill
Boston
Scituate
Rockland
Randolph
3
Brockton
Plymouth
495
MASSACHUSETTS
95
24
RHODE
ISLAND
Providence

Atlantic
Ocean

Miles
0   10

★ Indicates home to one
or more of the top 30
favorite restaurants

Map 2 (Boston / Cambridge detail)

MASSACHUSETTS

Mystic River

Somerville
Chez Henri ★
Dali ★
Elephant Walk ★
93
Charlestown
1
Kirkland St.
★ **East Coast Grill**
Olives ★
Upstairs at the Pudding ★
Blue Room ★
The Helmand ★
★ ★
River St.
Rialto
Main St.
Salamander ★
Downtown
Boston
Cambridge
Mass Ave.
Charles R.
Figs* ★
Maison Robert
L'Espalier ★
Anago
Cafe Louis ★
Biba
Aujourd'hui
90
★★
Ginza
Elephant Walk
Ginza ★ ★★
Capital Grille ★★★
★★ **Pignoli**
Icarus **Appetito**
Beacon St.
Legal Sea Foods* ★
★★
Grill 23 & Bar
Providence
Brookline
Ambrosia on Huntington
★
Hamersley's Bistro
Huntington Ave.
Tremont St.
Jae's*
Mass Ave.
93

*Check for other locations
Boston

Boston's Favorite Restaurants

Each of our reviewers has been asked to name his or her five favorite restaurants. The 40 spots most frequently named, in order of their popularity, are:

1. Olives
2. Aujourd'hui
3. Hamersley's Bistro
4. Rialto
5. Elephant Walk
6. Biba
7. Ambrosia on Huntington
8. Salamander
9. L'Espalier
10. Icarus
11. Jae's Cafe & Grill
12. Legal Sea Foods
13. Dali
14. East Coast Grill
15. Capital Grille
16. Pignoli
17. Grill 23 & Bar
18. Il Capriccio
19. Cafe Louis
20. Figs
21. Tuscan Grill
22. Blue Room
23. Chez Henri
24. Maison Robert
25. Appetito
26. Providence
27. Upstairs at the Pudding
28. Ginza
29. Anago
30. Helmand
31. Rowes Wharf
32. Julien
33. Bay Tower Room
34. Cheesecake Factory
35. Stellina
36. Henrietta's Table
37. Locke-Ober Cafe
38. Caffe Bella
39. Metropolis Cafe
40. Lala Rokh

It's obvious that many of the restaurants on the above list are among the most expensive, but Bostonians also love a bargain. Were popularity calibrated to price, we suspect that a number of other restaurants would join the above ranks. Thus, we have listed over 100 Best Buys on pages 18–19.

Top Ratings*

Top 40 Food Ranking

28 Aujourd'hui	Metropolis Cafe
L'Espalier	Ambrosia on Huntington
Olives	Rowes Wharf
27 Hamersley's Bistro	Tuscan Grill
Saporito's	Seasons
Rialto	Brown Sugar Cafe
Caffe Bella	Bristol
26 Julien	R Place
Il Capriccio	Pomodoro
White Rainbow	**24** Maison Robert
Morton's of Chicago	Grapevine
Marcuccio's	Helmand
Cafe Louis	Pignoli
Grill 23 & Bar	Red Raven's
Ginza	Silks
Icarus	Galleria Italiana
Salamander	Elephant Walk
Terramia	Matt Murphy's Pub
25 Anago	Cranebrook Tea Room
Biba	Dali

Top Spots by Cuisine

Top American (New)
28 Aujourd'hui
27 Hamersley's Bistro
26 White Rainbow
      Icarus
25 Seasons

Top American (Reg./Trad.)
26 Grill 23 & Bar
25 Rowes Wharf
24 Cranebrook Tea Room
      Capital Grille
23 Blue Ribbon BBQ

Top Asian/Fusion
26 Salamander
25 Ambrosia on Huntington
24 Elephant Walk
23 Jae's Cafe & Grill
20 Billy Tse

Top Bar-B-Q
24 East Coast Grill
23 Blue Ribbon BBQ
      Uncle Pete's Hickory Ribs
22 Redbones
21 Pit Stop Bar-B-Q

Top Bars/Grills
26 Grill 23 & Bar
23 Mistral
20 Les Zygomates
      Casablanca
19 Sonsie

Top Breakfast
28 Aujourd'hui
25 Rowes Wharf
      Seasons
23 Sound Bites
      Claremont Cafe

---

* Excluding restaurants with low voting and those outside the
Boston metropolitan area.

Top Brunch

28 Aujourd'hui
26 Icarus
25 Biba
Metropolis Cafe
Rowes Wharf

Top Burgers

25 Ambrosia on Huntington
23 Mistral
20 Mr. & Mrs. Bartley's
Audubon Circle
19 Tim's Tavern

Top Caribbean/Cuban

23 Chez Henri
22 Green Street Grill
19 Mucho Gusto Cafe
Legal C Bar
17 Rhythm & Spice

Top Chinese

23 East Ocean City
Ho Yuen Ting
Chau Chow
22 Lotus Blossom
Eastern Pier

Top Chowder

25 Bristol
22 Ritz Cafe
Locke-Ober Cafe
Legal Sea Foods
21 Turner Fisheries

Top Continental

26 White Rainbow
22 Locke-Ober Cafe
Cafe Budapest
19 Andover Inn
18 Cafe Escadrille

Top Delis/Sandwiches

21 Hi-Rise Bread Co.
Baker's Best
20 Charlie's Sandwich
Rubin's
19 Parrish Cafe

Top Desserts

27 Rialto
26 Grill 23 & Bar
25 Metropolis Cafe
Ambrosia on Huntington
Seasons

Top Eclectic/International

28 Olives
25 Biba
Metropolis Cafe
24 Red Raven's
Blue Room

Top Family

23 Matt Murphy's Pub
23 Carlo's Cucina Italiana
Figs
22 Redbones
New Shanghai

Top French

28 L'Espalier
26 Julien
Cafe Louis
24 Maison Robert
Silks

Top French Bistros

27 Hamersley's Bistro
25 Metropolis Cafe
24 Cafe Celador
23 Chez Henri
21 Restaurant Zinc

Top Hotel Dining

28 Aujourd'hui
Four Seasons
26 Julien
Le Meridien Hotel
25 Rowes Wharf
Boston Harbor Hotel
Seasons
Regal Bostonian Hotel
Bristol
Four Seasons

Top Indian

23 Rangoli
22 India Quality
New Mother India
21 Bombay Bistro
Kebab-N-Kurry

Top Irish Pubs

24 Matt Murphy's Pub
14 Green Dragon Tavern
Grafton St. Pub & Grill
Amrheins
12 Finnegans Wake

13

Top Italian (North)

27 Saporito's
26 Il Capriccio
Marcuccio's
25 Tuscan Grill
24 Tosca

Top Italian (North & South)

26 Terramia
25 Pomodoro
24 Pignoli
Galleria Italiana
Donatello

Top Italian (South)

23 Carlo's Cucina Italiana
Galleria Umberto
22 Daily Catch
Pat's Pushcart
Trattoria A Scalinatella

Top Japanese/Korean

26 Ginza
23 Jae's Cafe & Grill
Tatsukichi
22 Sakurabana
Gyuhama

Top Landmarks

24 Maison Robert
Ritz-Carlton Din. Rm.
22 Locke-Ober Cafe
21 Library Grill
16 Ye Olde Union Oyster Hse.

Top Lunch Spots

26 Cafe Louis
25 Biba
Ambrosia on Huntington
23 Claremont Cafe
19 Sonsie

Top Mediterranean

27 Rialto
Caffe Bella
24 Cafe Celador
23 Maurizio's
Mistral

Top Mex/Tex-Mex

22 Anna's Taqueria
21 Forest Cafe
La Paloma
Tacos El Charro
20 Casa Romero

Top Middle Eastern

23 Lala Rokh
22 Sultan's Kitchen
Phoenicia
Kareem's
19 Zaatar's Oven

Top Newcomers/Rated

26 Marcuccio's
Restaurant Clio
24 Penang
23 Fava
Franklin Cafe

Top Newcomers/Unrated

Bok Choy
Exchange
Harvey's
La Bettola
Vault

Top People-Watching

27 Rialto
25 Biba
23 Mistral
19 Ciao Bella
17 Armani Cafe

Top Pizza

23 Galleria Umberto
Figs
22 Regina Pizzeria
Florentina
21 Santarpio's Pizza

Top Power Lunch

28 Aujourd'hui
26 Julien
25 Seasons
22 Ritz Cafe
Locke-Ober Cafe

Top Pre-Theater

24 Galleria Italiana
23 Jae's (Stuart St.)
22 Red Herring
21 David's
Montien

Top Seafood (American)

26 Grill 23 & Bar
24 East Coast Grill
Providence
22 Legal Sea Foods
21 Turner Fisheries

14

Top Seafood (Ethnic)

23 Giacomo's
    Ho Yuen Ting
    Chau Chow
22 Eastern Pier
    Grand Chau Chow

Top Spanish/Portuguese

24 Dali
22 Tapeo
20 Atasca
    O'Fado
    Tasca

Top Steakhouses

26 Morton's of Chicago
    Grill 23 & Bar
24 Capital Grille
23 Oak Room
20 Palm

Top Thai/Malaysian

25 Brown Sugar Cafe
24 Penang
23 Siam Cuisine
21 Rod Dee
    Erawam of Siam

Top Vietnamese/Cambodian

24 Elephant Walk
23 Dong Khanh
    Viet Hong
    Saigon Vietnamese
22 Ducky Wok

Top Worth a Trip

28 L'Etoile/M. Vin.
27 White Barn Inn/ME
    Al Forno/RI
    Arrows/ME
    Savoir Fare/M. Vin.

Top 40 Decor Ranking

28 Aujourd'hui
Bristol
27 L'Espalier
Julien
Restaurant Clio
Bay Tower Room
26 Ritz-Carlton Din. Rm.
Rowes Wharf
Oak Room
Cranebrook Tea Room
Silks
Top of the Hub
Rialto
25 Mistral
Ambrosia on Huntington
Icarus
Biba
Hungry i
Spinnaker Italia
24 Pignoli

Maison Robert
Seasons
Wayside Inn
Hamersley's Bistro
Ritz Cafe
Capital Grille
Salamander
23 Dali
Pillar House
Grill 23 & Bar
Locke-Ober Cafe
Tosca
Helmand
Veronique
Hampshire House
Andover Inn
Cafe Budapest
22 White Rainbow
Barker Tavern
Mamma Maria

Top Outdoor

Armani Cafe
Cafe Louis
Casa Romero
Daddy-O's
Davio's/Cambridge
Gardner Museum Cafe

Henrietta's Table
Maison Robert
Spasso
Stephanie's on Newbury
Union Square Bistro
Upstairs at the Pudding

Top Romantic

Cafe Budapest
Casa Romero
Chanterelle
Dali
Hungry i
Icarus

Julien
L'Espalier
Oak Room
Salamander
Trattoria A Scalinatella
Trattoria Pulcinella

Top Views

Anthony's Pier 4
Aurora
Bay Tower Room
Biba
Davio's/Cambridge
Jimmy's Harborside

Joe's American/Waterfront
Mill Falls
Rowes Wharf
Spinnaker Italia
Tavern on the Water
Top of the Hub

Top 40 Service Ranking

29 Aujourd'hui
27 L'Espalier
26 Julien
    Ritz-Carlton Din. Rm.
    Bristol
25 Grill 23 & Bar
    White Rainbow
    Rialto
24 Rowes Wharf
    Hamersley's Bistro
    Ritz Cafe
    Seasons
    Oak Room
    Icarus
    Maison Robert
    Saporito's
23 Cafe Celador
    Salamander
    Silks
    Morton's of Chicago

Lala Rokh
Brown Sugar Cafe
Bay Tower Room
Cafe Louis
Locke-Ober Cafe
Mucho Gusto Cafe
Ambrosia on Huntington
Il Capriccio
Grapevine
Cranebrook Tea Room
Red Raven's
Mistral
Capital Grille
Anago
22 Caffe Bella
Cafe Budapest
Mamma Maria
R Place
Le Bocage
Upstairs at the Pudding

Best Buys

Top 80 Bangs For The Buck

This list reflects the best dining values in our *Survey*. It is produced by dividing the cost of a meal into the combined ratings for food, decor and service.

1. Anna's Taqueria
2. Baja Betty's Burritos
3. Galleria Umberto
4. Sound Bites
5. Charlie's Sandwich
6. Wrap Culture
7. Hi-Rise Bread Co.
8. 1369 Coffee House
9. Sami's
10. Purple Cactus
11. Saigon Vietnamese
12. Baker's Best
13. Brown Sugar Cafe
14. Zaatar's Oven
15. Blossoms Cafe
16. Mr. & Mrs. Bartley's
17. New Yorker Diner
18. Boca Grande
19. Blue Ribbon BBQ
20. Sultan's Kitchen
21. Audubon Circle
22. Bini Vini
23. Viet Foods
24. Mucho Gusto Cafe
25. Rosebud Diner
26. Other Side Cosmic Cafe
27. Matt Murphy's Pub
28. Manhattan Sammy's Deli
29. Cybersmith
30. Pho Pasteur
31. Delux Cafe
32. Regina Pizzeria
33. Doyle's Cafe
34. Ducky Wok
35. Cafe Jaffa
36. V. Majestic
37. Miracle of Science B+G
38. Rod Dee
39. Johnny's Luncheonette
40. Demo's
41. Pentimento
42. Pinardi's
43. Cafe Barada
44. Tacos El Charro
45. Milk Street Cafe
46. Centre Street Café
47. Taste of India
48. Taqueria la Mexicana
49. Burren
50. Cornwall's
51. Rudy's Cafe
52. Rangoli
53. Country Life Vegetarian
54. Amarin of Thailand
55. Erawan of Siam
56. Caffe Vittoria
57. Siam Cuisine
58. Phoenicia
59. Sevens Ale House
60. Sichuan Garden
61. India Samraat
62. Tim's Tavern
63. Halfway Cafe
64. India Pavilion
65. Gardner Museum Cafe
66. Dehli Darbar
67. Bombay Cafe
68. Bangkok Bistro
69. Bombay Bistro
70. India House
71. Kareem's
72. Penang
73. Santarpio's Pizza
74. House of Siam
75. Harry's
76. Bangkok Cuisine
77. Atasca
78. Grand Canal
79. Addis Red Sea
80. B & D Deli

Additional Good Values
(A bit more expensive, but worth every penny)

Akbar India
Amrheins
Anchovies
Artu
Bangkok Basil
Bangkok Blue
Bernard's
Bertucci's
Blue Diner
Bluestone Bistro
Bob the Chef
Border Cafe
Buddha's Delight
Buteco
Cafe Paradiso
Carlo's Cucina Italiana
Changsho
Chef Chow's House
Christopher's
Circle Pizza
Eastern Pier
Five Seasons
Goemon
Green Dragon Tavern
Green Papaya
Indian Cafe

India Quality
Jose's
King & I
La Paloma
Lotus Blossom
Mary Chung
Mildred's
Neighborhood Rest.
New Asia
New Bridge Cafe
New Mother India
North East Brewing Co.
Passage to India
Poppa & Goose
Rasol
Redbones
Roggie's
Rubin's
S&S Rest. & Deli
Sawasdee Thai
Shalimar of India
Skewers
Tandoor House
Tasca
Thai House
Wonder Bar

Alphabetical Directory of Restaurants

Abbondanza Ristorante ⊕
786 Main St. (restaurant), Everett, 617-xxx-xxxx

Aoba Bea Sea ⊞

Aldo Bistro ⊞

Amber Inside ⊞

Aku Aku ⊕

Boston

F | D | S | C

Abbondanza Ristorante Ⓜ ▽ 17 | 9 | 18 | $15
195 Main St. (Broadway), Everett, 617-387-8422
☑ This Everett Italian old-timer with "nursing home decor" is perhaps "not exactly Florence" (no one ever said Everett was), but most feel you get "what you'd expect" from a "reliable" "local eatery" including good service.

Addis Red Sea ⓈⓂ 19 | 19 | 17 | $18
544 Tremont St. (Clarendon St.), Boston, 617-426-8727
▮ You "feel transported" far from Boston at this "charming", "authentic Ethiopian" in the South End; "go with a group" and "be prepared to get your fingers dirty" since "you eat with your hands" in an ambiance like a "cozy dark cave"; as always, some decry "uncomfortable chairs", but the "spicy, unusual" fare makes up for it.

Aigo Bistro ⓈⓂ 21 | 18 | 19 | $30
Concord Depot, 84 Thoreau St. (Sudbury Rd.), Concord, 978-371-1333
☑ It's named after the Provençal word for garlic, and just like that pungent bulb, this Concord Mediterranean isn't to everyone's taste; by location alone it's a "suburban surprise", but while some call it "a gem" with "inventive", "flavorful" fare, others see a "Boston wanna-be" with "ordinary food"; on balance, most find "sophisticated" tastes in a "small, cozy" setting.

Akbar India ⓈⓂ 16 | 13 | 17 | $16
1250 Cambridge St. (Prospect St.), Cambridge, 617-497-6548
☑ In restaurant-dense Inman Square, this Indian earns praise for its "wonderful garlic naan" and "great" weekend lunch buffets that let diners "try a little bit of everything"; a few find it "unexceptional" with "greasy food" and unimpressive decor, but overall it's a "good" local option.

Aku-Aku ◖ⓈⓂ 8 | 9 | 11 | $15
149 Alewife Brook Pkwy. (bet. Burlington & Overland Sts.), Cambridge, 617-491-5377
☑ Surveyors seem to love the pun possibilities ("ack-ack", "so-so") more than the food at this "typical Chinese-Polynesian" near the Alewife train station in Cambridge; while some cite "good old-fashioned" fare, many feel this "tacky" place with "Americanized" food "has seen better days" – unless you dig "blue Naugahyde booths" and giant "scorpion bowl" drinks.

Al Dente 🅂🅼   14 | 10 | 16 | $19 |
109 Salem St. (Parmenter St.), Boston, 617-523-0990
◪ Though this North End Italian ranks as a "favorite" with a few, overall it draws mixed reviews, ranging from "ok" to "good" to "better than average", with special note made of the lobster ravioli and low-cost daily lunch specials; service is "friendly" but gets zings for being sometimes "slow" and "baffled."

Alloro 🅂   22 | 14 | 18 | $27 |
351 Hanover St. (bet. Fleet & Prince Sts.), Boston, 617-523-9268
◼ "Great if you can get a seat" say admirers of this "small, quaint" North End Mediterranean; though some say the "creative" daily changing menu is "less daring than in the past", most think it offers "well-cooked food with minimalist sauces" enhanced by "good wines" and "attentive service", all of which makes up for "cramped quarters" and "no dessert and coffee."

Amarin of Thailand 🅂🅼   21 | 19 | 19 | $18 |
287 Centre St. (Galen St.), Newton, 617-527-5255
◪ A "suburban surprise", this Newton Four Corners Thai is a "restful" retreat with "elegant" decor, "attentive service" and a kitchen that most find "reliable", producing "sharp clean tastes" from a "menu where spicy means spicy"; still, a few thrill seekers label the cooking "safe but exciting."

Amarin II 🅂🅼   18 | 16 | 18 | $20 |
27 Grove St. (Spring St.), Wellesley, 781-239-1350
◪ "Less formal" than its Newton sibling, this Wellesley Thai wins fans for its "consistently good food" and service, with compliments going to "fresh vegetables" and the "best pad Thai"; a handful of doubters "wouldn't drive too far" for what they call "average" fare, but some ask "where else can you eat in Wellesley?"

AMBROSIA ON HUNTINGTON 🅂🅼   25 | 25 | 23 | $45 |
116 Huntington Ave. (opposite Marriott Copley), Boston, 617-247-2400
◪ The decor is "fabulous" and Tony Ambrose's "beautifully sculpted" French-Asian fusion fare is equally "eye-pleasing" at this Back Bay standout; though an insistent minority finds it "pretentious all-around", even they agree that this "grand dining room" is "good for impressing" anyone from a client to a date.

Amelia's ◖🅂🅼   13 | 14 | 15 | $17 |
Marina Bay, 305 Victory Rd., N. Quincy, 617-471-1453
◪ "It's all about location" at this Marina Bay American where you should "go on a nice day for the view"; as for the food, beyond "good specials at reasonable prices" and a nod toward "very good salads", it can seem "boring" and "bland" when not looking across the Harbor.

Amrheins [S][M] 14 | 13 | 16 | $15

80 W. Broadway (A St.), S. Boston, 617-268-6189

◪ Classic "old Irish Boston"; you'll find "no surprises" at this South Boston landmark "where the pols hang out"; one person's "great" South Boston "home cooking" is another's "overcooked", "mediocre" grub, but either way it's "a trip back in time" complete with service by a "prehistoric staff" and a setting that can be very "smoky."

ANAGO [S][M] 25 | – | 23 | $36

Lenox Hotel, 65 Exeter St. (Boylston St.), Boston, 617-266-6222

■ Just opened in new quarters in the Lenox Hotel (thus outdating its decor rating), this New American owned by husband and wife team Bob Calderone and Susan Finegold may no longer be the small hidden "gem" that it was in its former Cambridge home, but admirers hope that its knack for turning "superb ingredients" into "delicious" bistro fare will "survive the move" to the Back Bay.

Anchovies 🌙[S][M] 16 | 14 | 15 | $15

433 Columbus Ave. (bet. Braddock Park & Holyoke St.), Boston, 617-266-5088

◪ It may be "too smoky" with "disorganized" service, but this South End Italian-American is always "crowded" because "regulars" consider it a "great neighborhood place" with "cheap eats" and "good pizza" – in sum, "a welcome dose of the ordinary in the trendy South End."

Andale! Tacquieria Mexico [S][M]≠ – | – | – | M

513B Medford St. (Broadway), Somerville, 617-625-5454

The few surveyors who know this Mexican newcomer in Somerville report "friendly owners" who offer "quick, cheap food", with special nods for the "burritos packed with flavor."

Andover Inn [S][M] 19 | 23 | 21 | $35

Chapel Ave. (Rte. 28), Andover, 978-475-5903

◪ High marks go to the "beautiful old inn setting" of this "elegant", "old-school" American-Continental on the grounds of Andover Academy, but to some the ambiance hovers "between sedate and sedating" and the food also provokes debate: "always excellent", "wonderful variety" vs. "mediocre", "boring"; still, it's a good place to "bring older relatives" and the Sunday evening rijsttafel is "fun."

Angelo's [M] 19 | 14 | 17 | $30

575 Boylston St. (bet. Clarendon & Dartmouth Sts.), Boston, 617-536-4045 🌙

237 Main St. (William St.), Stoneham, 781-279-9035

◪ Whether at the Stoneham original with its "storefront" ambiance or spiffier Back Bay spin-off, surveyors have a common plaint about this Italian duo: "expensive", which may be why some find the food "very good" and "prepared with panache" while others call it "competent but unimaginative" and "not worth the price"; Stoneham is BYO.

Angelo's Seafood [S][M] ▽ 20 | 12 | 16 | $22
297 Chelsea St. (Day Sq.), E. Boston, 617-567-2500
■ "When pretensions won't do, go here" say admirers of this East Boston Italian seafooder that does a good job with "simple grilled" fare; it's low on decor and "service can be slow", hence some find it "a little expensive for what it is", but "the fish is always fresh" and the "owners are friendly."

Anna's Taqueria [S][M]≠ 22 | 9 | 17 | $7
1412 Beacon St. (Summit Ave.), Brookline, 617-739-7300
■ It's no surprise that there's "always a line" at this Mexican just outside Coolidge Corner – its "huge, fresh burritos" and other "tasty", "filling" eats are considered a "real deal" and "great for a quick bite that's not junk food", as long as you don't mind "no-frills" decor.

Anthony's Pier 4 [S][M] 14 | 16 | 15 | $30
140 Northern Ave. (Pier 4), Boston, 617-423-6363
◪ "If it's nostalgia you crave", Anthony Athanas' "time warp" Harbor seafooder is the place, but for culinary cravings, it's not such a sure bet; while loyalists say this "old standby" still serves "solid" fish, critics harpoon it as "tired" and mostly catering to "tourists"; but it's an "icon" and no one faults the "excellent view", "great wine list" or "hassle-free parking."

Antico Forno [S][M] 21 | 15 | 17 | $22
93 Salem St. (bet. Cross & Parmenter Sts.), Boston, 617-723-6733
■ A "real find", this "friendly", "intimate" North End Neapolitan yearling delivers "refreshing, rustic", "stick to your ribs" food, much of it cooked in the namesake beehive-shaped, wood-burning brick oven; "authentic grilled vegetables", "sensational gnocchi" and what some call "Boston's best pizza" earn special mention.

Antonio's [M] 18 | 10 | 17 | $22
288 Cambridge St. (opposite Mass General), Boston, 617-367-3310
◪ The setting is "crowded and noisy", but this Italian near Mass General is "saved by its kitchen", which turns out "generous portions" of "freshly prepared" fare along with "good specials"; a few nitpickers say the food "tends to swim in sauce", but since the "price is right" and service "neighborly", most are content.

APPETITO [S][M] 20 | 18 | 19 | $24
1 Appleton St. (Tremont St.), Boston, 617-338-6777
761 Beacon St. (Langley St.), Newton, 617-244-9881
◪ "Enjoyable neighborhood options" describes this pair of "bustling" Italians where "lively pastas" and other "consistent" fare come in "hearty portions"; if some find the food "boring", more consider them a "best buy", which is why no reserving for dinner (Newton) can mean "a long wait"; the South Ender's bar is "popular with a young crowd."

Arirang House 🟥Ⓜ　　▽ 14 | 6 | 14 | $12 |
162 Mass Ave. (Berklee School of Music), Boston, 617-536-1277
◼ "Don't go for the atmosphere" ("needs refurbishing"),
but do go for the "decent buffet" with "plentiful hot and
cold" offerings at this Symphony Hall Korean; the variety
makes it "great for vegetarians and nonvegetarians" alike,
and some consider it "the best pre-symphony deal."

Armani Cafe 🟥Ⓜ　　17 | 19 | 15 | $28 |
214 Newbury St. (bet. Exeter & Fairfield Sts.), Boston,
617-437-0909
◪ A "chichi" and "lively" Newbury Street Italian in the
Armani Boutique with "too many cellular phones" belonging
to "too many beautiful people"; while fans find "nicely
presented" "imaginative food", foes feel the "menu is twice
the price it should be" and say you should expect second-
class service "if you speak English" at this "Eurotrash"
haunt; although "it has its ups and downs", the "convenient,
fun location" can make it "a great hangout" for a drink.

Armida's 🟥　　▽ 18 | 10 | 20 | $30 |
135 Richmond St. (Paul Revere House), Boston, 617-523-9545
◼ "Service is tops" at this family-run North End Italian
where the staff makes you "feel like a relative"; besides
good vibes, there's "good food" too, with surveyors praising
the "great shrimp scampi" and "haddock Milanese"; the
decor could use a boost though.

Artu 🟥Ⓜ　　21 | 13 | 17 | $18 |
6 Prince St. (bet. Hanover St. & North Sq.), Boston, 617-742-4336
89 Charles St. (bet. Mt. Vernon & Pinckney Sts.), Boston,
617-227-9023
◼ Though "nothing to look at", these North End and
Beacon Hill Italian cafes offer plenty to taste, i.e. "the
most delicious sandwiches" and antipasti, "fresh grilled
veggies" and other "reasonable" "Italian country food"
served in a "casual atmosphere"; despite a few gripes
about "slow service" and "cramped" quarters, they're
deemed "very satisfying", especially "for lunch."

Arturo's 🟥Ⓜ　　21 | 18 | 19 | $24 |
411 Chandler St. (bet. June St. & Park Ave.), Worcester,
508-755-5640
◼ "The best regional Italian in Worcester" proclaim
supporters of this "family-oriented" ristorante; the food
is "surprisingly good" given its strip mall location, so few
mind if the room is "somewhat cramped."

Assaggio ◑🟥Ⓜ　　▽ 20 | 22 | 22 | $25 |
29 Prince St. (Hanover St.), Boston, 617-227-7380
◪ Not many voters know this Italian yearling, but those
who do describe it as "typical North End", with food that's
"good" if "nothing great", enhanced by "pleasant service",
"nice decor" and a variety of wines.

Atasca S   20 | 19 | 20 | $20 |
279A Broadway (Columbia St.), Cambridge, 617-354-4355
■ This "piece of Portugal" in Cambridge may be "tiny" and cramped", but it's "totally surprising" – a "quaint hideaway" offering "satisfying grilled" dishes, seafood and "excellent wine" in an "unpretentious", "friendly" atmosphere; admirers call it an "all-around sure bet."

Atlantic Fish Company S M   15 | 14 | 14 | $23 |
777 Boylston St. (bet. Exeter & Fairfield Sts.), Boston, 617-267-4000
◪ There are two schools of thought on this Back Bay fish house: fans say it's "second only to Legal" for "good" "basic" seafood, while the less impressed grumble "run-of-the-mill"; neither camp is swept away by the atmosphere.

Atlas Bar & Grill ◐ S M   ▽ 13 | 20 | 16 | $15 |
145 Ipswich St. (Landsdowne St.), Boston, 617-437-0300
◪ Surveyors salute the "Atlas burger – all others are weak in comparison" at this American on the first floor of Jillian's (an entertainment complex) behind Fenway; but it's the "funky, dark, industrial decor" and "people-watching" that draw the most comment, leading skeptics to conclude "they obviously did not spend as much time" on the menu.

Audubon Circle S M   20 | 21 | 18 | $15 |
838 Beacon St. (Arundel St.), Boston, 617-421-1910
■ "A small, quirky" New American menu awaits diners at this "hip" yet "low-key" "yuppie training ground" near (what else?) Audubon Circle; "what they do they do well" say supporters of its "rockin' burgers", "killer potstickers" and other "well-presented" food; add in "great beers" and "sleek" decor and it's an "easy place to be."

AUJOURD'HUI ◐ S M   28 | 28 | 29 | $56 |
Four Seasons Hotel, 200 Boylston St. (bet. Arlington & S. Charles Sts.), Boston, 617-351-2071
■ "Elegant and sublime", this New American in the Four Seasons Hotel takes the triple crown as Boston's No. 1 for food, decor and service; exuding "pure class", it offers a "beautiful eating experience" complete with "heavenly flavors", "exquisite service", "peace and quiet" and a "wonderful view of the Public Garden"; naturally, such "blissful indulgence" is "expensive", but savvy surveyors say "try the prix fixe."

Aurora S M   ▽ 16 | 18 | 17 | $27 |
30 Congress St. (Sleeper St.), Boston, 617-350-6001
◪ An offbeat combo of Russian and American fare comes with "one of the most beautiful views of the Boston skyline" at this ship anchored on the Harbor; the Russian offerings (including delicious stuffed cabbage and over 100 vodkas) are more adventurous, but the tourist zone location means they're losing out to fried fish and the like.

Back Bay Brewing Company S M | 15 | 17 | 15 | $19 |
755 Boylston St. (bet. Exeter & Fairfield Sts.), Boston, 617-424-8300

◪ Upstairs at this bi-level Back Bay brewpub you'll find an "ambitious" New American menu served in a "tranquil" setting, while downstairs there's "average pub food" and a "loud bar scene"; opinions on the beers vary from "world-class" to "so-so", and "cigar smoke" can be a problem – no surprise since it's a yuppie "watering hole."

Baja Betty's Burritos M≠ | 19 | 13 | 19 | $9 |
3 Harvard Sq. (Harvard & Washington Sts.), Brookline, 617-277-8900

◪ A "nice addition to Brookline Village", this "Cal-style Mexican" with "giant burritos" and a "great condiment bar" makes for "delicious, healthy takeout" (there's also limited seating); but even though fans think this "cool little joint" with "nice" folks is "the first Mexican burrito shack to get it right", some find it "expensive for what it is."

Baja Mexican Cantina S M | 14 | 13 | 14 | $17 |
111 Dartmouth St. (Columbus Ave.), Boston, 617-262-7575

◪ "Casual, neighborhood" Mexican South Ender liked for its "good drinks" (especially the margaritas) and "moderate prices" even if views on the "not exactly classic", "almost fusion-style" food vary: "enjoyable", "interesting" vs. "mediocre"; the decor strikes some as "cool", others as "gaudy", but the place is "fun with a group."

Baker's Best S M | 21 | 12 | 16 | $12 |
27 Lincoln St. (Walnut St.), Newton, 617-332-4588

◪ "Excellent for takeout", this Newton American has a "good selection" of "delicious" food including "intriguing salads", "veggie antipasto", "worthy sandwiches" and "great desserts"; "dull surroundings" are tempered by a "helpful staff", and while some judge it "overpriced", it's "always reliable"; brunch can be "noisy" and "crowded."

B & D Deli S M | 15 | 9 | 12 | $12 |
1653 Beacon St. (Washington St.), Brookline, 617-232-3727

◪ "Not quite Manhattan, but not bad" say supporters of this Washington Square "classic deli", calling it "latke heaven" and praising its "good pastrami on rye", "super bagels", hot dogs and the like; but an equal number feel it's "long past its glory days" and "needs an overhaul"; on one point many agree: "breakfast is best."

Bangkok Basil S M | 16 | 14 | 16 | $16 |
1374 Beacon St. (Centre St.), Brookline, 617-739-1236

◪ While some praise the "fiery creations" and "excellent" pad Thai at this Coolidge Corner Thai, others don't get all fired up over "average" fare; still, locals consider it a "friendly", "satisfying neighborhood place" and note that "Indonesian dishes add to the standard menu."

Bangkok Bistro §Ⓜ 19 | 14 | 17 | $17
1952 Beacon St. (Cleveland Circle), Brighton,
617-739-7270

☑ "Nice people" give this Cleveland Circle Thai a "warm neighborhood feeling"; enthusiasts also rave over its "tantalizing tofu" and "outrageous curry", but most give a more modest assessment: "good food", "nothing wild."

Bangkok Blue §Ⓜ 20 | 16 | 18 | $19
651 Boylston St. (opposite Boston Public Library), Boston,
617-266-1010

■ "Upscale" Copley Square Thai that's seen as "a pleasant departure from Boston's increasingly cookie-cutter Thai food scene"; "aesthetic presentations" with "nice touches like flowers on plates" earn kudos, as does the "good value" lunch menu, sidewalk seating and "extremely friendly staff."

Bangkok Cuisine §Ⓜ 20 | 14 | 18 | $17
177A Mass Ave. (bet. Boylston St. & Huntington Ave.),
Boston, 617-262-5377

☑ The "clutter of colonial artifacts" and a "cramped" room hurt the decor rating of this Thai near the Berklee School of Music, but its "convenient" location and "good food" make it "reliable for a pre-symphony dinner"; expect a "solid, predictable meal" served by a staff that knows how to "get you in and out in time."

Bangkok House §Ⓜ 17 | 15 | 18 | $18
50 JFK St. (Mt. Auburn St.), Cambridge, 617-547-6666

☑ "Dependable" Harvard Square Thai where most diners find "satisfying", "reasonably priced" food and "especially quick service"; they're divided on the decor, however, with fans feeling it's "nice for a Thai restaurant" and foes finding it "sketchy looking."

Bangkok Seafood §Ⓜ ▽ 18 | 9 | 15 | $17
20 Charles St. (Beacon St.), Boston, 617-723-5939

■ "Charles Street Thai without the crowds", but with "consistently good" food; this "intimate eatery" in a "great neighborhood" strikes some as "more authentic" than its neighbors, making it a "reliable" choice for tasty Thai on Beacon Hill.

Barker Tavern, The § 21 | 22 | 21 | $32
21 Barker Rd. (bet. Hatherly & Jericho Rds.), Scituate,
781-545-6533

☑ This Scituate American is a "place to dress up" and remember when "taverns were in and food was well prepared but heavy" and "unimaginative"; the best advice may be to "forget the fancy new stuff" and stick with simple things like "swordfish to die for" or veal chops; it's both a "family" place and a "pricey spot for special occasions", with "lovely decor" and bartenders who "mix a great drink."

Barking Crab, The [S] [M] — 15 | 14 | 12 | $18

88 Sleeper St. (Northern Ave.), Boston, 617-426-2722

◪ For "a vacation in the city", reviewers recommend this "terrific little crab shack Downtown"; the "shirt-sleeve environment", "wood-burning stove" and waterfront location are hits, but as for the seafood, reactions range from "fresh as it gets" to "adequate"; some also warn "you may need to bark to get service."

Barrett's on Boston Harbour [S] [M] — 13 | 18 | 15 | $25

2 Constitution Plaza (Water St.), Charlestown, 617-242-9600

◪ "On the Harbor", this "relaxing" Charlestown American generates more excitement with its "beautiful view" than its "unimaginative" food, though Sunday brunch is "worth it"; "slow service" gives you more time to savor the sights.

Bawarchi [S] [M] — ▽ 19 | 16 | 18 | $14

636 Beacon St. (Commonwealth Ave.), Boston, 617-424-1499

■ "Great Indian food" at "reasonable prices" plus a "good lunch buffet" are applauded by admirers of this Kenmore Square addition; though a few are put off by the "very dark interior" and find the place "about the same as the rest", more say the "friendly owners" and staff "make diners feel at home."

BAY TOWER ROOM [M] — 21 | 27 | 23 | $44

60 State St. (Congress St.), Boston, 617-723-1666

◪ "Unbeatable views" and a "romantic setting" are the hallmarks of this 33rd-floor Financial District New American; to impress out-of-towners or "celebrate a special occasion" it's hard to top, but while some find the food "surprisingly good", others call it "forgettable" and "overpriced", advising "check the weather" – "if not for the view, don't bother."

Bella's [S] [M] — 20 | 16 | 18 | $24

933 Hingham St. (Rte. 3), Rockland, 781-871-5789

◪ Regulars find comfort in this "good old-fashioned" Rockland Italian where the "traditional" fare is "not too expensive" and served in a "friendly" if unexciting atmosphere; a few demanding types cite "uncreative" food and insist it "needs to come into the '90s", but for most it's a "reliable" "midweek" kind of place.

Bennigan's ◑ [S] [M] — 10 | 11 | 12 | $16

191 Stuart St. (bet. S. Charles & Tremont Sts.), Boston, 617-227-3754

■ "Adequately adequate" sums up opinions on this "standard chain" American in the Theater District; the food is "basic" at best, but the "convenient" location and "reasonable prices" "keep people coming" back for a "quick bite" or "socializing" over "after-work drinks."

	F	D	S	C
Bernard's [S][M]	20	16	18	$19

Mall at Chestnut Hill, 199 Boylston St., Chestnut Hill, 617-969-3388

■ In the Mall at Chestnut Hill, this "gourmet Chinese" with "eager to please" service offers an "eclectic menu" of "creative", "fresh and light" dishes that are a "healthy alternative" to typical Chinese fare, though it can be "disappointing if you want traditional"; some also feel it's "too expensive", but lunch is "a good value."

	F	D	S	C
Bertucci's [S][M]	16	13	15	$15

22 Merchants Row (State St.), Boston, 617-227-7889
39-45 Stanhope St. (bet. Columbus Ave. & Stuart St.), Boston, 617-247-6161
90 Main St., Andover, 978-470-3939
412 Franklin St. (Five Corners), Braintree, 781-849-3066
Westgate Mall, 345 Westgate Dr. (Rte. 24), Brockton, 508-584-3080
4 Brookline Pl. (Boylston St.), Brookline, 617-731-2300
5 Cambridge Park Dr. (MBTA Alewife Station), Cambridge, 617-876-2200
21 Brattle St. (Harvard Sq.), Cambridge, 617-864-4748
799 Main St. (Mass Ave.), Cambridge, 617-661-8356
14 E. Littleton Rd. (Rte. 110), Chelmsford, 978-250-8800
150 Worcester Rd./Rte. 9 (Rte. 126), Framingham, 508-879-9161
90 Derby St. (Gardner St.), Hingham, 781-740-4405
414 Washington St./Rte. 16 (Rte. 126), Holliston, 508-429-4571
1777 Mass Ave. (Lexington Ctr.), Lexington, 781-860-9000
388 Boston Post Rd. E. (Rte. 20), Marlborough, 508-460-0911
4054 Mystic Valley Pkwy. (Rte. 16), Medford, 781-396-9933
435 Andover St. (Turnpike St.), N. Andover, 978-685-4498
275 Centre St. (Newton Corner), Newton, 617-244-4900
1405 Providence Hwy. (Sumner St.), Norwood, 781-762-4155
North Shore Mall, Andover St. (Rtes. 114 & 128), Peabody, 978-532-2600
197 Elm St. (Davis Sq.), Somerville, 617-776-9241
450 Paradise Rd. (Rte. 1A), Swampscott, 781-581-6588
Silver City Galleria Mall, 2 Galleria Mall, Taunton, 508-880-0222
14 Audubon Rd. (Salem St.), Wakefield, 781-245-4488
475 Winter St. (Rte. 128), Waltham, 781-684-0650
380 Washington St. (bet. Forest St. & Rte. 16), Wellesley, 781-239-0990
17 Commerce St. (New Boston St.), Woburn, 781-933-1440
15 Newbury St./Rte. 1 (Rte. 128), W. Peabody, 978-535-0969
683 VFW Pkwy. (Newton St.), W. Roxbury, 617-327-0898

◪ "Yummy pizzas" at "reasonable prices" explain why diners flock to this Italian chain; there's pasta and other dishes too, but regulars advise "stick with the pizzas" and don't miss the "tasty, hot, fresh" soft rolls; since they're "family-friendly" and good for "a crowd", they can be "extremely noisy" with "disorganized" service.

BIBA S M 25 | 25 | 22 | $46
272 Boylston St. (bet. Arlington & S. Charles Sts.), Boston, 617-426-7878
◪ Lydia Shire and Susan Regis' Back Bay Eclectic–New American combines "urban chic" with an "exotic, creative menu"; meals begin with the "best bread" and continue with "complex", "unusual" dishes served in a "dramatic" Adam Tihany–designed setting; on the downside, service still earns a "snobby" label and some feel the kitchen "tries too hard to be avant-garde."

Billy Tse ◐ S M 20 | 14 | 18 | $19
240 Commercial St. (Richmond St.), Boston, 617-227-9990
■ This Chinese–Pan-Asian earns kudos for its "well-prepared" fare with choices for "both the adventurous and nonadventurous", as well as for being "the only good take-out place" near the North End; a few find it "overrated" and "too noisy", but if in the area, you may agree it's "very good if you can't get to Chinatown."

Bini Vini S M 17 | 13 | 14 | $12
999 Beacon St. (St. Mary's St.), Brookline, 617-730-8464
■ "Delicious" "brick-oven pizzas" and other "light, fresh" fare make this "tiny" spot on the Brookline-Boston border a "perfect neighborhood pizza place", especially when you add in "wonderful outside dining"; though some report "patronizing service" and find it "nothing special", locals feel it's a refreshing "alternative."

Bishop's S M 20 | 13 | 19 | $24
99 Hampshire St. (Lowell St.), Lawrence, 978-683-7143
◪ "Big portions" of "dependable Middle Eastern" fare draw diners to this Lawrence legend; the room reminds some of "an aircraft carrier", but it's "worth the drive" and a "great value" for "all the pita bread you can eat", "hummus that can't be beat" and "superb french fries."

Bison County BBQ S M 16 | 12 | 14 | $17
275 Moody St. (Crescent St.), Waltham, 781-642-9720
◪ This "novel concept" in Waltham strikes most as a "solid BBQ" spot serving up "decent" Texas-style ribs and the likes of bisonburgers; doubters find the food "interesting but tame" and "a bit greasy", though "huge portions", "friendly staff" and "unpretentious", "funky surroundings" help make it a "casual" local option.

Bisuteki S M 17 | 16 | 19 | $23
Howard Johnson, 777 Memorial Dr., Cambridge, 617-492-7777
Howard Johnson, 407 Squire Rd., Revere, 781-284-7200
◪ You get "a lot of show" for your money at these Japanese steakhouses where "flying knives" and cooking "right at the table" ensure an "entertaining meal", if not necessarily an outstanding one; for best results, go with children or "a large group" and "keep your hands off the table."

Black Crow Caffe 🅢Ⓜ
20 | 16 | 17 | $21

2 Perkins St. (Centre St.), Jamaica Plain, 617-983-9231

◪ A "funky neighborhood place", this Jamaica Plain Eclectic has a "comfortable", "congenial" atmosphere and a "limited but tasty" menu with an "unusual earthy flair"; phobes feel it may be "a little too pricey" given "minute portions", but the "great people" who run it help keep it "crowded."

Black Goose 🅢Ⓜ
16 | 14 | 14 | $20

21 Beacon St. (Bowdoin St.), Boston, 617-720-4500

◪ Hang with the "State House hip" at this "trendy Beacon Hill" Italian; views on the food vary ("understated", "consistently good" vs. "bland", "mediocre") and some find service "subpar", but it's a "great lunch spot" that brings diners back with its "convenient location", "nice outdoor area" and "people-watching."

Black Rose 🅢Ⓜ
10 | 11 | 12 | $15

160 State St. (Commercial St.), Boston, 617-742-2286

◪ "Irish conversation", "friendly waitresses" and "cold beer" are the longtime draws at this Irish pub near Faneuil Hall; though many have long come here "to drink, not eat", the post-Survey opening of a second-floor steakhouse adorned with Gaelic murals and mahogany may boost future food scores and inspire some to ditch the beer-soaked "sticky atmosphere" downstairs.

Blossoms Cafe & Catering Ⓜ⇗
17 | 12 | 14 | $10

99 High St. (Congress St.), Boston, 617-423-1911

◪ This Financial District "nice alternative for lunch" offers "imaginative, fresh", "high-quality" fare served "cafeteria style"; while most enjoy its "interesting" creations, some find the food "too heavy for the working crowd" and a bit "overpriced"; no dinner.

Blue Diner ●🅢Ⓜ
14 | 13 | 14 | $14

150 Kneeland St. (South St.), Boston, 617-338-4639

◪ Though many surveyors agree that this "old-time diner" has "lost its charm since moving" from its original site, it remains a popular Downtown destination for the "late-night club crowd" because it's "one of the few places open 24 hours"; its "classic diner food" may be "overpriced" and service can be "ditzy", but "when nowhere else" is open, it's there.

BLUE RIBBON BBQ 🅢Ⓜ
23 | 12 | 17 | $14

1375 Washington St. (Elm St.), W. Newton, 617-332-2583

◼ "When you need a fix" of "finger-licking ribs and all the fixings", this "real bargain" in West Newton is "as close to Southern BBQ as you can get" in Yankeeland; regulars say it's "better to take out" because there's "no atmosphere", but after all "decor isn't the point" – "world-class" BBQ is.

Blue Room, The 🆂Ⓜ　　24⎦ 20⎦ 21⎦ $31⎦
1 Kendall Sq. (Hampshire St.), Cambridge, 617-494-9034
⬛ "Hasn't missed a beat since changing owners" is how most feel about this "vibrant" Kendall Square Eclectic – some even call it "much improved with [chef/co-owner] Steve Johnson at the helm", turning out "creative" food marked by "fantastic flavors" and served amidst "chic decor"; though a few dissent ("lost its punch"), "noise" and "long waits" attest to its popularity.

Bluestone Bistro 🆂Ⓜ　　18⎦ 11⎦ 14⎦ $15⎦
1799 Commonwealth Ave. (Chiswick Rd.), Brighton, 617-254-8309
⬛ This "glorified pizza joint" specializes in "creative" pies with a "variety of toppings" and "awesome crust"; despite "cramped seating" and decor that could use a "spiff up", a "young crowd" returns to enjoy "affordable", "casual" dining – "don't expect more and you'll be ok."

Blue Wave Rotisserie Grill 🆂Ⓜ　18⎦ 17⎦ 16⎦ $22⎦
142 Berkeley St. (bet. Columbus Ave. & Stuart St.), Boston, 617-424-6664
⬛ "Fun and loud" describe this Back Bay Cal-American; most like its "casual California atmosphere", "reasonable prices" and "creative" fare, but foes think the food "has gone downhill" and the "room is showing its age", and even some fans knock the staff with "attitude."

Bob the Chef 🆂　　19⎦ 14⎦ 16⎦ $16⎦
604 Columbus Ave. (Mass Ave.), Boston, 617-536-6204
⬛ The South End's answer to "down-home Southern cooking", this Soul Fooder is the place for "great fried chicken" and other eats "that make you feel good"; despite a few squawks that it "lost some of its charm" after recent renovations, many consider it the "best" of its kind and highly recommend the "great jazz brunch."

Boca Grande 🆂Ⓜ🚭　　15⎦ 8⎦ 11⎦ $9⎦
149 First St. (Bent St.), Cambridge, 617-354-5550
1728 Mass Ave. (Linnaean St.), Cambridge, 617-354-7400
⬛ Popular with "students on a budget", this Cambridge duo dishes out the usual Cal-Mexican chow, with nods going to its "oversized burritos" made "while you wait"; though a few find the food "bland", more report that "large portions" of "filling", "authentic" fare "seriously satisfy" cravings without seriously denting the wallet.

Bok Choy 🆂Ⓜ🚭　　–⎦ –⎦ –⎦ M⎦
202-204 Washington St. (Station St.), Brookline, 617-738-9080
Husband and wife Matt Murphy and Siobhan Carew (who also own Pomodoro and Matt Murphy's) look East for inspiration at their New Wave Asian in Brookline Village, where they offer intriguing dishes (i.e. Mongolian-style oxtails) in an earth-toned setting; as at their other venues, no plastic is accepted and you should arrive early.

Bombay Bistro §M
21 | 15 | 18 | $17

1353 Beacon St. (Harvard St.), Brookline, 617-734-2879

◪ This Coolidge Corner Indian doles out "delicious" if "somewhat oily" fare plus "very accommodating service" from a staff happy to "explain new dishes"; while some say the menu has become "more daring", others feel it's still "too safe", but either way most agree that "consistently good", "high-quality food" makes this local "favorite" "stand above the crowd."

Bombay Cafe §M
20 | 15 | 16 | $17

175 Mass Ave. (Boylston St.), Boston, 617-247-0555

■ Boasting a "great location" near the Hynes, this Indian with "colonial decor" delivers "reasonably priced" "fine" food, with special note going to "super shrimp samosas"; a handful feels "the daily buffet needs some variety", but there's a "great brunch."

Bombay Club §M
19 | 18 | 16 | $19

57 JFK St. (Harvard Sq.), Cambridge, 617-661-8100

■ "Very trendy Indian" with a "gracious owner", "great view of Harvard Square" and "better than average food" complemented by "unbelievable breads" and a "terrific wine list"; a few find it "too pricey except for the [lunch] buffet", which all agree is "a good deal."

Boodle's of Boston ◗§M
17 | 17 | 17 | $28

Back Bay Hilton Hotel, 40 Dalton St. (Belvidere St.), Boston, 617-266-3537

◪ This Back Bay steakhouse with a "great beer selection" strikes admirers as "perfect before the symphony" and enjoyable anytime thanks to "good steaks", "wonderful Boston baked beans" and "old-style service" in a "warm atmosphere"; dissenters counter that it's "bland and uncreative", but most come away satisfied.

Border Cafe §M
16 | 15 | 14 | $16

32 Church St. (Palmer St.), Cambridge, 617-864-6100
817 Broadway (Rte. 1), Saugus, 781-233-5308

◪ The "under-30 crowd" goes to revel in the "loud" "party atmosphere" and "soft prices" at these "crowded" Tex-Mexers in Harvard Square and Saugus; despite "long waits" and sometimes "sour" service, "tasty 'ritas" and "plates piled high" with "decent" chow keep most happy, even if critics "can't understand" their popularity.

Boston Beer Garden §M
13 | 12 | 14 | $15

734 E. Broadway (L St.), S. Boston, 617-269-0990

◪ Though some say this "loud" South Boston "barroom" featuring a variety of beers is "not a place to eat", others claim it serves "decent, cheap" food and a good Sunday brunch ("got to have the salmon eggs Benedict"); just "don't go with a headache."

Boston Beer Works ◗ⓈⓂ   15 | 15 | 14 | $16 |
61 Brookline Ave. (Fenway Park), Boston, 617-536-BEER
☑ "Good beer near Fenway" sums up the main appeal of this brewpub; some find the American food "good for a bar", others say the kitchen is no heavy hitter, but it's a natural "pre- and post-game" if you don't mind "crowds", "noise" and "slow" service.

Boston Sail Loft ⓈⓂ   15 | 15 | 14 | $18 |
80 Atlantic Ave. (Commercial St. & Lewis Wharf), Boston, 617-227-7280
1 Memorial Dr. (bet. Kendall Sq. & Main St.), Cambridge, 617-225-2222
☑ Blessed with "wonderful locations" on the Charles River in Cambridge and smack on the Harbor, these "casual" American seafooders deliver "large portions" of mostly "standard" fare, though the likes of "great fried calamari" and "bargain fish and chips" earn praise; if some say they "look more like pickup bars than restaurants", the "after-work" crowd doesn't seem to mind.

Botolph's on Tremont ◗ⓈⓂ   19 | 16 | 17 | $22 |
569 Tremont St. (Clarendon St.), Boston, 617-424-8577
☑ This Italian–New American "South End staple" with a "great location" offers "good" pizzas and pastas and "a great brunch at a reasonable price"; while a few feel the "menu is uninspired" and there's "nothing to distinguish it from the crowd", most appreciate the fact that it's "steady, not a flash in the pan."

Brandy Pete's Ⓜ   13 | 9 | 14 | $16 |
267 Franklin St. (Batterymarch St.), Boston, 617-439-4165
☑ A 1922 American "institution" that's "convenient and consistent for lunch" in the Financial District; but picky eaters maintain you should "skip the food" and just enjoy this "archetypal old Irish political" place as a "great after-work watering hole."

Brew Moon ⓈⓂ   17 | 18 | 16 | $19 |
115 Stuart St. (bet. S. Charles & Tremont Sts.), Boston, 617-523-6467 ◗
250 Granite St. (South Shore Plaza Rd.), Braintree, 781-356-2739 ◗
50 Church St. (bet. Brattle St. & Mass Ave.), Cambridge, 617-499-2739 ◗
114 Broadway (Rte. 1N), Saugus, 781-941-2739
■ This "hip" quartet of brewpubs is "a cut above the usual", delivering "food better than you'd expect" such as "great molasses pork chops", "delectable corn chowder" and "huge pizzas" in a "unique atmosphere"; there's also "a good selection of beer" (including "fabulous root beer") and a "great jazz brunch"; a few feel the "very diverse menu" tries too hard and is "overpriced."

BRISTOL, THE ◐ [S] [M] 25 | 28 | 26 | $33

Four Seasons Hotel, 200 Boylston St. (bet. Arlington & S. Charles Sts.), Boston, 617-351-2071

■ "An alternative to Aujourd'hui at a much-reduced price", this street-level cafe in the Four Seasons Hotel offers "excellent" New American cooking and "lots of bang and elegance for the buck"; there's a "great afternoon tea" and "pastry buffet" served in a "classy but comfortable setting" with a "wonderful view" and a "delightful staff"; to the few who say the "food can be expensive", the vast majority responds "given the cost vs. quality here, this may be Boston's best dining bargain."

BROWN SUGAR CAFE [S] [M] 25 | 18 | 23 | $15

129 Jersey St. (Boylston St.), Boston, 617-266-2928

■ A "tiny storefront" serving "gorgeously presented", "reasonably priced" "tasty Thai" in the Fenway; there's "great papaya salad" and "vegetarian fried rice" brought to table by a "very friendly", "helpful staff"; the "wacky location" means it's "tough to find" and "tough to park" and also probably explains why it's "still undiscovered."

Buddha's Delight [S] [M] 18 | 8 | 13 | $13

5 Beach St. (Washington St.), Boston, 617-451-2395
404 Harvard St. (bet. Beacon St. & Commonwealth Ave.), Brookline, 617-739-8830

◪ "Fake meat even a confirmed carnivore can love" is the word on this pair of Asians offering "an exquisite selection of vegan mock meats" at "great prices" (most entrees under $8); while a minority feels the food is "hit or miss" and can vary from "good to greasy", all agree the "dull atmosphere" needs dressing up.

Bugaboo Creek Steak House [S] [M] 12 | 16 | 14 | $18

551 Mahar Hwy. (Pearl St.), Braintree, 781-848-0002
345 Cochituate Rd. (bet. Rtes. 9 & 30), Framingham, 508-370-9001
North Shore Mall, Rte. 114, Peabody, 978-538-0100
Arsenal Mall, 617 Arsenal St., Watertown, 617-924-9000

◪ "Shtick-o-rama" steakhouse chain where a "talking tree and singing moose" are part of the theme; enthusiasts insist "except for the wait", it's a "great place for families" and the "food's fine", but phobes say "average food at best" and warn "the gets on your nerves quickly ambiance" is what happens when you combine "Outback, Disney and a bad LSD trip with screaming kids."

Bull & Finch Pub ◐ [S] [M] 12 | 15 | 14 | $17

84 Beacon St. (bet. Arlington & Charles Sts.), Boston, 617-227-9605

◪ A "tourist mecca" offering "typical stadium fare", this Beacon Hill American that inspired *Cheers* can be "fun" and "a good place to have a hamburger", but most know "you don't go for the food" but rather "just to say I've been."

Burren, The 🅂🅜   15 | 15 | 13 | $13
247 Elm St. (Davis Sq.), Somerville, 617-776-6896
■ "Boston finally has a pub that feels like Ireland" – a "dark and smoky" Somerville spot boasting "pretty good fare" like "fish 'n' chips", "delicious rich Guinness", the "best traditional Irish music" and "lots of brogues."

Buteco 🅂🅜   17 | 9 | 17 | $15
130 Jersey St. (Park Dr.), Boston, 617-247-9508
■ "Food with flavor" is what fans find at this "authentic" Fenway Brazilian offering "lots of rice and beans, "delicious plantains" and "fried yuca"; the setting is "nondescript", but the "reasonable prices" are adequate compensation.

Cactus Club 🅂🅜   15 | 16 | 15 | $19
939 Boylston St. (Hereford St.), Boston, 617-236-0200
☑ The "good margaritas" and "amazing sangria" at this "noisy" Back Bay Tex-Mex "college hangout" make for a "happening" bar; the "food is inconsequential", but even the prickly admit "it's good for a night out."

Cafe Barada 🅂   17 | 11 | 17 | $13
201 Mass Ave. (Lake St.), Arlington, 781-646-9650
☑ This "authentic", "informal, inexpensive" Arlington Middle Eastern wins admirers for its "tasty" "home-cooked" fare; while the "decor is depressing" ("like an airport cafeteria"), it's "a great place to go before or after a movie."

Café Brazil 🅂🅜   19 | 11 | 19 | $18
421 Cambridge St. (Harvard Ave.), Allston, 617-789-5980
■ A "spicy and hearty" "taste of Brazil" in Allston that's the perfect choice when you're in the mood for meat; service is "friendly" and "accommodating" and when the guitarist is playing, the "nice live music" helps turn the "simple decor" into a "pleasant atmosphere."

Cafe Budapest 🅂🅜   22 | 23 | 22 | $41
Copley Square Hotel, 90 Exeter St. (bet. Boylston St. & Huntington Ave.), Boston, 617-266-1979
☑ For "memorable" "Magyar meals", this "beautiful" Back Bay Hungarian is "a favorite" of many who revel in the "delightful old-world experience" complete with "romantic strolling violins"; loyalists claim "all is impeccable", but foes feel "it's showing its age", with "stuffy service" and "food drenched in butter."

Cafe Celador   24 | 20 | 23 | $34
5 Craigie Circle (bet. Brattle St. & Concord Ave.), Cambridge, 617-661-4073
■ "Hidden" on "a side street", this "romantic" French bistro with the "coziest basement in Cambridge" comes with "charm and style" and a "constantly changing menu" that includes "interesting" and "innovative" Italian and Mediterranean dishes; a few counter "claustrophobic", "precocious and pretentious"; P.S. parking's tough.

Cafe China S | 20 | 13 | 17 | $19
1254 Cambridge St. (Prospect St.), Cambridge, 617-868-4300
■ A "small, quiet" Inman Square "nouveau Chinese" offering "interesting", "nicely arranged food combinations" as well as "French desserts and cappuccino", which makes for a "charming variation on the usual Chinese"; there's a "homey atmosphere" and a "pleasant owner and staff", so it's "a nice place to hang out."

Cafe de Paris S M ⊄ | 10 | 9 | 8 | $12
19 Arlington St. (bet. Boylston & Newbury Sts.), Boston, 617-247-7121
◪ This "cafeteria-style" French cafe near the Public Garden and the "fancy parts of Newbury and Boylston Streets for shopping" has a "fantastic location" for an "ok coffee shop" with "sluggish service"; while you can eat "dessert any time of the day" here, reviewers wonder whether "they mean Paris, Texas because France it ain't."

Cafe Escadrille M | 18 | 17 | 18 | $27
26 Cambridge St. (Rte. 128, exit 33A), Burlington, 781-273-1916
◪ Supporters of this "elegant" Burlington Continental serving "excellent Caesar salad, crab cakes and scampi" swear it's a "wonderful place" where "you can never go wrong", while detractors deem it an "old, musty" "master of mediocrity" with "food and decor from the '50s" and "too much of a bar scene for peaceful dining."

Cafe Fleuri S M | 20 | 19 | 20 | $31
Le Meridien Hotel, 250 Franklin St. (Pearl St.), Boston, 617-451-1900
◪ For "movers and shakers on expense accounts", the "bright, pretty" French cafe in the Le Meridien is where to go for "power breakfasts" and "great business lunches" in the Financial District; the atrium setting is "good if you like a lot of sunlight", but for some "the decor is dated"; on Saturday there's a "wonderful" midday chocolate dessert buffet and on Sunday the "best brunch in Boston."

Cafe Jaffa S M | 19 | 11 | 15 | $13
48 Gloucester St. (bet. Boylston & Newbury Sts.), Boston, 617-536-0230
■ "The best bargain in Back Bay dining" is offered at this "good and quick" Middle Eastern; it's a "sure bet" for "very generous portions" of the "best baba ghanoush" and "great shwarmas and kebabs."

Cafe Japonaise M | 21 | 14 | 13 | $22
1034 Commonwealth Ave. (Babcock St.), Boston, 617-738-7200
◪ A Comm Ave. newcomer serving a "limited menu" of "creative and elegant" Japanese-French fusion fare including "sushi and sashimi to die for"; yet it's "never crowded" – perhaps because the location is "drab" and service can be "unfriendly."

CAFE LOUIS Ⓜ   26 | 21 | 23 | $39
234 Berkeley St. (Newbury St.), Boston, 617-266-4680
■ "A little gem in a clothing store" (Louis of Boston), this Back Bay New French may be "cramped" but Michael Schlow's "superb" fare wins raves, as do his "great presentations" ("gives tall food a good name") gripes about the "so-so room" are mainly due to its "smallness", but given a chef who "really celebrates food", it adds up to dining "as stylish as Louis' clothes"; bargain hunters should take note of the "interesting lunches" and "free parking."

Cafe Marliave Ⓢ Ⓜ   15 | 13 | 16 | $21
10 Bosworth St. (bet. Tremont & Washington Sts.), Boston, 617-423-6340
☑ "A Boston tradition", this Downtown Crossing "standard Italian" serving "old-time food" along the lines of "delicious manicotti" is "always satisfying" and has been "the same for the past 30 years"; critics, on the other hand, call it a "shabby" "tired", "too much red sauce" "institution."

Cafe Paradiso Ⓢ Ⓜ   15 | 12 | 12 | $13
255 Hanover St. (bet. Cross & Richmond Sts.), Boston, 617-742-1768 ◗
1 Eliot Pl. (Harvard Sq.), Cambridge, 617-868-3240
☑ "Fast food without the shame of chains" can be had at this pair of cafes in the North End and Harvard Square featuring "decent calzones and quiche" and "delicious desserts and cappuccinos"; "too much smoke" and "too much neon" hurt the decor score, but with "gelati as good as in Italy", the duo is a "people-watching" paradiso.

Cafe Promenade Ⓢ Ⓜ   20 | 18 | 17 | $31
Colonnade Hotel, 120 Huntington Ave. (W. Newton St.), Boston, 617-425-3240
☑ "Super before the symphony", this New American with a "great location" in the Colonnade Hotel can be "quiet and relaxing" even if service is "much too slow"; Saturday evenings September–May offer "the best opera nights."

Cafe Shiraz Ⓢ Ⓜ   ▽ 13 | 12 | 16 | $18
1030 Commonwealth Ave. (bet. Babcock St. & Brighton Ave.), Boston, 617-566-8888
☑ Loyalists like the "intriguing kosher" eats at this primarily Persian place on Comm Ave. near BU's West Campus, but foes feel the "food is bland" and "if you're not kosher, don't bother."

Cafe Soho Ⓢ   17 | 14 | 18 | $19
11 Springfield St. (Cambridge St.), Cambridge, 617-354-7040
☑ A "funky" Inman Square American where an "eager to please staff" delivers "generous portions" of "fairly priced" "down-home food" and a "great brunch"; a few critics call it "Cafe So-So", claiming "the menu falls short."

Cafe St. Petersburg S 17 | 16 | 19 | $24
236 Washington St. (Harvard St.), Brookline, 617-277-7100
◪ This "rare Russian" in Brookline offers diners "beautiful decor" and an "old-world atmosphere" complete with a "schmaltzy piano"; it's where the "Russians eat", but the question is do they serve cuisine that "convinces doubters that Russian food isn't boring" or do they merely do "great presentations of tasteless food"?; your call, comrade.

Cafe Suisse S M ▽ 20 | 16 | 20 | $29
Swissôtel Boston, 1 Ave. de Lafayette (bet. Chauncey & Washington Sts.), Boston, 617-422-5577
■ "Swiss specialties" mark this Downtown Crossing Continental whose hotel location makes for "the perfect place to enjoy lunch" or the "Sunday buffet"; even with a "great unsung chef", it's "empty all the time."

Cafe Sushi S M 21 | 13 | 17 | $21
1105 Mass Ave. (Putnam Ave.), Cambridge, 617-492-0434
■ "Fresh fish, no-frills" sums up the "consistently good" "inexpensive sushi" served at this "nice Japanese neighborhood spot" just outside Harvard Square; while some find the atmosphere "tacky", "who cares about the decor when the fish is good?"

Cafe Three Hundred M⇗ ▽ 21 | 15 | 13 | $13
300 Summer St. (D St.), Boston, 617-426-0695
■ It doesn't do dinner, but this American with "innovative entrees" is a "great lunch spot" that brings "South End style to South Station"; a "cute find", "especially in that area", its "great decor" comes from being surrounded by an art gallery.

CAFFE BELLA M 27 | 19 | 22 | $33
19 Warren St. (Main St. & Rte. 139), Randolph, 781-961-7729
■ Though "no longer a secret", Patrick Barnes' "excellent" Mediterranean fare still has fans shaking their heads and saying "I can't believe it's in Randolph"; the strip mall location means it's "tiny", "crowded" and "noisy", and no reserving means a "long wait", but it's "worth it" to enjoy "wonderfully fresh", "real Tuscan food" and other delights that earn it "best on the South Shore" accolades; special note is made of the "super wine list."

Caffe Lampara S M 16 | 15 | 16 | $19
55 Needham St. (Centre St.), Newton, 617-964-4244
◪ "An easy option for inexpensive dining", this "consistent" "suburban Italian" wins votes as a "good place for a grown-up meal with kids" provided you "stick to regular Italian dishes" ("above-average pastas", "great pizza", Caesar salad, etc.) "rather than creative ones"; pickier palates sniff "mediocre", "loud" and "not the place for a special occasion."

Caffe Luna [S][M] 19 | 16 | 17 | $20

Old Chestnut Hill Shopping Ctr., 11 Boylston St. (Hammond St.), Chestnut Hill, 617-734-8400

■ "Great food and superior service make up for the strip mall location" at this "reliable" Chestnut Hill Northern Italian proffering "sensational warm goat cheese salad", "great pizzas" and the "best suburban pasta"; be advised that it's "busy before and after the movies" next door and there's "always a wait on weekends."

Caffe Vittoria ☾[S][M]🚫 19 | 19 | 15 | $16

294 Hanover St. (Prince St.), Boston, 617-227-7606

■ This "bustling" coffeehouse is "the perfect place to catch the North End scene"; of course it's "touristy", but because it's "open late" party-people have a prime "after-club stop" for "great" coffee and desserts.

California Pizza Kitchen [S][M] 14 | 12 | 14 | $15

Prudential Ctr., 800 Boylston St. (Rine Rd.), Boston, 617-247-0888
Natick Mall, 1245 Worcester Rd. (Rte. 9), Natick, 508-651-1506

◪ "A step above your standard chain", this "gourmet" pizza chain offers "interesting albeit bizarre" toppings like "Thai chicken" and "Peking duck"; for some it's "ok in a pinch" and "a good break from walking in the mall", but from a more critical viewpoint the food is "assembly line–like", the decor is poor and the "staff has an attitude"; nevertheless, it's one of the most highly trafficked restaurants in our Survey.

Callahan's [S][M] 13 | 8 | 14 | $16

100 Needham St. (bet. Rtes. 9 & 128), Newton, 617-527-0330

■ It may offer "cheap eats" for "carnivores only", but critics complain that this "depressing" Newton steakhouse is "not what it was" – "one-time local leader has lost it"; but others cite "good burgers" and "at least there's never a wait."

Cambridge Brewing Co. [S][M] 12 | 12 | 12 | $15

1 Kendall Sq. (Broadway & Hampshire St.), Cambridge, 617-494-1994

◪ "Beer made with love" (including "great seasonal" varieties) and an outdoor patio for "people-watching" are the main attractions at this "loud and crowded" Kendall Square brewpub frequented by "MIT types" "trying to be cool"; as scores suggest, "food is served only as a cushion for the suds."

Cambridge Common ☾[S][M] 13 | 11 | 13 | $14

1667 Mass Ave. (Wendell St.), Cambridge, 617-547-1228

■ Loyal locals converge on this "casual and cheap" American just outside Harvard Square more for the "beer on tap" and "great neighborhood feel" than the "standard" "stick to your ribs" "comfort food" like "macaroni and cheese", "meat loaf and potatoes" and "lasagna of the day."

Cantina Italiana 🅢🅜　　　20 | 13 | 17 | $24
346 Hanover St. (Fleet St.), Boston, 617-723-4577
■ This "low-frills" North Ender "has been around forever" and still "has a following" for its "generous portions" of "consistent", "hearty homemade Italian food" and "very friendly service"; "the decor is late '70s", but devotees don't seem to mind.

CAPITAL GRILLE 🅢🅜　　　24 | 24 | 23 | $42
359 Newbury St. (bet. Hereford St. & Mass Ave.), Boston, 617-262-8900
250 Boylston St. (Rte. 9E), Chestnut Hill, 617-928-1400
■ Whether at the newer Chestnut Hill location or the Back Bay original, expect "super" "dry-aged" steaks with all "the trimmings" including potent cocktails, a "fine wine list", a "manly", "million-dollar" atmosphere and, of course, "noise"; some grouse that it's "too expensive", especially "for the suburbs", and claim "cigar smokers ruin" the Back Bay site (Chestnut Hill prohibits smoking).

Captain's Wharf 🅢🅜　　　16 | 10 | 15 | $17
356 Harvard Ave. (Coolidge Corner), Brookline, 617-566-5590
☑ If you "still eat fried fish", this "cheap" Brookline seafooder with "goofy nautical decor" is a "nice example of a great genre" where "old-fashioned seafood plates" are served to the "geriatric set"; mutineers simply sneer – "it gives seafood a bad name."

Carla's 🅢　　　19 | 20 | 20 | $27
171 Nahatan St. (Central St.), Norwood, 781-769-9000
☑ Set in an "old fire station", this "fancy" "suburban Italian" with "wonderful lobster ravioli" and a staff that "makes an effort to do more" is "the place to go if you're in Norwood"; the few who find it "overpriced" have the option of going "to the bar for a less expensive meal."

Carlo's Cucina Italiana 🅢🅜　　　23 | 11 | 20 | $19
131 Brighton Ave. (Harvard Ave.), Allston, 617-254-9759
■ Allston's "tiny", "always packed" "local neighborhood treasure" offers "wonderful home-cooked Italian food" and "excellent service" at "amazingly low prices", leading customers to contend that it "beats anything in the North End"; there are "long lines" and "there's no place to wait", so "get there early."

Carl's Pagoda 🅢🅜⇗　　　20 | 7 | 14 | $20
23 Tyler St. (bet. Beach & Kneeland Sts.), Boston, 617-357-9837
☑ Loyalists claim this Chinatown legend serves the "only authentic Chinese-Cantonese food (for better or worse) in Boston" and single out the "excellent steamed sea bass" for kudos, but detractors deem it a "dive" that's "living on an old reputation."

Casablanca ●ⓈⓂ 20 | 19 | 17 | $24
40 Brattle St. (Harvard Sq.), Cambridge, 617-876-0999
☑ Respondents who "loved the movie" "love" this "cool without trying" Harvard Square "institution" where chef Ana Sortun's "delicious, innovative" Mediterranean fare is complemented by a "romantic and sophisticated" atmosphere and a "hopping bar" (which some say is "better than the restaurant"); despite scattered reports that "service needs overhauling", it remains a "great late-night place."

Casa Elena ⓈⓂ 16 | 9 | 15 | $16
45 Lexington St. (Main St.), Watertown, 617-926-3222
☑ "Basic", "no-frills" Mexican–South American–Spanish in Watertown doling out "plenty of good reasonably priced" food; they "need to spruce up the decor" though – maybe that's why there's "always a table available."

Casa Mexico ⓈⓂ 18 | 16 | 17 | $20
75 Winthrop St. (JFK St.), Cambridge, 617-491-4552
☑ "Great for a date", this "dark and cozy" basement Mexican in Harvard Square features a "straightforward menu" of "authentic" fare including the "best refried beans on the planet", "excellent enchiladas" and "siren salsa"; too bad the margaritas are, in a word, "weak."

Casa Portugal ⓈⓂ 16 | 12 | 18 | $19
1200 Cambridge St. (bet. Prospect & Tremont Sts.), Cambridge, 617-491-8880
☑ Diners head to this "gem in Inman Square" for "generous portions" of "tasty, well-spiced" Portuguese; although some feel the quality has "gone downhill", for many it remains a perfect destination for a "home-cooked" meal.

Casa Romero ⓈⓂ 20 | 21 | 19 | $27
30 Gloucester St. (bet. Commonwealth Ave. & Newbury St.), Boston, 617-536-4341
■ Reviewers rave about the "beautiful outdoor patio" at this "upscale" Back Bay Mexican offering "fresh and delicious" "authentic" food and the "best salsa and margaritas around" in a "romantic atmosphere"; amigos assert that it's "worth the search" (the entrance is off an alley) and recommend it "for a special night out."

Centre Street Café ⓈⓂ⇗ 20 | 12 | 16 | $14
597 Centre St. (bet. Goodrich Rd. & Pond St.), Jamaica Plain, 617-524-9217
■ This "earthy, crunchy" Jamaica Plain Eclectic with "a good vegetarian selection" and "great breakfasts" is a favorite "neighborhood place" where "funky, interesting food" is doled out in a "cramped" but "relaxed" and "friendly" atmosphere that several surveyors say could use some spiffing up; P.S. "they charge [50 cents] less for takeout if you bring your own container."

Changsho [S][M] 19 | 19 | 18 | $19
1712 Mass Ave. (bet. Linnaean & Martin Sts.), Cambridge, 617-547-6565
◪ Fans of this "wonderful, subtle, sublime Chinese in a lovely setting" just outside Harvard Square praise the "beautiful decor" ("no tacky dragons"), "best Peking duck" and "excellent dim sum Sunday brunch"; while faultfinders feel "this one-time leader" is "slipping", the majority maintains "it's still better than most."

Chanterelle French Country Bistro [S][M] 18 | 21 | 19 | $32
226 Newbury St. (bet. Exeter & Fairfield Sts.), Boston, 617-262-8988
◪ A "very romantic country French bistro" on Newbury Street that takes many armchair travelers on "a little trip to Provence" with its "fabulous" fare at "reasonable prices" and "informed, efficient" staff; the less transported find the food "heavy" and the service "stiff."

Charley's Saloon [S][M] 14 | 14 | 15 | $18
284 Newbury St. (Gloucester St.), Boston, 617-266-3000
Mall at Chestnut Hill, Rte. 9 (bet. Hammond Pond Pkwy. & Langley Rd.), Chestnut Hill, 617-964-1200
■ These "basic Americans" are "dependable" and "decent" for "burgers, fries" and "brunch"; though "there's no character or charm", they're "convenient" and "good for a quick bite" at "reasonable" prices.

Charlie's Sandwich Shoppe [M] 🚫 20 | 13 | 17 | $11
429 Columbus Ave. (bet. Dartmouth & Newton Sts.), Boston, 617-536-7669
■ For the "best breakfast in town", this South End coffee shop is "truly a Bostonian hangout" with "by far the best turkey hash (or any hash for that matter)" and a "get to know your neighbor setting" (meaning you may "share a table with strangers"); it doesn't serve dinner and devotees "wish it was open on Sundays."

Chart House [S][M] 18 | 19 | 19 | $28
60 Long Wharf (Atlantic Ave.), Boston, 617-227-1576
◪ Fans go overboard about the "spectacular setting", "fantastic seafood" and "excellent steaks" at this "pricey" American chain link on the Harbor, while foes sniff "reliably mediocre for big overcooked fish and larger undercooked beef"; you'll have to chart your own course on this one.

Chau Chow ☽[S][M] 23 | 7 | 14 | $16
52 Beach St. (Harrison Ave.), Boston, 617-426-6266
■ "Great food in simple surroundings" sums up this Chinatown seafood specialist, which also serves "excellent sauteed pea pod stems with garlic"; there's "no decor" and it can be "crowded", but it's "cheap", serves "late-night Chinese" and offers "a real deal."

Chau Chow City ◐ [S] [M] — | — | — | M

83 Essex St. (Chauncey St.), Boston, 617-338-8158

The Luu family has added another jewel to their Chinatown crown with this tri-level entry (the biggest of their eateries); the menu is huge as well, ranging from old Cantonese favorites to Hong Kong–style seafood dishes; be sure to check out the fish tanks as many of the fish specials aren't listed on the menu; daily dim sum begins at 8:30 AM.

CHEESECAKE FACTORY [S] [M] 18 | 17 | 16 | $20

Cambridgeside Galleria, 100 Cambridgeside Pl., Cambridge, 617-252-3810

Atrium Mall, 300 Boylston St., Chestnut Hill, 617-964-3001

◪ An "exhaustive" "something for everyone" menu, "obscene portions" and "cheesecake to die for" keep these branches of the national chain "crowded" with "long lines" and "ridiculous waits"; critics counter "it's a factory alright" – a "pinnacle of mediocrity" for "people who believe that size equals quality."

Chef Chang's House [S] [M] 18 | 12 | 16 | $17

1006 Beacon St. (St. Mary's St.), Brookline, 617-277-4226

◪ The "Peking duck is a fix that must be had twice a year" at this long-lived Chinese on the Boston-Brookline line with "fast service" making it "the place to go before a game at Fenway"; what some call "an old reliable friend" others find "passable" and "disappointingly bland", but "an extensive selection of dishes" keeps it "crowded on Sundays."

Chef Chow's House [S] [M] 16 | 12 | 16 | $15

354 Chestnut Hill Ave. (Cleveland Circle), Brighton, 617-566-2275

230 Harvard St. (Coolidge Corner), Brookline, 617-739-2469

■ This "middle of the road" Chinese duo with Hunan and Szechuan offerings is "ok" for a "fast and filling" meal; there are "generous portions", wallet-friendly prices and "no pretenses here."

CHEZ HENRI [S] [M] 23 | 19 | 21 | $33

1 Shepard St. (Mass Ave.), Cambridge, 617-354-8980

■ Since it offers "fantastic tastes presented beautifully" in a "lively and hip" atmosphere, fans forgive this French-Cuban bistro in Cambridge for being "noisy" and "cramped"; while a few feel it has lost something since chef Corinna Mozo left, most maintain Paul O'Connell's food is "always a delight" – "every bite is nothing short of delicious" and the "the prix fixe dinner is terrific."

Chiengmai ◐ [S] [M] 15 | 11 | 15 | $16

81 Union St., Newton, 617-964-8044

◪ While some say this "hole-in-the-wall" Newton Thai serves food that's "consistently tasty and presented nicely" by a "pleasant and friendly staff", others find it "bland and uninspiring" with "uneven quality"; all agree the decor in the basement setting "needs sprucing up."

China Pearl ⓈⓂ
19 | 11 | 13 | $17

9 Tyler St. (Beach St.), Boston, 617-426-4338

■ The "fab" dim sum – among the "best in Boston" – is what receives raves at this "raucous", "crowded" Chinatown Chinese; but the "rest of the food" rates "unimaginative" and "spotty" reviews.

Christopher's ●ⓈⓂ
15 | 14 | 15 | $16

1920 Mass Ave. (Porter Sq.), Cambridge, 617-876-9180

■ This "cheap" and "casual" Porter Square Eclectic with an adjoining bar offering live late-night music is "practically an institution" thanks to "great burgers", "reliable sandwiches" and "dependable vegetarian options"; service can be "slow", but it's a "safe bet if you're trying to please many appetites."

Ciao Bella ⓈⓂ
19 | 17 | 18 | $28

240A Newbury St. (Fairfield St.), Boston, 617-536-2626

■ Most agree that "great people-watching matches great food" ("you gotta get the swordfish chop") at this "trendy", "high energy", "top sidewalk" Italian overlooking Newbury Street; if the "model-type waitresses" (and clientele) have "a little too much attitude", it's still "a happening place."

Circle Pizza ⓈⓂ⇗
15 | 5 | 9 | $10

361 Hanover St. (Fleet St.), Boston, 617-523-8787

☑ Supporters say this "fun place" in the North End is "still a classic pizza joint" with "great thin crusts", "huge" slices, "fast service" and "tacky" decor; critics concede it "used to be great, but it's still good."

Cityside at the Circle ⓈⓂ
12 | 11 | 12 | $16

1960 Beacon St. (Chestnut Hill Dr.), Boston, 617-566-1002

■ "Fairly priced" Cleveland Circle American that's a "BC hangout" and also "convenient to Circle Cinema"; while the "basic" bar fare takes a backseat to the scene – it's a "place to meet, not to eat" – there's a "nice deck to have a drink on."

Claddagh ⓈⓂ
10 | 10 | 12 | $16

119 Dartmouth St. (Columbus Ave.), Boston, 617-262-9874

☑ A few generous souls say this South End Irish bar/restaurant boasts the "best ribs in the Boston area" and is also a good "value for Sunday brunch", but scores suggest it's "nothing special"; still, some regulars find the "newly renovated old-world place" "significantly improved."

Claremont Cafe Ⓢ
23 | 17 | 20 | $26

535 Columbus Ave. (Claremont Park), Boston, 617-247-9001

■ This "hidden jewel" in the South End may be "the best neighborhood restaurant in Boston", with "superb" and "fabulously comforting" Eclectic cuisine, a "friendly staff" and a "cozy feel"; breakfasts are "excellent", brunches "wonderful" and "dinner is outstanding"; "wish it were bigger" seems to be the only complaint.

Clarke's S M
12 | 11 | 12 | $15
21 Merchants Row (State St.), Boston, 617-227-7800
■ While some speak up for the "good burgers" at this
Faneuil Hall–area American that doubles as a "pickup joint",
others consider it a "place to drink" with "mediocre food."

Club Cafe ● S M
15 | 16 | 16 | $26
209 Columbus Ave. (Berkeley St.), Boston, 617-536-0966
◪ Enthusiasts of this South End Eclectic, "home base
for the upscale gay community", say it's "such a pleasant
place" with "a great location" and a "fabulous bar scene"
that "you forgive the mediocre food"; but critics claim
there's so much "attitude you could cut it with a knife"
and dub it "Club Snub."

Colonial Inn S M
15 | 19 | 16 | $26
48 Monument Sq. (Rte. 2), Concord, 978-369-9200
◪ The "pretty historic setting" and "lovely building",
especially the "great front porch", make this Concord
Center American "worth a visit" even if some say the food is
"from 1776" and "hasn't improved since the shot heard
'round the world"; the safest bet is to "try it for afternoon
tea", "cocktails" or the "special Sunday brunch."

Commonwealth Brewing Co. S M
13 | 15 | 14 | $17
138 Portland St. (Causeway St.), Boston, 617-523-8383
■ Reviewers agree that "great beer" rather than "mediocre
food" makes this brewpub near North Station "the place
to go before a game" at the nearby Fleet Center; get ready
for "rowdy surroundings" and "bachelor chow" – "burgers
and fries" and "good ribs" – from "yet another" place for
"ordinary pub food."

Coolidge Corner
Clubhouse ● S M
14 | 11 | 14 | $14
*307A-309 Harvard St. (bet. Babcock & Beacon Sts.),
Brookline, 617-566-4948*
◪ A "popular local sports bar", this Coolidge Corner
American in Brookline delivers "massive servings" of
burgers, fries and wings; while critics call it a "grungy"
"factory" serving "just ok greasy food", insiders insist
"lots of TVs" and "lots of beer" (35 on tap) in a "laid-back"
atmosphere add up to "a good place to watch a game."

Copley's ● S M
19 | 21 | 20 | $34
*Fairmont Copley Plaza, 138 St. James Ave. (bet. Dartmouth &
Trinity Sts.), Boston, 617-267-5300*
◪ Located in the "elegant" Fairmont Copley Plaza in the
Back Bay, this upscale American is "in transition" and
"worth watching"; while a few feel there have been "too
many ownership changes" and "Sunday brunch has lost
its punch", the majority maintains the "food is much better"
and the "beautiful room and elegant service" still make it
a fine "place to take your mother."

Cornwall's ◐ⓈⓂ
| 15 | 16 | 18 | $15 |

510 Commonwealth Ave. (Kenmore Sq.), Boston, 617-262-3749

■ Boosters of this "quintessential, age-old" "English pub" in Kenmore Square call it "a cozy subterranean hideaway" that's especially fun "before a Red Sox game", giving it points for a "great beer selection", "home-cooked food" and "board games" that you can "play at your table."

Cottonwood Cafe ⓈⓂ
| 19 | 19 | 17 | $25 |

222 Berkeley St. (St. James Ave.), Boston, 617-247-2225
Porter Exchange Mall, 1815 Mass Ave. (Roseland Ave.), Cambridge, 617-661-7440

◪ "Good locations" in Porter Square and the Back Bay make these Southwesterners good destinations for "funky power lunches" and brunches; fans rave about the "consistently good" "creative cuisine", "great margaritas" (especially the "fresh fruit" versions) and "terrific atmo"; a minority doesn't cotton to the "tired formula" of "faux Mex food" "masquerading as high-end fare."

Country Life Vegetarian ⓈⓂ
| 17 | 9 | 12 | $12 |

200 High St. (Rowes Wharf), Boston, 617-951-2534

◪ For "cheap", "all you can eat" "natural food", the "crunchy" crowd heads to this "cafeteria-style" Vegetarian in the Financial District offering "yummy" "bargain buffets" and "excellent fruit salad" in a "depressing" setting that's "a flashback to the '70s"; foes feel the fare is "unexciting" – a triumph of "volume over quality."

Court House Seafood Ⓜ
| ▽ 21 | 7 | 15 | $13 |

498 Cambridge St. (6th St.), Cambridge, 617-491-1213

■ There may be "no atmosphere", but this "spotlessly clean" East Cambridge seafooder next to the fish market of the same name is where "police and ambulance workers eat" when they want "fresh fish" at "bargain prices."

CRANEBROOK RESTAURANT & TEA ROOM Ⓢ
| 24 | 26 | 23 | $39 |

229 Tremont St. (Lakeview St.), Carver, 508-866-3235

◪ This "elegant" Carver New American in a "lovely country setting" is "wonderful" "for special occasions" thanks to a "romantic" atmosphere and "beautifully presented" food; although a handful find the fare "not as perfect as it should be for the price", it's the "only show in town."

Cybersmith ⓈⓂ
| 12 | 15 | 10 | $11 |

36 Church St. (bet. Brattle St. & Mass Ave.), Cambridge, 617-492-5857

◪ To some, the "'90s atmosphere" at this combination cafe and computer playground in Harvard Square is "entertaining" and "great for coffee on a rainy afternoon"; but a drop in ratings since our last *Survey* supports those who think it's a "weak concept" that exists "more for the computers" than the "airport-type food."

Daddy-O's [S][M] 20 | 16 | 18 | $23

134 Hampshire St. (bet. Elm & Norfolk Sts.), Cambridge, 617-354-8371

◪ There's definitely a "bohemian influence" on the "comfort food" at this "way cool" Cambridge American where "quirky", "creative" twists "breathe new life into familiar dishes" like "macaroni and cheese"; but foes call it "inconsistent" fare coming from a "funky and weird menu"; still, everyone agrees the "nice outdoor patio" is "a treat in the summer."

Daily Catch, The [S][M] 22 | 9 | 16 | $22

261 Northern Ave. (Fish Pier), Boston, 617-338-3093
323 Hanover St. (bet. Prince & Richmond Sts.), Boston, 617-523-8567 🚫
441 Harvard St. (bet. Beacon St. & Commonwealth Ave.), Brookline, 617-734-5696 🚫

◪ The "excellent fresh" fish with an Italian accent served at these "no-frills" seafood-only spots includes "fried calamari that melts in your mouth" and the "best squid ink pasta"; although some don't like "eating from the frying pans" that the food is cooked in, or the "too cramped and small" "kitchen" atmosphere, that doesn't deter devotees who feel they net "wonderful" fare that's "worth the wait."

Dakota's [M] 18 | 19 | 17 | $27

34 Summer St. (Arch St.), Boston, 617-737-1772

◪ A "power lunch place for the Financial District", this "old reliable" American grill with "sleek", "sophisticated" decor offers "excellent steaks", "well-prepared fish" and a "great salad bar"; it's "unbelievably noisy" and the service can be "inattentive", but when you want "to be seen", it's a "very good" choice.

DALI [S][M] 24 | 23 | 21 | $26

415 Washington St. (Beacon St.), Somerville, 617-661-3254

■ For "a romantic dinner" in "one of the most beautiful restaurants in the area", this Somerville Spaniard with "outstanding service" boasts a "staggering array of tapas" that are "the highlight of the menu" and "better than the entrees" as well as "the best sangria around"; most want to dally at Dali ("Salvador would love it") and their only complaint is "no reservations" means "long waits."

Dalya's [M] 21 | 19 | 21 | $30

20 North Rd. (Rtes. 4 & 62), Bedford, 781-275-0700

■ This "charming" Bedford Mediterranean in an "obscure location" surprises many with its "superb cuisine" "artfully presented", "excellent wine list", "gracious staff" and "comfortable, homey decor"; all this and "reasonable prices" too – no wonder respondents rave "absolutely worth the drive."

Davide Ristorante Ⓜ
22 | 19 | 22 | $37

326 Commercial St. (bet. Battery & Clark Sts.), Boston, 617-227-5745

■ "Upscale Northern Italian" on the outskirts of the North End offering "great food", "fine wines" and "superior service" in a "romantic" if slightly "dated" atmosphere; while a few feel it's "expensive", more maintain it's "what great Italian is all about."

David's Ⓢ
21 | 19 | 21 | $31

123 Stuart St. (bet. S. Charles & Tremont Sts.), Boston, 617-367-8405

■ "Good for a quick pre- or post-theater meal", this Theater District American with a Mediterranean accent offers "super food and service"; the "very pretty decor" makes you feel "like you're eating on a stage set" plus "they have their act together" and serve you "promptly."

Davio's Ⓢ Ⓜ
21 | 18 | 19 | $30

269 Newbury St. (bet. Fairfield & Gloucester Sts.), Boston, 617-242-4810
Royal Sonesta Hotel, 5 Cambridge Pkwy. (opposite Cambridgeside Galleria), Cambridge, 617-661-4810

☑ Diners are downright divided on this Davio duo on Newbury Street and in Cambridge's Royal Sonesta Hotel; loyalists like the "always dependable", "unusual" and "creative Italian food", "romantic atmosphere" and "courtly" staff, while foes feel it's "not what it used to be", labeling it "overrated" with sometimes "surly" service; however, all agree the "outdoor terraces" at both locations (Cambridge is on the Charles River) make for "good people-watching."

Delhi Darbar Ⓢ Ⓜ
19 | 14 | 14 | $15

Harvard Sq., 8 Holyoke St. (bet. Mass Ave. & Mt. Auburn St.), Cambridge, 617-492-8993

■ The "appealing Indian fare" proffered at this "pleasant oasis in Harvard Square" includes a "wonderful and cheap lunch buffet" ($6.95); regulars warn "when they say spicy, they mean it" and advise it's "not the place to go when you are in a hurry" – service is the "slowest in town."

Delux Cafe ◑ Ⓜ ≠
21 | 18 | 16 | $16

100 Chandler St. (Clarendon St.), Boston, 617-338-5258

■ Where "Greenwich Village meets Beantown", this South End Eclectic "dive with great fare" focuses on a "twentysomething crowd" ("just try to count the tattoos") that comes for "gourmet food at grunge prices" and "funky" decor that includes "old record covers plastered on the walls"; longtime enthusiasts "enjoyed it more before it was discovered" as now it's "impossibly crowded" – and, like it was from day one, "smoky."

Demo's [S][M]≠ | 19 | 6 | 13 | $11 |

146 Lexington St. (bet. Main & 128th Sts.), Waltham, 781-893-8359
60-64 Mt. Auburn St. (bet. Main St. & Rte. 16), Watertown, 617-924-9660

■ Insiders insist these "working man's" "Greek cafeterias" in Watertown and Waltham serve the "best cheap eats in Boston"; there's "no atmosphere" ("except for the fluorescent lights") and you have "to stand in line for food", but "huge portions" of "great shish kebab" and other Greek treats make up for the inconvenience.

De Pasquale's [S][M] | 20 | 9 | 17 | $20 |

374 Main St. (Harvard St.), Medford, 781-395-9591

◪ It's the "good portions" of "fabulous comfort food" and "friendly service" that bring diners back to the "only Italian in Medford"; however, the "typical checkered tablecloth" decor and "basement" locale lead some to say this 1939 pioneer needs "updating."

Dick's Last Resort ◐[S][M] | 10 | 9 | 10 | $17 |

55 Huntington Ave. (Prudential Ctr.), Boston, 617-267-8080

■ "Go only as a last resort" is the consensus on this "gimmicky" Prudential Center American that "specializes in berating the clientele"; though there are a few fans of the "cheap" "buckets of ribs and chicken", most maintain the combination of "abuse and bad food" should be reserved for "rowdy frat boys" whose idea of "fun" is dining with "Beavis and Butt-head."

Dino's Sea Grille [S] | 13 | 11 | 14 | $19 |

640 Arsenal St. (Coolidge Ave.), Watertown, 617-923-7771

◪ Opinions about this Watertown seafooder are oceans apart, with fans hooked on "good" "simple" menu choices and foes carping it's so "overpriced" and "unimaginative" that "you could do it at home for less money"; what "a pity because this area needs decent restaurants."

Division Sixteen ◐[S][M] | 16 | 14 | 13 | $19 |

955 Boylston St. (bet. Hereford St. & Mass Ave.), Boston, 617-353-0870

◪ "Monstrously big burgers" and other "elegant junk food", "superstrong drinks" and "late-night Eurotrash-watching" are the draws at this Back Bay American "pickup joint"; it's "dark", "smoky" and "if you're not a wealthy European with a fancy for fried food, you may feel out of place."

Dixie Kitchen [S][M] | 18 | 10 | 14 | $16 |

182 Mass Ave. (St. Germain St.), Boston, 617-536-3068

■ When Bostonians crave "good" Cajun-Creole cooking, many head to this Symphony Hall "hole-in-the-wall"; despite "slow Southern service" and "not much atmosphere" ("a liquor license would help"), it's still a "low-key find" for "down-home food" at dirt cheap prices.

Dockside ◐ⓈⓂ
| 10 | 11 | 10 | $16 |

229 Centre St. (Rte. 60), Malden, 781-321-3000

▧ A "McDonald's with beer", this "very average sports bar" in Malden offers "ok food" in a "light, fun, entertaining atmosphere"; "order by noon if you want your dinner by six."

Dodge Street Bar & Grill ⓈⓂ ▽
| 17 | 12 | 15 | $16 |

7 Dodge St. (bet. Lafayette & Washington Sts.), Salem, 978-745-0139

▧ "The place to go in Salem if you're 24 and have nothing to do", this "fun little bar/restaurant" offers "large portions" of "good basic" Regional American fare ("yummy catfish", "ribs that Fred Flintstone would love") in a "typical local bar" setting; be warned "eat before 9 PM or be blasted out by the band."

Dolphin Ⓜ
| 19 | 13 | 17 | $19 |

1105 Mass Ave. (Remington St.), Cambridge, 617-661-2937
7 South Ave. (Rte. 27S), Natick, 508-655-0669

▧ Legions of loyalists call these "always busy" Harvard Square and Natick seafooders "solid standbys" for "good fresh fish served in plain settings"; afishionados assert that they're "better and cheaper than Legal", but an across-the-board drop in scores supports critics who carp "uninspired" and "past their prime"; N.B. an expansion at the Natick locale means "less of a wait."

Dom's ⓈⓂ
| 21 | 18 | 21 | $37 |

100 Salem St. (Bartlett Pl.), Boston, 617-367-8979

▧ "The unique concept", where the "owner sits at the table" and "finds out your likes and dislikes and creates something" for you, receives as many comments as the cuisine at this North End Italian; "excellent food" and the fact that "the customer is made to feel like a king" lead admirers to call it "one of the hub's hidden delights"; but foes feel the in-your-face format is "passé" and possibly painful ("don't let Dom sit on your lap – he'll try and it hurts").

Donatello Ristorante ⓈⓂ
| 24 | 22 | 22 | $34 |

44 Broadway (Rte. 1N), Saugus, 781-233-9975

■ Supporters say this "wonderful suburban" in Saugus is the "best Italian north of Boston", with a "veal chop to die for" and "great littlenecks in garlic"; "not too stuffy", but with "a lot of class" and a "superb European-trained staff", it's definitely "the place for a special evening."

Dong Khanh ⓈⓂ⇎ ▽
| 23 | 10 | 17 | $12 |

81-83 Harrison Ave. (Beach St.), Boston, 617-426-9410

▧ The few who've visited this bare-bones Vietnamese-Chinese say it's "very cheap", "very delicious" and "worth the drive to Chinatown"; the "lightness of each course" and "friendly service" may help offset the "slow kitchen."

Doyle's Cafe [S][M]≠ 14 | 19 | 17 | $14
3484 Washington St. (Williams St.), Jamaica Plain, 617-524-2345
■ The "quintessential Irish pub", this "dark, smoky" Jamaica Plain 1882 "institution where food is clearly secondary" to "Guinness, burgers and kitsch" is a "friendly, crowded" "pols place" and the "definitive neighborhood hangout"; insiders insist it has the "best Sunday brunch in Boston."

Du Barry [M] 17 | 16 | 17 | $27
159 Newbury St. (bet. Dartmouth & Exeter Sts.), Boston, 617-262-2445
◩ Boosters of this "old favorite", "lovely little" Classic French "tucked away on Newbury Street" say it "deserves to go on forever", claiming "it's as close to France as you can get without getting on a plane" and advising "go in summer and dine in the garden"; detractors, on the other hand, dis "bland food" and "boring decor."

Duckworth Lane [S][M] 16 | 19 | 16 | $23
1657 Beacon St. (Washington St.), Brookline, 617-730-8040
83 Main St. (Pleasant St.), Charlestown, 617-242-6009
66 Chestnut St. (Rte. 135), Needham, 781-444-8200
344 Walnut St. (Washington St.), Newton, 617-244-0004
◩ With four locations, this rapidly expanding, "reasonably priced" Eclectic bistro/wine bar chainlet offers a "huge menu" in a "cool atmosphere" culled from yard sale art; surveyors say it's a "good concept" with "real potential", but at the moment it's "hit or miss" – "they need to raise the quality of the food."

Ducky Wok [S][M] 22 | 15 | 20 | $16
122-126 Harvard St. (Commonwealth Ave.), Allston, 617-782-6888
■ It may have a "rotten name", but this "bright, shiny" newcomer with "cool fish tanks" has brought "a Chinatown menu to Allston"; "listen to the waiters" and get ready for "great whole fish specials" and "incredible stir-fried watercress" at this "inexpensive", "delightful" spot that's a "step above the others."

Durgin Park [S][M] 14 | 11 | 12 | $21
Faneuil Hall, 30 N. Market St. (Clinton St.), Boston, 617-227-2038
■ "It is what it is"; this 1827 "landmark" in Faneuil Hall is the home of "huge portions" of "old-fashioned New England–style food" like "chowdah" and "Indian pudding" – "a must for tourists" ("lunch is the best time to go") but "not for serious eating"; harsher critics call it "the land of bland" and warn "sharing tables isn't cozy, it's annoying" and "rude" service is part of the shtick.

Dynasty ⓈⓂ
16 | 12 | 12 | $17

33 Edinboro St. (bet. Beach St. & Surface Rd.), Boston, 617-350-7777

▣ "Great dim sum" "seven days a week" is the reason to go to this otherwise "standard Downtown Chinese", a large, "typically decorated" place that's "a little worse for the wear"; service seems to be "good if you're Chinese" and "nasty if you're not."

EAST COAST GRILL & RAW BAR ⓈⓂ
24 | 18 | 19 | $28

1271 Cambridge St. (Prospect St.), Cambridge, 617-491-6568

■ "Expanded" but "still crowded", Chris Schlesinger's "funky" Inman Square seafood and barbecue restaurant is "still smokin' after all these years" with "big portions of wonderful grilled food" "beyond your dreams of spicy" washed down with "wicked margaritas"; despite criticisms – "parking is impossible", there are "uncivilized waits" and it's "incredibly noisy" – "it always puts a smile on your face."

Eastern Pier Seafood ⓈⓂ
22 | 12 | 19 | $19

237 Northern Ave. (Atlantic Ave.), Boston, 617-423-7756

▣ "Off the beaten track", this "can't miss" Chinese seafooder on the Pier dishes up "better fish than any of the nearby Occidental restaurants" ("try the shrimp with scallions"); some find the decor "cheesy", but it's "a nice away-from-Chinatown alternative" with "courteous service."

East Ocean City ◑ⓈⓂ
23 | 13 | 16 | $20

25 Beach St. (bet. Harrison Ave. & Washington St.), Boston, 617-542-2504

■ Touting "excellent" "seafood fresh from the tanks", this "bright and open" Chinatown favorite with a "menu as long as a Stephen King novel" "lives up to its billing"; even with a "drab outside", "bland decor" inside and "inconsistent service", it "seems to have become a hot spot."

eat ⓈⓂ
20 | 15 | 18 | $23

253 Washington St. (Union Sq.), Somerville, 617-776-2889

▣ "A worthy newcomer", this "warm and cozy" Somerville Eclectic draws applause for its "caring host" (Charlie Robinson) and "delicious" "affordable comfort food" doled out in a "deliberately downscale setting" (which a few find "weird"); "friendly but terribly slow service" is the only major complaint about this "very promising restaurant"; P.S. "weekly guest chefs on Monday are a clever idea."

El Cafetal ⓈⓂ
– | – | – | I

479 Cambridge St. (Brighton Ave.), Brighton, 617-789-4009

The handful of adventurous souls who've sampled this "no-frills" Brighton Colombian give a nod to the "authentic" fare and "friendly people running" the place but point out that it can be difficult to enjoy your meal "with Hispanic TV in the background."

ELEPHANT WALK 🟥Ⓜ   24 21 20 $28

900 Beacon St. (Park Dr.), Boston, 617-247-1500
70 Union Sq. (bet. Prospect St. & Somerville Ave.),
Somerville, 617-623-9939

◪ A "unique" French-Cambodian blend yields "exotic
atmosphere, tastes and textures" at this "attractive", family-
run Kenmore Square and Somerville duo where "novel"
fare (including mee siem, a noodle dish, and "mind-blowing
tuna with chile") plus a "great" beer list "reward the
adventurous diner"; though dissenters cite "arrogant staff"
and feel it's "slipping", the majority says "wild elephants
couldn't keep us away" from such "intriguing" flavors.

Enzo's on the Charles 🟥Ⓜ   14 13 15 $23

Days Inn, 1234 Soldiers Field Rd. (Storrow Dr.), Boston,
617-254-0550

◪ Some "mourn the move from Brookline" to the Days Inn
on Soldiers Field Road, feeling "the location" will hurt this
Italian; "poor service" and high prices for wines also take
knocks, but a "great host" (Enzo himself) and "terrific
pastas" might turn the tide.

Erawan of Siam 🟥Ⓜ   21 22 20 $19

459 Moody St. (High St.), Waltham, 781-899-3399

■ "Fine" "well-prepared" fare (including the "best melon
curry"), "rich, sumptuous decor" and "attentive service"
make this "always agreeable" Waltham Thai "an easy place
to enjoy a quiet unhurried dinner"; only a few think it "tries
too hard on the decor and not hard enough on the food."

Exchange, The Ⓜ   -   -   -   E

148 State St. (India St.), Boston, 617-726-7600
Small and sophisticated, this New French near the Custom
House Tower has a soothing dining room attached to a
noisier bar; chef Prabhas Navaraj (ex Locke-Ober) turns
out interesting updates on classics (crab cakes with a
coulis of mango and cranberry, baby chicken stuffed with
foie gras) that are enhanced by refined service; while
some might wish the wines were less pricey, on the whole
it's a welcome return to quietly elegant dining.

Fajitas & 'Ritas Ⓜ   14 10 13 $14

25 West St. (bet. Tremont & Washington Sts.), Boston,
617-426-1222
48 Boylston St. (Harvard & Washington Sts.), Brookline,
617-566-1222 🟥

◪ Although these Brookline and Downtown Crossing
Tex-Mexers are "very casual" and "very cheap", most
maintain "you get what you pay for"; much is made of the
environment ("it's a dump"), but for "fajitas in a hurry"
and what some say are "the best margaritas in Boston",
it's "exactly what the name says it is."

Fava 23 | 15 | 19 | $28

1027 Great Plain Ave. (Eaton Sq.), Needham, 781-455-8668

◪ "If [chef-owner] Paul Booras would relocate to Boston, I'd eat there every night" cheer boosters of his "brilliant" Needham New American; everyone agrees the "inventive chef" whips up "beautifully executed food", but the "very tight seating" and "overwhelmed service" need to be remedied so this place can live up to its "good potential."

Felicia's [S][M] 17 | 13 | 17 | $24

145 Richmond St. (Hanover St.), Boston, 617-523-9885

◪ Felicia fans claim this "quintessential North End" Italian is "underrated because it still has a fairly traditional menu", but faultfinders retort "it's seen better days" and "too much sauce" marks "typical Italian food from the '50s and '60s."

57 Restaurant [S][M] 17 | 16 | 18 | $31

Radisson Hotel, 200 Stuart St. (Park Sq.), Boston, 617-423-5700

◪ "Convenient" to the Theater District, this American-Continental in the Radisson Hotel serves "good basics" including prime rib and swordfish; but what some consider a "comforting menu that I remember from 20 years ago", others calls "boring" and a sign of a "tired" spot that's "well past its prime"; "free parking" is a plus.

FIGS [S][M] 23 | 16 | 18 | $22

42 Charles St. (Chestnut St.), Boston, 617-742-3447
67 Main St. (Monument Ave.), Charlestown, 617-242-2229
1208 Boylston St. (Hammond St.), Chestnut Hill, 617-738-9992
92 Central St. (Rte. 135), Wellesley, 781-237-5788

■ "Gourmet pizzas with crunch" rule at these "harried", "congested" pizza and pasta places created by Todd and Olivia English of Olives; pros praise the pies as "ingenious", "heavenly" and "the best in Boston"; many "hate the wait" and paying "$50 for pizza and pasta", but the majority believes "it's the biggest culinary bargain" around.

Filippo Ristorante [S][M] 17 | 17 | 17 | $30

283 Causeway St. (Endicott St.), Boston, 617-742-4143

◪ Dine amidst "marble mirrors and oil paintings" at this "opulent" Abruzzi-influenced Italian near the Fleet Center, a safe bet "before a game at the Garden" with "good wines" and "unusual dishes"; a few find the food "too rich" and "overpriced", but they make up for it with "good portions."

Finally Michael's [S][M] 16 | 16 | 17 | $26

1280 Worcester Rd. (Rte. 9W), Framingham, 617-237-6180

◪ "Vegetarians need not apply" – this "very suburban" Framingham Regional American is for an "older meat and potatoes" crowd that raves about the "best rack of lamb" and "good value" "early-bird specials"; the younger sets sees it as an "old tired place" with a "boring menu" and "average food", claiming "the only redeeming feature is the bar" where it's a "bargain to eat."

Finnegans Wake [S][M] | 12 | 15 | 15 | $16

2067 Mass Ave. (bet. Hadley & Russell Sts.), Cambridge, 617-576-2240

◪ This "authentic" Irish pub near Porter Square is "good if you like potatoes" and "shepherd's pie", but patrons basically "go for the Guinness" and "free bar snacks" during happy hour and soak up the "great ambiance."

Fire & Ice ◐[S][M] | – | – | – | I

50 Church St. (Harvard Sq.), Cambridge, 617-547-9007

Create-your-own-meal is the concept behind this dramatic-looking Harvard Square New American where diners mix and match meats, seafood, vegetables and sauces and then hand the ingredients over to a chef at the open grill; dishes are teamed with sides like rice and beans, tortillas or moo shu pancakes, making for filling, affordable eats.

Fire King Bistro [S][M] | 22 | 19 | 17 | $23

19 North St. (Rte. 3A), Hingham, 781-740-9400

◪ Everyone agrees that "amazing breads and pastries" make this "unique for the South Shore" Hingham Harbor Eclectic a "good choice" for an "excellent lunch"; although the "imaginative menu" can be "hit or miss" and the service "pot luck", most maintain the "cool decor" and "lovely patio seating" are adequate compensation.

Fishery [S][M] | 18 | 13 | 17 | $18

720 Mass Ave. (bet. Inman & Prospect Sts.), Cambridge, 617-868-8800

◪ "Reliable but no standout" sums up this no-frills Central Square seafooder where "the owner is always there watching over the preparation" of "good" fin fare; a few fans go so far as to say it's "better than Legal" and "a lot cheaper" too.

Five North Square [S][M] | 21 | 18 | 20 | $28

5 North Sq. (Prince St.), Boston, 617-720-1050

◪ A "tranquil", "traditional", "very romantic" North End Italian that's a "great place to celebrate an anniversary"; some say it's a "little too small", "crowded" and "touristy", but experienced diners overlook this as they enjoy "Caesar salad made at the table" and some of the "best veal parmigiana in Boston."

Five Seasons [S][M] | 23 | 13 | 16 | $18

669A Centre St. (Green St.), Jamaica Plain, 617-524-9016

■ The "only real Vegetarian option in Boston", this Jamaica Plain "old standby" also serves seafood and free-range chicken; "it's the best health food joint around" with "delicious" "hearty fare", "impressive tuna steaks" and "fresh salads right out of the backyard garden"; regulars warn "it can get crowded" and there's "no waiting area."

575 ◖ S M
17 | 18 | 14 | $24

94 Mass Ave. (Commonwealth Ave.), Boston, 617-247-9922

◪ Proponents of this "trendy" Mass Ave. Med-Japanese praise the "great maki" and "some of the city's best sushi" as well as the "friendly" atmosphere that includes a happening "bar scene"; but detractors insist "it's passé", the "staff has an attitude" and they "need to stabilize the menu and decide if it's fusion or Western with sushi."

Flora S
23 | 21 | 21 | $28

190 Mass Ave. (bet. Chandler & Lake Sts.), Arlington, 781-641-1664

■ The "mature, hip" crowd that hangs out at this "bank turned American bistro" calls it a "winner" and "worth the trip to Arlington" for "upscale comfort food" in "a gorgeous space"; "ask to dine in the vault room" for a particularly "delightful" experience and to avoid the "deafening noise" in the main dining area.

Florence's S M
19 | 13 | 21 | $23

190 North St. (Richmond St.), Boston, 617-523-4480

◪ While the "tacky atmosphere" is off-putting to some, others feel that if you "concentrate on the food" at this "basic" Southern Italian in the North End you'll find "a menu for everyone" with "wonderful mussels" and "inventive" dishes like "amazing Gorgonzola risotto."

Florentina M
22 | 16 | 19 | $24

143 Main St. (bet. Broadway & 3rd St.), Cambridge, 617-577-8300

■ This "pleasant surprise in Kendall Square" is a "popular lunch place" for "MIT students and faculty" in search of "quick and filling" pizzas and pastas, but it's "almost always empty" at dinner – a pity since it offers "fantastic appetizers" and "creative and wide-ranging entrees."

Florentine Cafe S M
18 | 20 | 17 | $23

333 Hanover St. (Prince St.), Boston, 617-227-1777

◪ It's the "hopping sidewalk and bar scene" that makes this North End Italian a "good summer place" – "it's like being in Tuscany except the waiters wear Dockers"; while loyalists like the "creative cuisine" and foes feel the "food could be better", all agree on the "great open-air ambiance."

Forest Cafe S M
21 | 6 | 15 | $20

(fka Mexican Cuisine)
1682 Mass Ave. (bet. Harvard & Porter Sqs.), Cambridge, 617-661-7810

■ This "hole-in-the-wall" between Harvard and Porter Squares "confirms the rule that you have to go to a dive to get good Mexican food"; expect "incredibly authentic and delicious" dishes ("not just nachos and quesadillas") including "inventive seafood" and the "ultimate chile rellenos" dished out in a "smoky" "barroom atmosphere."

Franklin Cafe ◑ⓈⓂ   23 | 16 | 20 | $23
278 Shawmut Ave. (Hanson St.), Boston,
617-350-0010

✉ The "new hip spot in Boston", this "dark", "hidden",
"sexy" South End Contemporary American serves up
"generous portions of gutsy food" ("try the meat loaf") at
"reasonable prices"; while satisfied surveyors say it's a
"cool place" with a "great bar scene" and "very friendly
staff", it's also "loud and smoky", "parking is practically
impossible" and there are "long waits", but once you get
in you can expect "awesome drinks."

Frank's Steak House ⓈⓂ   16 | 13 | 16 | $20
2310 Mass Ave. (Rice St.), Cambridge, 617-661-0666

✉ "When you want a cheap steak and an iceberg lettuce
salad", this "family-owned" North Cambridge Traditional
American specializing in sizzling sirloin is the place; but
what some carnivores see as "solid family food", others
call "uninspired" with "no frills" and "no style"; N.B. a
recent redo may improve decor scores next time around.

Fraser's on the Avenue ⓈⓂ   14 | 13 | 15 | $20
1680 Mass Ave. (bet. Hudson & Martin Sts.), Cambridge,
617-441-5566

✉ Reviewers can't seem to reach a consensus on this
"convenient" Eclectic near Harvard Square; supporters
say it's "cozy, comfy and creative" and claim the "new
menu with lower prices" makes it "a good deal with a
neighborhood feel", but a drop in scores since our last
Survey sides with critics who contend "the menu keeps
changing, but not for the better", "location is its only virtue"
and it's "overpriced for what it is."

Fuddruckers ⓈⓂ   13 | 8 | 10 | $11
8 Park Pl. (Stuart St.), Boston, 617-723-3833

✉ A "glorified McDonald's", this "not very exciting"
"burger and fries" "cafeteria" in the Theater District
doesn't win many devotees with its downscale interior
and the "side of beef hanging on display"; but many
maintain "if you must have a fast-food hamburger, this is
it"; plus, it's a "fun place for kids."

GALLERIA ITALIANA ⓈⓂ   24 | 17 | 19 | $35
177 Tremont St. (Boylston St.), Boston,
617-423-2092

■ This "popular", "crowded" Theater District Italian offers
"extraordinary" food and "one of the best wine selections
around" in an "ultra-stylish" setting "that's exactly like
trattoria dining in Tuscany"; despite a few complaints about
"spotty service" and "high prices", the majority calls it
"marvelous", though some will "wait and see" if the new
chef can "keep up the quality."

Galleria Umberto Ⓜ⊄   23 | 10 | 14 | $9
289 Hanover St. (bet. Prince & Richmond Sts.), Boston, 617-227-5709

■ You'll find "great simple food" at "cheap" prices at this lunch-only "cafeteria-style" "Italian food hall" in the North End, along with "unbelievably long lines" of fans who swear the "outrageous pizzas" and "superb calzones" are "worth waiting" for, especially since the "pizza cutters" are "a show unto themselves."

Gardner Museum Cafe Ⓢ   18 | 19 | 16 | $17
Isabella Stuart Gardner Museum, 280 The Fenway (Huntington Ave.), Boston, 617-566-1088

■ Within the elegant Isabella Stuart Gardner Museum in the Fenway is this "cozy" and "congenial" Mediterranean; it's an artful choice for a "light and diverse" "ladies' lunch", particularly if you "sit outside and enjoy the garden."

Gargoyles on the Square Ⓢ   24 | 20 | 22 | $32
215 Elm St. (Summer St.), Somerville, 617-776-5300

■ "A terrific find in the middle of nowhere", this "intriguing, innovative and intimate" New American in Davis Square serves "beautifully presented, excellent food"; it may be "cramped", but the "romantic atmosphere" and "superb martinis" make it "great for a date."

Geoffrey's Cafe & Bar Ⓢ Ⓜ   20 | 17 | 18 | $20
578 Tremont St. (bet. Clarendon & Dartmouth Sts.), Boston, 617-266-1122

☑ Locals are pleased that things are "back to normal" after a fire last year at this "super popular" South End Eclectic, a "fabulous restaurant" for "good home cooking"; while regulars say if you "get into the waiters' camp attitude you'll enjoy it", others find service "annoying" and say it's "not worth the lengthy wait to be seated."

Giacomo's Ⓢ Ⓜ   23 | 17 | 20 | $25
355 Hanover St. (bet. Fleet & Prince Sts.), Boston, 617-523-9026 ⊄
431 Columbus Ave. (Dartmouth St.), Boston, 617-536-5723

■ "There's always a line", but most feel it's "worth the sacrifice" to dine on "seafood and pasta like no one else's" at these "cozy little Italians" in the North and South End; the "friendly staff" may "rush you in and out", but about the only other complaint is "wish they'd move to bigger digs."

Giannino's Ⓢ Ⓜ   20 | 19 | 19 | $27
20 University Rd. (bet. Memorial Dr. & Mt. Auburn St.), Cambridge, 617-576-0605

■ This "reliable", "elegant alfresco" Northern Italian in the Charles Hotel courtyard is "removed from the chaos of Harvard Square" and "nice to take advantage of in warm weather"; fans "love the half-size entree" option, and "efficient service" makes it "convenient for pre-theater."

Ginger Tree 🅂🅼   15 | 12 | 14 | $17
1366 Beacon St. (Centre St.), Brookline, 617-277-6869

◼ The "excellent weekend dim sum buffet" is the highlight at this "local" Chinese, and the "courteous staff" gets nods, but the regular menu is deemed "mediocre" by most.

GINZA 🅂🅼   26 | 18 | 19 | $26
16 Hudson St. (bet. Beach & Kneeland Sts.), Boston, 617-338-2261 ◖

1002 Beacon St. (St. Mary's St.), Brookline, 617-566-9688

◼ Bringing a "bit of Tokyo to Beantown", this "crowded" Chinatown Japanese and its younger Beacon Street sibling earn plaudits for their "inventive", "work of art" fare, with the lion's share of praise going to "awesome", "sublime sushi" that's "whimsical" and "dazzlingly prepared"; kudos also go to the "helpful staff", good sake, "late" hours in Chinatown and easier parking in Brookline.

Glenn's Restaurant & Cool Bar 🅂🅼   ▽ 22 | 18 | 19 | $33
44 Merrimac St. (Green St.), Newburyport, 978-465-3811

◼ This Newburyport New American wins raves for "huge portions" of "imaginative food" including the "best tuna in the area"; although the Sunday jazz brunch is also praised, it makes for a "noisy" meal.

Goemon Japanese Noodle 🅂🅼   16 | 11 | 14 | $14
738 Commonwealth Ave. (St. Mary's St.), Boston, 617-739-3474

◼ "For a cheap bowl of hot noodles on a cold day", head to this Japanese noodler near Boston University; but expect "minimalist decor and service" at this "authentic", "healthy" Asian "answer to McDonald's."

Golden Palace ◖🅂🅼   19 | 12 | 13 | $19
14 Tyler St. (bet. Beach & Kneeland Sts.), Boston, 617-423-4565

◼ "Another reliable favorite for dim sum", this Chinatown veteran also offers "pretty good regular dishes" on the rest of the menu; "fast service" is another plus.

Golden Temple ◖🅂🅼   20 | 19 | 18 | $20
1651 Beacon St. (Washington Sq.), Brookline, 617-277-9722

◼ A "popular" Washington Square Chinese known for "new Asian" "gourmet" dishes like Chardonnay chicken as well as "good traditional-style" fare; it's still praised by many for its "glitzy", "gorgeous decor" and "great mai tais", but critics who say it's "gone downhill" wonder "why do people still worship at this temple?"

Good Life, The ◖🅂🅼   16 | 15 | 16 | $17
28 Kingston St. (Bedford St.), Boston, 617-451-2622

◼ "There's funky '50s fun", "retro-style food" and "awesome drinks" at this "lively" American near Downtown Crossing; even if the "food is just ok" – "it's a good life, not a great one" – you can still "sip a chocolate martini and listen to Frank Sinatra" here.

Grafton Street Pub & Grill [S][M] 14 | 16 | 15 | $20
1280 Mass Ave. (bet. Linden & Plympton Sts.), Cambridge, 617-497-0400
◪ A Harvard Square Irish blessed with a "great location", "nice beer selection" and "a hopping bar scene", all of which compensates for food that critics find "heavy and bland"; whether it's a good "hangout for Harvard profs and students" or a "depressing slice of yuppie hell" will have to be your call.

Grand Canal [S][M] 14 | 21 | 15 | $17
57 Canal St. (Causeway St.), Boston, 617-523-1112
◪ "Go for the Irish atmosphere" and the "beautiful room" with "high Victorian style" at this New American–Irish near North Station; it's definitely "charming", but beyond the "quaint" feeling and "courteous staff", most find only "basic", albeit "serviceable", "bar fare."

Grand Chau Chow ◐ [S][M] 22 | 11 | 16 | $19
41-45 Beach St. (Harrison Ave.), Boston, 617-292-5166
■ This Chinese seafooder is "worth the trip to Chinatown" for "great fish and lunch specials" at "inexpensive" prices; the "staff is helpful" and the "setting is more upscale" (though less than grand, as ratings attest) than that of its sibling Chau Chow across the street.

Grand China [S][M] 16 | 12 | 14 | $18
686 Washington St. (Kneeland St.), Boston, 617-482-8898
◪ The "very traditional" Chinese cuisine at this "massive banquet hall" in Chinatown is "not for wimps" since you'll hear very "little English" as you dine on "good but not great dim sum"; the other offerings get little comment.

GRAPEVINE, THE [S][M] 24 | 20 | 23 | $31
26 Congress St. (Derby St.), Salem, 978-745-9335
■ A "surprising find" in Salem, this "enchanting" New American earns high marks for its "sophisticated menu" of "wonderful fare" and its ability to "cater to vegetarians"; the "intimate setting", "terrific staff" and "excellent wine list" make it worth "the trek to the North Shore."

Green Dragon Tavern [S][M] 14 | 16 | 14 | $16
11 Marshall St. (Union St.), Boston, 617-367-0055
■ There's "decent" "pub fare" and "great Guinness" at this Irish-American near Faneuil Hall; though it can be "too noisy", the "historic atmosphere" and "live music" can be "a lot of fun."

Green Papaya [S][M] 20 | 14 | 17 | $17
475 Winter St. (Rte. 128, exit 27B), Waltham, 781-487-9988
■ Supporters say this popular Waltham spot is "the best Thai in the 'burbs" so "get there early for lunch as there's always a line" on weekdays; even though decor is "sparse" and they need to "tone down the lighting", there's a "friendly, relaxed ambiance" and food that's "unpretentiously good."

Green Street Grill [S][M] 22 | 11 | 17 | $24
280 Green St. (bet. Magazine & Pearl Sts.), Cambridge, 617-876-1655
■ They "take chiles seriously" at this "funky" Central Square Caribbean "hole-in-the-wall" where "inventive and enticing" "spicy fare" that's "not for the fainthearted" is served in a "dark, smoky" atmosphere, which some sniff is just "a glorified bar"; insiders insist "the live music and half-price menu on Mondays are not to be missed."

Greg's [M] 18 | 10 | 16 | $18
821 Mt. Auburn St. (Belmont St.), Watertown, 617-491-0122
◪ "Get there early and bring your appetite" because they serve "large portions" of "great, cheap food" at this "basic red sauce joint" in Watertown; but to foes it's "dated", has "no atmosphere" and is "not worth the frequent waits."

Grendel's Restaurant & Bar [S][M] 14 | 14 | 13 | $15
89 Winthrop St. (JFK St.), Cambridge, 617-491-1160
◪ This "earthy", "unchanging", "cheap eats" Eclectic is a "Harvard Square institution" and "the place in Boston where you're most likely to meet the Bill Gates of tomorrow"; loyalists like the salad bar and the fact that on "weeknights the bar menu is $2"; while critics find it "old" and "dingy", to most it's a "comforting" "college hangout."

Grille at Hobbs Brook [S][M] – | – | – | M
Doubletree Guest Suites, 550 Winter St. (Rte. 128), Waltham, 781-487-4263
This American grill hidden off Route 128 in Waltham's Doubletree Guest Suites offers some sophisticated surprises such as garlic-rubbed tuna on a bed of red bliss potatoes and grilled chops and steak laced with wine reductions; herbs are grown in an adjacent garden and many of the interesting wine choices are featured in Monday evening wine dinners.

Grillfish [S][M] 19 | 19 | 16 | $24
162 Columbus Ave. (Arlington St.), Boston, 617-357-1620
◪ An "affordable" South End seafood "sleeper" that admirers rate "fantastic", particularly for "basic" "fresh fish", "Mediterranean calamari" and "awesome chowder" served in a "beautiful room"; but naysayers don't understand "long waits" for "small portions" of "unadventurous" food.

GRILL 23 & BAR [S][M] 26 | 23 | 25 | $42
161 Berkeley St. (Stuart St.), Boston, 617-542-2255
◪ "What an experience – from the meat to the cigars" say fans of this "brassy" Back Bay steak and seafooder offering "excellent steak and fish" along with "superb service" and a "great wine list"; if some find the "noise" and smoke "intolerable", most say that for "old-fashioned red meat" dining you "can't go wrong" – just bring an "expense account" and "your 'old boy network' friends."

G'Vanni's 🇸🇲
18 13 17 $26

2 Prince St. (Hanover St.), Boston, 617-523-0107

◪ For "authentic" Northern Italian cuisine "like nònna's", many "crowd" into this "very small" spot in the North End; most deem the food "excellent", including some of the "best homemade ravioli around", but a minority is "not impressed" by "average" fare, judging it "nothing special."

Gyuhama ●🇸🇲
22 15 16 $26

827 Boylston St. (bet. Fairfield & Gloucester Sts.), Boston, 617-437-0188

◼ "Club kids" head to this "hip" Back Bay Japanese for "late-night grazing" on "excellent" (if "expensive") sushi accompanied by "cool drinks" and rock 'n' roll; "indifferent service" and "long waits" are drawbacks; "luckily, the fish is fresher than the decor."

Halfway Cafe ●🇸🇲
15 12 17 $14

174 Washington St. (VFW Pkwy.), Dedham, 781-326-3336
394 Main St. (Lexington St.), Watertown, 617-926-3595

◪ Yet another "place to grab a burger and a beer" sums up these "pseudo college sports bars" in Watertown and Dedham; supporters swear that "their slogan – 'good food cheap' – is right on the money", praising their "large menus" offering "huge amounts of food"; critics cry "crowded", "commercial" and "not classy."

HAMERSLEY'S BISTRO 🇸🇲
27 24 24 $44

553 Tremont St. (Clarendon St.), Boston, 617-423-2700

◼ Gordon Hamersley's South End French-American bistro is even "better since it expanded" according to its many admirers; the "sublime seasonal" fare, including the never-out-of-season "garlic chicken", is backed up by "gorgeous" decor, "impeccable service" and an "interesting wine list"; a few dissenters find it "overrated" and pricey, but for most surveyors the "inventive cuisine" is "worth every cent."

Hampshire House 🇸🇲
19 23 21 $34

84 Beacon St. (Arlington St.), Boston, 617-227-9600

◪ Located above the Bull & Finch Pub (aka *Cheers*), this "classy" Beacon Hill American grill boasts a "gorgeous" "old English library" setting with views of Boston Common plus "above-average" food and "impeccable service", making it a natural for "Sunday brunch"; however, some call it "the place to take an older relative", finding it a bit "old school" and "not exciting"; N.B. it's often closed for private functions, so call ahead.

Hanmiok 🇸🇲
▽ 20 9 13 $16

351 Washington St. (Market St.), Brighton, 617-783-2090

◼ "East meets West" at this "excellent blend" of Chinese, Japanese and Korean influences in Brighton; while "service is obliging", there's "not much atmosphere" and the "open kitchen makes it a smoky room."

Hard Rock Cafe ●ⓈⓂ   13 | 19 | 15 | $18

131 Clarendon St. (bet. Boylston St. & Columbus Ave.), Boston, 617-424-7625

☑ "Noisy tourist trap" it may be, but "teenagers need to go to" this Back Bay outpost of the rock 'n' roll–themed chain, which is more a "pop museum experience" than an eating outing; spoilsports grouse about the "boring food", "pricey" burgers and "loud music" ("you've gotta have rocks in your head to eat here"), but it can be "fun" "for the kids."

Harry's ●ⓈⓂ⌿   19 | 9 | 16 | $15
149 Turnpike Rd./Rte. 9, Westborough, 508-366-8302
Harry's Too ⓈⓂ
153 Turnpike Rd./Rte. 9, Westborough, 508-898-2200

■ "Fun and funky" with "great fried seafood at family prices" describes this "diner-like" Westborough American; the "best fried clams around" are the reason it's "an old favorite" and "always crowded"; N.B. just behind the original is a new offshoot offering sauteed seafood and wine as well as some of the signature fried dishes.

Hartwell House Ⓜ   17 | 21 | 19 | $28
94 Hartwell Ave. (Rtes. 4 & 225), Lexington, 781-862-5111

☑ The "beautiful setting" makes this Lexington Continental-American a "very enjoyable" "place to take your mom", and the "elegant" ambiance is also perfect for a "special occasion or wedding"; however, since many cite "unexciting", "out-of-date fare", so the consensus is "nice atmosphere and service, average food."

Harvard Gardens ●ⓈⓂ   13 | 10 | 14 | $15
316 Cambridge St. (Grove St.), Boston, 617-523-2727

☑ An "ok" "Beacon Hill joint", this Italian-American pizza/ pasta place "serves the neighborhood well" with "simple", "casual" fare; but it's not much to look at and some say it's best if "you're starving" and "short on money."

Harvey's ⓈⓂ   – | – | – | M
99 St. Botolph St. (W. Newton St.), Boston, 617-266-3030
Set on two levels, this South End American combines a lively bar, late hours on weekends and a menu of familiar well-executed food; it's an early hit with the neighbors, which tends to happen when you serve a good burger, bratwurst with kraut and roast chicken at square prices.

HELMAND, THE ⓈⓂ   24 | 23 | 20 | $25
143 First St. (Bent St.), Cambridge, 617-492-4646

■ "One of the Cambridge's most pleasant surprises", this Afghan draws raves for its "truly unique" cuisine – an "out of this world pumpkin appetizer", "outstanding lamb", "good vegetarian selections" and "fresh baked bread" made in a dining room oven; with "solicitous staff", "gorgeous decor" and "warm" ambiance, this "well-kept secret" is "worth a return trip."

HENRIETTA'S TABLE 🅂🅼   22 | 20 | 20 | $28
Charles Hotel, 1 Bennett St. (University Pl.), Cambridge,
617-661-5005
■ "The closest we have to Chez Panisse", meaning "pure,
fresh food simply done", is the word on this Harvard
Square New Englander that "makes you want to eat
your vegetables"; the "bright and airy" "farmhouse setting"
"belies the amazingly sophisticated" fare and "great service";
it's "good for power lunches" and brunch is "fabulous."

Hill Tavern, The ◑🅂🅼   15 | 14 | 14 | $18
228 Cambridge St. (Garden St.), Boston, 617-742-6192
☑ This Beacon Hill New American serving "solid" "late-
night" "pub grub" is where "good-looking people go to
meet good-looking people"; but foes knock a "bad attempt
at a yuppie menu" and "snooty service."

Hilltop Steak House 🅂🅼   16 | 11 | 15 | $20
210 Union St. (Rte. 3, exit 7), Braintree, 781-848-3363
855 Broadway/Rte. 1, Saugus, 781-233-7700
☑ "Average steaks served in a herd-like atmosphere" sums
up these "institutions" where diners are "penned like cattle"
waiting to have their number called for a table; while fans
call them "consistent" "American classics" offering "cheap
drinks", "generous portions" and "great value", others moo
they're a " bum steer."

Hi-Rise Bread Co. 🅂🅼   21 | 15 | 16 | $12
208 Concord Ave. (Huron Ave.), Cambridge, 617-876-8766
Hi-Rise Pie Co. 🅂≠
56 Brattle St. (Church St.), Cambridge, 617-492-3003
☑ "Delightful" Cambridge bakeries manned by star baker
René Becker that offer "phenomenal breads" and "delicious
sandwiches"; while those who find them "overpriced" dub
them "hi-rent", the cost doesn't deter the majority since
"great smells" and "watching the bakers at work" make
for the "best lunch around."

Houlihan's 🅂🅼   12 | 13 | 14 | $17
Faneuil Hall, 60 State St., Boston, 617-367-6372
☑ "Just another standard American joint" when it comes
to food, but this branch of a national chain near Faneuil Hall
serves as a "watering hole" for an "after-work" crowd that
doesn't mind "ok burgers" when they're served in "one of
the better fun bars."

House of Blues 🅂🅼   16 | 20 | 16 | $20
96 Winthrop St. (JFK St.), Cambridge, 617-491-2583
☑ The "unforgettable" "Sunday morning gospel brunch is
a real hoot" that "will leave you stuffed" at this Harvard
Square Southern; but while some say the everyday
food is "tasty", others counter "good thing there's music";
"a backdrop of fine folk art" creates a "funky" feel, but
sometimes a "house of attitude" hits a sour note.

House of Siam S M | 20 | 16 | 18 | $17 |
21 Huntington Ave. (Exeter St.), Boston, 617-267-1755
■ The "excellent" Thai food at this Copley Square spot gets high marks for "great flavors"; despite decor that's "not quirky enough to make it individualistic", most think the cuisine "rocks."

Ho Yuen Ting Seafood S M⇄ | 23 | 6 | 13 | $17 |
13A Hudson St. (bet. Beach & Kneeland Sts.), Boston, 612-426-2316
■ "Don't let the basement" setting of this "authentic" "hole-in-the-wall" Chinese seafooder in Chinatown "scare you" because it's "a treasure"; respondents rave that the "sizzling hot pots", "best salted squid" and "yum, yum twin lobsters" offer "great value for the money."

Hsin-Hsin Chinese Noodle S M | 14 | 7 | 14 | $13 |
25 Mass Ave. (bet. Commonwealth Ave. & Marlborough St.), Boston, 617-536-9852
☑ Fans of this Back Bay Chinese praise the filling "cheap noodles" and the "lunch specials, which are a steal"; cynics sneer who cares if there are "large portions" if it's only "basic Asian" fare anyway?

HUNGRY I, THE S M | 22 | 25 | 22 | $39 |
71 Charles St. (bet. Mt. Vernon & Pinckney Sts.), Boston, 617-227-3524
■ The "best date place in Boston" and the "most romantic spot around" is how many view this subterranean Beacon Hill French offering "wonderful food" plus "exquisite", "charming" decor that's "better in the winter with a roaring fireplace"; "attentive staff" and a "very lovely Sunday brunch" round out the picture.

ICARUS S M | 26 | 25 | 24 | $41 |
3 Appleton St. (bet. Arlington & Berkeley Sts.), Boston, 617-426-1790
■ "Lovely" sums up this South End New American that has long been considered a "romantic" "date place" as well as a "clubby", "special event celebration" venue; "the best game preparations" are a highlight of the "gussied-up", "adventurous" menu, which is served in a "charming", "soothing" setting by a "helpful" staff; what more could one ask for? – how about "very good brunches" and "great" Friday night jazz in the lounge.

Ida's M⇄ | ▽ 19 | 11 | 16 | $22 |
3 Mechanic St. (Hanover St.), Boston, 617-523-0015
☑ This "very tiny" North End Italian "hasn't changed in 45 years" and still offers "homestyle" dishes with "great spaghetti sauce" at a nice price; but those looking for some elbow room cry "cramped."

Iguana Cantina S M　　　　18 16 16 $18
1656 Wooster Rd. (Rte. 9), Framingham, 508-875-1188
313 Moody St. (Rte. 20), Waltham, 781-891-3039
■ Despite "nutty", "tacky" decor, including "politically incorrect murals", these "loud", "moderately priced" Waltham and Framingham Tex-Mexers pack 'em in for "decent" "basic" fare; bashers say the grub's "heavy" and not worth the "long waits"; P.S. reviewers praise the Waltham location's "nice outdoor patio."

Il Baccio S M　　　　17 18 16 $25
226 Hanover St. (Cross St.), Boston, 617-742-9200
■ The name means kiss, and most surveyors embrace, if only lukewarmly, this "stylish", "trendy" North End Italian for its "imported marble floors", hopping bar area, "enormous portions" and "top" lunchtime sandwiches; the less enchanted point to a kitchen that needs work, "distracted service" and the absence of a no-smoking section.

IL CAPRICCIO M　　　　26 21 23 $40
888 Main St. (Prospect St.), Waltham, 781-894-2234
■ "A jewel in the suburbs"; Richard Barron's "consistently excellent" Northern Italian fare and Jeanne Rogers' wine expertise earn this "romantic hideaway" votes as "best of the many in Waltham"; a "stylish" art deco setting that "feels like Downtown" serves as backdrop for food that's "serious" and "quite inspired"; toss in "intelligent" wine events and you have real "Boston quality", with "prices to match."

Il Giardino Cafe M　　　▽ 21 13 21 $20
132 Brookline Ave. (Kenmore Sq.), Boston, 617-267-6124
■ "An oasis near Fenway", this Italian offers pizza, subs and the usual lineup of traditional dishes such as "lemon chicken to die for"; you can get your order to go or sit down and be treated to "service with a smile" from an "efficient" staff.

Il Moro S　　　　– – – M
143 Pleasant St. (Washington St.), Marblehead,
781-639-8682
Another entry in the Italian-Mediterranean ranks, this Marblehead newcomer near the Warwick Theater serves the likes of spinach-stuffed swordfish chops, shark skewers over rice primavera and pastas, all made more enjoyable by a fairly large wine list and moderate prices.

Imperial Seafood House ● S M　17 11 15 $18
70 Beach St. (Harrison Ave.), Boston, 617-426-8439
■ Called the "Hilltop Steak House of Chinatown" because it's "noisy", "reliable and inexpensive", this Chinese is "most fun for dim sum with a large group" on Sunday; as its name suggests, the emphasis is on seafood, leading a few crabs to carp that there's "too much shrimp" on the menu.

India House 🅂Ⓜ   20 16 18 $17
239 Harvard St. (Longwood Ave.), Brookline, 617-739-9300
▪ "Ask for it spicy" at this "cheap" "entry into the Brookline Indian surge" that's praised as "a glimmer of what Indian in Boston could be"; while nothing stands out about the decor, the "very friendly" staff will bring some orders out in a "beautiful copper pot."

Indian Cafe 🅂Ⓜ   19 15 15 $17
1665 Beacon St. (Winthrop Rd.), Brookline, 617-277-1752
▪ This "very good" "neighborhood" Indian in Brookline's Washington Square offers "basic" fare in a "comfortable atmosphere"; the unimpressed think "there are better" places, but concede that they "aren't worth the trip."

Indian Club 🅂Ⓜ   ▽ 18 15 18 $16
1755 Mass Ave. (Porter Sq.), Cambridge, 617-491-7750
▪ "Delicious and strangely underrated" is how boosters describe this Cambridge Indian with fare that's "not too heavy"; the more circumspect say "uneven but generally quite good" and steer you toward the "yummy pakoras."

India Pavilion ◗🅂Ⓜ   19 14 17 $16
17 Central Sq. (Western Ave.), Cambridge, 617-547-7463
▪ "Tucked away" in Central Square, this Indian offers "not thrilling but dependable" vittles; surveyors recommend the "excellent" Friday–Sunday lunch buffet that comes with the right mix of rices and spices.

India Quality 🅂Ⓜ   22 7 16 $16
536 Commonwealth Ave. (Brookline Ave.), Boston, 617-267-4499
■ Sure this Kenmore Square Indian is a "dive" with "lots of bulky, time-darkened antiques and narrow spaces between tables", but "who cares" when there are "superb samosas and chicken tikka" at very "cheap" prices?; spice-seekers sigh if only "all Indians were this good."

India Samraat 🅂Ⓜ   18 11 17 $15
51A Mass Ave. (bet. Commonwealth Ave. & Marlborough St.), Boston, 617-247-0718
▪ "Patronized by many Indians" (always a good sign), this family-run Back Bay restaurant is "simple and pleasant" with "good vegetarian specials"; a few think it's only "average", but at these prices it can afford to be.

Iruna Ⓜ   17 12 17 $18
56 JFK St. (Mt. Auburn St.), Cambridge, 617-868-5633
▪ "Tucked away in an alley", this "utterly unpretentious", "inexpensive" Spaniard is a "peaceful haven" from bustling Harvard Square; you'll find Basque omelets, "tasty paella", "great garlic soup" and gazpacho; however, where some see consistency others see mediocrity – it "hasn't been good since 1968."

Isabella §Ⓜ 23 | 19 | 20 | $25

566 High St. (Eastern Ave.), Dedham, 781-461-8485

■ You might have to "go midweek to avoid the long waits" at this "noisy", "cosmopolitan" New American in Dedham garnering rave reviews for an "interesting" and "varied" menu that's "consistently excellent" and "reasonably priced"; you can also expect a "comfortable atmosphere" and an "efficient staff"; in sum – "what a find!"

Jacob Wirth §Ⓜ 15 | 16 | 15 | $19

31 Stuart St. (Tremont St.), Boston, 617-338-8586

■ "In a world of bars made to look like 1890s saloons", this "cavernous" German-American in the Theater District "is the real thing" ("wooden floor creaks"); while many say "too bad the food isn't hotter", it's "fine for a beer" before a show or on a "Friday to sing along" (8 PM).

JAE'S CAFE & GRILL §Ⓜ 23 | 19 | 18 | $23

212 Stuart St. (Arlington St.), Boston, 617-451-7788
520 Columbus Ave. (Concord Sq.), Boston, 617-421-9405
1281 Cambridge St. (Prospect St.), Cambridge, 617-497-8380
Atrium Mall, 300 Boylston St., Chestnut Hill, 617-965-7177

■ Now four strong, these "trendy", "awesome Pan-Asians" with "cool fish tanks" attract throngs of diners willing to tolerate "a lot of noise", "long waits" and "attitude" for a "large menu" of "exciting", "imaginative dishes" such as soft-shell crab sushi and "spicy Korean noodles with squid"; a contingent cries "overhyped", but they're outvoted.

Jake's Boss BBQ § 17 | 9 | 12 | $14

3492 Washington St. (Williams St.), Jamaica Plain, 617-983-3701

☑ "Bring wet naps" to this Jamaica Plain BBQ that fiercely divides 'cue fans: supporters gush "Jake is the man" for "excellent", "less greasy" "shredded pork that may be the best in Boston", but detractors dub the meat "fatty" and warn "don't believe the hype."

Jasmine Bistro §Ⓜ 18 | 15 | 19 | $23

412 Market St. (Washington St.), Brighton, 617-789-4676

☑ The few who know this "homey", "family-run" French-Hungarian-International in an "unlikely neighborhood in Brighton" say you can expect "gracious, attentive service" and "extremely fine food"; nitpickers, on the other hand, would like the menu and the "meager wine list" beefed up.

J.C. Hillary's Ltd. §Ⓜ 14 | 14 | 15 | $20

793 Boylston St. (Fairfield St.), Boston, 617-536-6300
985 Providence Hwy. (Rtes. 1 & 128), Dedham, 781-329-0800
55 Boston Post Rd./Rte. 20W, Wayland, 508-358-5124
311 Mishawum Rd. (Rte. 95), Woburn, 781-935-7200

☑ This American chain with "bland", "boring" food, "no character or ambiance" and "slow service" elicits yawns from reviewers who liken it to "Houlihan's"; but there's "something for everyone" and it's "dependably average."

Jerusalem Cafe 14 | 7 | 11 | $15
423 Harvard St. (Fuller St.), Brookline, 617-278-0200
◪ "After Israel, one wishes for more" from this "small, sparsely furnished" Brookline kosher Middle Eastern; others label the fare "good", but there's debate as to whether it's "reasonable" or "overpriced."

Jimbo's Fish Shanty S M 16 | 13 | 15 | $19
245 Northern Ave. (Boston Fish Pier), Boston, 617-542-5600
■ "If you still like fried food you'll love Jimbo's", a "poor man's Jimmy's Harborside" offering a similar menu to its sibling but in "cheesier surroundings" ("electric trains on the ceiling"); it's an old standby when visiting the World Trade Center for a "quick", "casual" meal.

Jimmy's Harborside S M 18 | 17 | 17 | $32
242 Northern Ave. (Boston Fish Pier), Boston, 617-423-1000
◪ "Bring your out-of-town guests" to this longtime Pier seafooder because it still has "the best view of the harbor" and is a "Boston tradition for lobsters" and basic seafood like Dover sole and swordfish; a minority thinks the "decor's tired looking" and that this "relic" "survives on nostalgia."

Jimmy's Steer House S M 19 | 14 | 18 | $20
1111 Mass Ave. (Quincy St.), Arlington, 781-646-4450
◪ Cynics say that upon entering this "senior citizens' land" steakhouse in Arlington you "age 30 years and get blue hair"; however, you don't have to be on a fixed income to appreciate "large portions" of "better than expected" beef at "cheap" prices; scores support those who say it "outshines the Hilltop and Frank's."

Joe's American Bar & Grill S M 15 | 16 | 15 | $21
279 Dartmouth St. (Newbury St.), Boston, 617-536-4200 ◖
100 Atlantic Ave. (Commercial Wharf), Boston, 617-367-8700
South Shore Plaza, 250 Granite Ave. (Rte. 30), Braintree, 781-848-0200
2087 Washington St. (Rte. 123), Hanover, 781-878-1234
◪ "College and postcollege youngsters" and "tourists" find this minichain "a fun spot" for a "Friday night relaxing beer", especially at those locations with outdoor patios; some say the "decor is more impressive than the food", which consists of standard pub items like burgers, pizza and chowder; the newest location is on the harbor in the former Cornucopia.

Joe Tecce's S M 16 | 15 | 17 | $25
61 N. Washington St. (Cooper St.), Boston, 617-742-6210
◪ Some may call it the "prototype North End tourist trap" Italian, but this "red sauce king" has "big portions", "martinis the size of bird baths" and you can count on it "to get you to the game on time"; even those who say the "food's overrated" concede it's still an "experience" "for those who prefer Disney World to Naples."

John Harvard's Brew House ◗ 🅢🅜   16   16   16 $18
33 Dunster St. (bet. Mass Ave. & Mt. Auburn St.),
Cambridge, 617-868-3585
1 Worcester Rd./Rte. 30 (Rte. 9), Framingham, 508-875-2337
▰ "A college crowd" frequents the Harvard Square branch
of this brewpub; while the "food isn't Ivy League", there
are a "cut above average" burgers, sausages and meat
loaf to wash down with "awesome" beer; the Framingham
location is less noisy and caters more to families.

Johnny D's Uptown 🅢🅜   16   13   16 $17
17 Holland St. (Davis Sq.), Somerville, 617-776-2004
▰ There's a "weird mix of bar, club and restaurant" at this
Davis Square Creole-Eclectic known primarily for "some
of the best live music in town"; regulars recommend the
"surprisingly good" fare on Tuesday–Friday from 4:30–6:30
PM when everything on the menu is half price.

Johnny's Luncheonette 🅢🅜   16   15   15 $14
30 Langley Rd. (bet. Beacon & Centre Sts.), Newton,
617-527-3223
▰ An "always busy" "'50s-style" Newton Centre American
diner that serves up "great omelets" ("go for breakfast") and
"awesome sweet potato french fries"; it's very child friendly,
prompting a few to carp "too many kids crying" here.

Jonah's 🅢🅜   17   16   16 $24
Hyatt Regency Hotel, 575 Memorial Dr. (Audrey St.),
Cambridge, 617-492-1234
▰ The Friday night seafood buffet is still a whale of a hit at
this Cambridge seafooder-steakhouse, but respondents are
"not impressed" with the rest of the "very costly" menu.

Jose's 🅜   18   10   15 $14
2390 Mass Ave. (Alberta Terrace), Cambridge, 617-354-8477
131 Sherman St. (Rindge Ave.), Cambridge, 617-354-0335
▮ These "funky little Cambridge hole-in-the-wall" Mexicans
are "favorites for stick to your ribs burritos" at cheap prices –
more "good finds for poor students."

Joyce Chen 🅢🅜   15   13   15 $18
390 Rindge Ave. (Alewife Brook Pkwy.), Cambridge, 617-492-7373
▰ A Cambridge Chinese "in a depressing location" that's
"still chugging along" despite the death of the namesake
owner three years ago; unfortunately, many feel "that
without Mother Joyce" it's headed "downhill."

JP Seafood Cafe 🅢🅜   22   13   19 $19
730 Centre St. (Pond St.), Jamaica Plain, 617-983-5177
▮ This Japanese-Korean in a "well-lit" but "spartan"
Jamaica Plain setting is "a wonderful find" for its wide-
ranging menu highlighted by "terrific sushi and crispy,
light tempura"; there's a "lovely staff" and even with
"occasionally long waits" for dishes, it's a "great
addition to the neighborhood."

Julia's [S] [M] 16 | 12 | 15 | $18
386 Market St. (Washington St.), Brighton, 617-782-5060
◪ "Classy food at a reasonable price" is the point at this "downscale" Brighton New American bar/restaurant; perhaps it's "never crowded" because some find it "bizarre to order an entree with everybody else just drinking."

JULIEN [M] 26 | 27 | 26 | $53
Le Meridien Hotel, 250 Franklin St. (bet. Oliver & Pearl Sts.), Boston, 617-451-1900
◪ "Prepare to be pampered" at this "elegant", "very French" hotel dining room; a bastion of "fine dining", it offers "sophisticated food in a sophisticated setting", but you'd better have a "sophisticated wallet" as well; still, given the "superb" French fare, "outstanding service" ("everything is done right") and one of "the most beautiful" rooms in town, the majority deems it "worth every penny."

Kareem's [M] ⊘ 22 | 10 | 18 | $16
600 Mt. Auburn St. (Arlington St.), Watertown, 617-926-1867
◪ There's "no pandering to shy taste buds" at this "no-frills" Syrian in Watertown with "wonderful shwarma and grape leaves"; the service score has jumped considerably since our last *Survey*, but the staff is apparently not always charming ("waitresses are pleasant after your sixth visit").

Karoun 19 | 17 | 18 | $23
839 Washington St. (Walnut St.), Newtonville, 617-964-3400
◪ "Not exciting but dependable" longtime Newtonville Armenian–Middle Eastern where highlights include belly dancing on weekends and hot-to-trot lamb kebabs; "slow" service and the need for a "remodeling" may explain why it's "always empty."

Kashmir [S] [M] 21 | 17 | 16 | $21
279 Newbury St. (Gloucester St.), Boston, 617-536-1695
■ This Newbury Street Indian "sleeper" serves what quite a few claim is the "best buffet lunch around"; the sidewalk cafe is also well received, but a number find the interior "too dark to see the menu."

Kaya ◐ [S] [M] 19 | 14 | 15 | $23
581 Boylston St. (Clarendon St.), Boston, 617-236-5858
1924 Mass Ave. (Porter Sq.), Cambridge, 617-497-5656
◪ The "lunch specials" are the way to go at this "pretty good" Porter Square and Back Bay Korean-Japanese duo that's a "sure bet for sushi" and "scallion pancakes to die for"; however, the "staff is in a fog" and the "atmo's so-so."

Kebab-N-Kurry [S] [M] 21 | 12 | 15 | $18
30 Mass Ave. (Beacon St.), Boston, 617-536-9835
◪ "Ignore the goofy name" and "low-level decor" at this Back Bay "hole-in-the-wall" and focus on "excellent" Indian cooking at "great prices"; connoisseurs suggest the seafood, roasted eggplant and "curry if you like it hot."

Ken's Steak House SM
16 | 13 | 17 | $26

95 Worcester Rd. (Speen St.), Framingham, 617-235-5414

◪ Carnivorous cognoscenti call this Framingham beefery a "trip down memory lane" and a "haven for blue-haired ladies"; while some say it's "gone downhill" and "needs a major overhaul", loyalists maintain you won't leave hungry and it's "fine for what it is."

King & I SM
20 | 14 | 18 | $18

145 Charles St. (Cambridge St.), Boston, 617-227-3320

◪ A Charles Street Thai with "little atmosphere" but unusually "large portions" of "relatively cheap", "high quality", "no nonsense" fare; followers feel "it's still good after so many years", especially for lunch.

Kokopelli Chili Co. S
– | – | – | I

1648 Beacon St. (Washington St.), Brookline, 617-277-2880

Santa Fe comes to Brookline at this SW specializing in chile of all sorts including beanless, meatless and even Cincinnati-style; there's plenty of turquoise and howling coyotes in the room and a menu featuring the usual suspects from the desert.

Kong Luh SM
▽ 22 | 10 | 21 | $19

9 Medford Ave. (Mass Ave.), Arlington, 781-643-2456

■ "Shhh . . . don't tell anyone about this hidden gem", a Northern Chinese housed in a simple storefront serving "out of the ordinary" Mongolian dishes and noodle soups; throw in "kind and attentive" service and you understand why folks "are very happy to have it in Arlington."

Korea House SM
19 | 10 | 16 | $18

111-117 Chiswick Rd. (Commonwealth Ave.), Brighton, 617-783-7030

◪ If you "don't expect much ambiance" from this Brighton Korean, you'll be pleased with the experience that includes "authentic" food and customers ("BC/BU Korean clientele").

Koreana SM
19 | 11 | 15 | $20

154 Prospect St. (Broadway), Cambridge, 617-576-8661

■ At this "crowded" Korean just outside Central Square, the table grills are "fun", especially for groups; the "decor borders on a cafeteria", but there's a "varied, interesting menu" including "excellent stews", "seafood soups" and "scrumptious barbecue"; it's a "good bet with no surprises", except for the sometimes "sullen" staff.

Kowloon ●SM
15 | 15 | 15 | $19

948 Broadway/Rte. 1N, Saugus, 781-233-0077

◪ The "puffy hair set" frequents this "tacky" ("a plumber's conception of Kublai Khan's pleasure palace") North Shore Chinese-Thai offering, of all things, live music (free) and comedy shows (cover charge); a few claim the "old-style" Chinese dishes remain "excellent", but more say stick with the "above-average Thai."

Kyoto 🅢🅜   18 | 16 | 19 | $24
201 Stuart St. (bet. Arlington & S. Charles Sts.), Boston,
617-542-1166
◼ A Theater District Japanese with "good sushi and
sashimi" where "the chef puts on a show"; it can be a
"fun place to go" with "a group" for "eating around the
hibachis", but it's "not for a romantic outing."

La Bettola 🌑🅢   - | - | - | E
480A Columbus Ave. (W. Newton St.), Boston, 617-236-5252
The owners of Galleria Italiana have brought in Rene
Michelina (ex NYC's Sign of the Dove) to oversee this
small, noisy South End Eclectic-Italian designed to resemble
a hidden Roman alley; the name means 'little neighborhood
place', but the ambitious menu covers wider ground, with
many Asian nuances (i.e. turmeric-scented pesto, gingered
caponata); the third restaurant in this space, it looks like it
has strong enough legs to last the course.

La Famiglia Giorgio 🅢🅜   15 | 11 | 15 | $17
112 Salem St. (Parmenter St.), Boston, 617-367-6711
250 Newbury St. (bet. Fairfield & Gloucester Sts.), Boston,
617-247-1569
Tremont House Hotel, 275 Tremont St. (Kneeland St.),
Boston, 617-292-2047 🌗
◼ "Cheap", "no-frills" Italians that deliver portions so
"huge" you can "get three meals out of one" and still
need to "bring a wheelbarrow" for your leftovers;
however, "quantity not quality is their trademark."

La Groceria 🅢🅜   19 | 16 | 17 | $23
853 Main St. (Mass Ave.), Cambridge, 617-497-4214
◼ This Central Square Italian has a coterie of followers who
call it a "reliable standby" for "generous portions" of old
favorites covered with the "best red sauce around"; but
the unimpressed label it "pedestrian", saying it "promises
more than it delivers."

LALA ROKH 🅢🅜   23 | 22 | 23 | $31
97 Mt. Vernon St. (Charles St.), Boston, 617-720-5511
◼ The "smart", "extremely helpful" "staff loves to educate
you on the food" at this well-loved Beacon Hill Persian;
patrons have nothing but praise for "the totally different
taste sensations" and "warm", "handsome" setting,
promising your visit will be like "a trip to another country."

Landing, The 🅢🅜   13 | 15 | 14 | $23
81 Front St. (State St.), Marblehead, 781-631-1878
◼ Some think "the great view" doesn't make up for "the
disorganized staff" and "plain" fish at this Marblehead
Harbor American-seafooder, while others claim it's a "good
place for drinks" and "pickups" (and we're not talking
takeout); either way, "you don't go there for the food."

La Paloma S   21 | 15 | 18 | $19
195 Newport Ave. (Hobart St.), Quincy, 617-773-0512
1037 Main St. (Rte. 18), S. Weymouth, 781-335-1773
■ "What every Mexican restaurant wants to become" boast acolytes of this "surprisingly good" South Shore duo where you start with "fantastic salsa" and move on to "superb enchiladas"; quibblers claim they're "less than authentic", but quickly admit "who cares with specials like these?"

Last Hurrah ◖S M   14 | 16 | 16 | $22
Omni Parker House, 60 School St. (Tremont St.), Boston,
617-227-8600
■ It "may have already had its last hurrah" according to disappointed visitors to this New England American in the basement of the Omni Parker House; nonetheless, it's in a convenient location and defenders contend the clam chowder is worth a try "after work" or the theater.

La Summa S M   18 | 14 | 19 | $26
30 Fleet St. (Hanover St.), Boston, 617-523-9503
◪ Owner Barbara Summa "loves her customers" and is "very accommodating" at this North End Southern Italian with "old-style", "straightforward, flavorful fare" that makes it "a standby for quality dishes"; a few dissenters say it "doesn't add up as well as it used to."

Le Bocage S M   24 | 21 | 22 | $41
72 Bigelow Ave. (Mt. Auburn St.), Watertown, 617-923-1210
◪ "There's relaxed elegance" at this "soothing", "romantic" Watertown Classic and Contemporary French known for using seasonal ingredients; most "can't say enough" about the "excellent food and fantastic service", but there are a few grumblings that "it used to be superb, now it's ordinary"; try the prix fixe menu to lessen the dent in your wallet.

Legal C Bar ◖S M   19 | 15 | 16 | $25
Park Plaza Hotel, 27 Columbus Ave. (Park Sq.), Boston,
617-426-5566
◪ Executive chef Jasper White's Caribbean twist on the old Legal Seafood Cafe in Park Square receives mixed reviews: proponents call it "a nice change" with "the same great seafood given a more lively presentation"; naysayers feel "the gimmick doesn't work", especially in light of "long waits" in a "noisy" room filled with smoke.

LEGAL SEA FOODS S M   22 | 15 | 18 | $27
Prudential Ctr., 800 Boylston St. (bet. Fairfield &
Gloucester Sts.), Boston, 617-266-6800
Copley Pl., 100 Huntington Ave. (bet. Dartmouth & Exeter Sts.),
Boston, 617-266-7775
Park Plaza Hotel, 35 Columbus Ave. (Arlington St.),
Boston, 617-426-4444
(Continues)

LEGAL SEA FOODS (Cont.)
Burlington Mall, 1131 Middlesex Tpke. (Rte. 128), Burlington, 781-270-9700
5 Cambridge Ctr. (bet. Ames & Main Sts.), Cambridge, 617-864-3400
43 Boylston St. (Hammond Pond Pkwy.), Chestnut Hill, 617-277-7300
Miltons Plaza, 1400 Worcester Rd. (bet. Speen St. & Rte. 126), Natick, 508-820-1115
Northshore Mall, Rtes. 114 & 128, Peabody, 978-532-4500
◪ The city's top vote-getter, this seafood chain under the command of Roger Berkowitz and newly installed exec chef Jasper White is a true "institution"; "consistent" and "comfortable like an old shoe", it has always excelled at "fresh fish, done simply", and fans feel that White's menu tinkering has "made a great thing better"; faultfinders cite "mall atmosphere", "high prices" and "boring" fare, but they're a minority – expect a "wait" at every branch.

Lei Jing ☽ [S] [M] — 13 | 13 | 12 | $20
20 Hudson St. (Kneeland St.), Boston, 617-292-6238
◪ Surveyors are widely split on this revamped (too late to be reflected in the decor score) Chinatown Chinese – do they make the "best dim sum" or the "worst"?; while a handful insist it's "great some days", ratings suggest that it can also be a letdown.

Le Lyonnaise [S] [M] — 19 | 19 | 17 | $42
416 Great Rd./Rte. 2A (Rte. 27), Acton, 978-263-9068
◪ This Acton French is a "real find" for "solid traditional" fare amidst "wonderful country atmosphere" that's like a "time capsule from the 1950s"; but be warned "you'd better be with someone you like because the service is slow."

Lemon Grass Grille [S] [M] — 19 | 15 | 16 | $19
156 Cambridge St. (Stanford St.), Boston, 617-720-4530
1710 Mass Ave. (Waltham St.), Lexington, 781-862-3530
■ Lexington and Beacon Hill duo offering "above average", "tasty Thai at reasonable prices"; regulars recommend the pad Thai, "awesome whole fish in ginger sauce" and "great spring rolls" brought to table by a "very pleasant" staff; P.S. "their hot dishes are really hot."

L'ESPALIER [M] — 28 | 27 | 27 | $63
30 Gloucester St. (bet. Commonwealth Ave. & Newbury St.), Boston, 617-262-3023
■ Like dining in someone's "très elegant" parlor, Frank McClelland's Back Bay French provides "incredible" food (rated No. 2 in Boston) and "superb service" to go along with the "exquisite" townhouse setting; though the "limited menu" is "prix fixe only" and "perfection comes with a serious price tag", for "special occasions" devotees place it "in a class by itself"; a few find it "stiff" and "precious" ("we had to whisper"), but such is life in "heaven's dining hall."

Les Zygomates [S][M] | 20 | 19 | 19 | $30 |
129 South St. (bet. Beach & East Sts.), Boston, 617-542-5108
◪ A "sophisticated", "boisterous" French bistro in the Leather District with a "wonderful wine selection" and "solid" kitchen turning out "honest" fare; some view it as "pretentious" and say watch out for the "attitude" onslaught; others who find the "bar area too crowded" tout the "great atmosphere in the back room."

Library Grill [S][M] ▽ | 21 | 25 | 22 | $32 |
Hampshire House, 84 Beacon St. (bet. Arlington & Charles Sts.), Boston, 617-227-9600
■ Get "a taste of mansion" living at this "superb" Traditional American atop the Hampshire House; the few reviewers who've discovered it say it's a "great all-around experience" with "impeccable service adding to the fine fare" and "atmosphere [that] makes you feel like an intellectual."

LOCKE-OBER CAFE [M] | 22 | 23 | 23 | $43 |
3 Winter Pl. (bet. Tremont & Washington Sts.), Boston, 617-542-1340
◪ This "last bastion of civility in Boston" where you "can have your table the whole night" is called "the dining equivalent of a good massage"; there's a "wood/silver/leather/cigar smoke" atmosphere, excellent Continental fare ("never succumbed to nouvelle") like "great lobster Savannah" and "professional" service; detractors who find it stuffy ("mandatory jacket") say "its time has passed."

L'Osteria [S][M] | 20 | 13 | 19 | $25 |
104 Salem St. (Cooper St.), Boston, 617-723-7847
◪ Off the beaten path, "quaint little Italian in the North End" that some label "worth seeking out" for "very good" dishes set down by a "wonderful staff"; the more subdued call it an "ordinary red sauce place" with a "cafeteria-like ambiance."

Lotus Blossom [S][M] | 22 | 20 | 20 | $21 |
394 Boston Post Rd. (Sudbury Farms), Sudbury, 978-443-0200
■ Located in a remodeled colonial home with a "stunning interior right out of *Architectural Digest*", it's apparent from the start that this Sudbury Chinese "dream" is not your typical Chinatown spot; expect "personable and efficient" service and "well-prepared" dishes that prompt some to label it "the best Asian in greater Boston."

L Street Diner [S][M] ▽ | 21 | 13 | 16 | $12 |
108 L St. (bet. 4th & 5th Sts.), S. Boston, 617-268-1155
◪ This "relaxing" South Boston diner offering "nothing but good food" may be "one of the best breakfast places around" (lunches and dinners are "excellent" too), but it's certainly "not where you go on a fancy date."

Lucia's Ristorante [S][M] 16 | 14 | 16 | $29
415 Hanover St. (Harris St.), Boston, 617-367-2353
53 Mt. Vernon St. (bet. Main & Washington Sts.), Winchester, 781-729-4585
◪ Although most give a nod to the "above-average" fare at this Italian duo, there are several complaints that they're "overpriced", "tacky" and "slow"; nevertheless, they must be doing something right because they're always "crowded."

Lucky Garden [S][M] 11 | 7 | 11 | $15
282 Concord Ave. (Huron Ave.), Cambridge, 617-354-9514
◪ This "consistent" "bare-bones" West Cambridge Chinese hasn't "changed in 20 years"; supporters peg it as "useful if you're in the neighborhood", but bashers claim it's the "quintessential" "cheap" Chinese with "sauces that all taste the same."

Lyceum Bar & Grill [S][M] 22 | 22 | 21 | $28
43 Church St. (Washington St.), Salem, 978-745-7665
■ "Underrated" New American in a "bewitching" setting with a "large, comfortable bar"; owner "George Harrington makes everyone feel at home" and there's an "impressive" menu lineup including a winning "portobello mushroom appetizer"; "if you're stuck in Salem", try it for live jazz on Friday or Saturday night, or for the "terrific brunch" with piano music on Sunday.

Maddie's Sail Loft [S][M]≠ 16 | 12 | 15 | $19
15 State St. (bet. Washington & Front), Marblehead, 781-631-9824
◪ "It's the atmosphere" and the drinks, not the "ok food", that's the attraction at this casual Marblehead seafooder frequented by the "20s and 30s" set; if you're not in the mood for crowds, "avoid it on weekends."

Ma Glockner's [S] 16 | 12 | 18 | $17
151 Maple St. (Rtes. 126 & 140), Bellingham, 508-966-1085
◪ This formerly "family-run" Bellingham American "recently changed hands" and reviewers have "mixed feelings" about the "break from tradition"; some welcome the "great new bar area" and "expanded menu" (steaks, seafood, pastas, etc.) that still includes "the best chicken" and "addictive cinnamon rolls", while others simply "can't see the appeal."

Magnolias Southern Cuisine 21 | 15 | 20 | $24
1193 Cambridge St. (Tremont St.), Cambridge, 617-576-1971
■ "One of the few neighborhood restaurants worth traveling to" is a "swell Southern belle" that draws applause for its "local color", "charming hospitality" and "terrific cooking" along the lines of "killer" catfish and fried green tomatoes – all of which "makes up for" the "uncomfortable seating" and "disappointing" setting; N.B. a post-*Survey* face-lift may improve decor scores the next time around.

Maharaja's ⓈⓂ   ▽ 18 | 8 | 16 | $14
2088 Mass Ave. (Walden St.), Cambridge, 617-492-9538
■ "When you ask for hot and spicy, they actually believe you and deliver" at this "small" Porter Square Indian where, despite "generous portions" of "flavorful" food at "very reasonable" prices, it's "easy to get a table"; perhaps the underwhelming decor drives potential patrons away.

MAISON ROBERT Ⓜ   24 | 24 | 24 | $43
Old City Hall, 45 School St. (bet. Tremont & Washington Sts.), Boston, 617-227-3370
◪ "Classy" and "trustworthy" describes the Robert family's Old City Hall French, "a Boston institution" known for "impeccable, traditional food", yet there have been "changes" lately – namely, installing Jacky Robert as chef, which admirers say has resulted in an "improved" menu; foes find the place "stuffy" and "overrated", but to most, its "calm", "protected" "elegance" makes it "special"; P.S. Ben's Cafe downstairs "has to be the best value in town."

Maluken ●ⓈⓂ   15 | 12 | 16 | $21
645 Beacon St. (Kenmore Sq.), Boston, 617-859-3149
◪ A Kenmore Square Japanese that's "a favorite lunch place" even if it's "often smoky from the previous night's karaoke parties"; respondents rate the sushi "just fair" but "worth it if it's midnight and that's what you crave."

Mamma Maria ⓈⓂ   24 | 22 | 22 | $36
3 North Sq. (bet. Little Prince & North Sts.), Boston, 617-523-0077
■ Don't let the "silly name" deter you – this North End Italian is a "serious" restaurant with "fabulous food", "excellent wines", "romantic decor", "knowledgeable" service and "valet parking to boot"; "everything, and I mean everything", is "great" at this "place for celebrating."

M&M Bar-B-Q Ⓢ   – | – | – | I
Columbia Rd. & Quincy St., Dorchester, 617-825-6852
M&M Station II Ⓢ⊄
195 Adams St. (Dorchester Ave.), Dorchester, 617-825-9667
Whether it's at their outdoor operation on the corner of Columbia Road and Quincy Street or the sit-down spot in the old jail near Fields Corner, Maurice and Marion dish up delicious North Carolina–style Soul Food – vinegary chopped pork, slabs of ribs, collard greens, yams and sweet potato pies; the street corner site usually sells out early.

Manhattan Sammy's Deli Ⓜ   19 | 8 | 15 | $12
1 Kendall Sq. (bet. Hampshire & Portland Sts.), Cambridge, 617-252-0044
◪ Noshers note this Kendall Square deli is "the closest Boston comes to a New York deli complete with stale air, fabulous brisket", "great corned beef" and the "best pastrami on rye in town"; if only it weren't located in a "dingy lower-level space."

Marcella's [S][M] 19 | 12 | 11 | $16

1808 Mass Ave. (Arlington St.), Cambridge, 617-547-5000

◪ "Service is rude" but the "sandwiches can't be beat" at this Porter Square deli; thick-skinned surveyors speak of "wonderful food", the "freshest preparations" and "great take-out chicken", while critics claim "they've cut back on portions and quality."

MARCUCCIO'S [S][M]≠ 26 | 21 | 20 | $30

125 Salem St. (bet. Parmenter & Prince Sts.), Boston, 617-723-1807

◪ At this North Ender, Charles Draghi's modern slant on Italian cuisine produces "innovative", "New Age" creations as well as "wonderful" traditional dishes; though it may "still be working out some service kinks", the "nouvelle" fare, "great tasting menu" (a bargain) and "imaginative decor" have many surveyors proclaiming Draghi "a rising star" and his restaurant "a terrific new find."

Marino Ristorante [S][M] 19 | 17 | 17 | $27

2465 Mass Ave. (bet. Porter Sq. & Washburn St.), Cambridge, 617-868-5454

◪ "Loud, bustling" North Cambridge Italian with a "lovely garden environment", "wonderful staff" and an "open kitchen" turning out "healthy, organic" food "expertly prepared" with "very fresh ingredients from their own farm"; though many maintain it's "a tad overpriced" and a few feel the "food always sounds better than it tastes", it's "still an oasis in Cambridge."

Marquee [M] 21 | 19 | 18 | $33

200 High St. (Atlantic Ave.), Boston, 617-345-5500

◪ While "not a marquee player yet", this "noisy" New American addition to the Financial District "deserves points for ambition" with "beautiful steaks" and the "best seared tuna around" headlining the "interesting menu"; "colorful murals" add to the ambiance, but service is one of the kinks that needs to be worked out.

Marrakesh [S] – | – | – | M

561 Cambridge St. (7th St.), Cambridge, 617-497-1614

Set in Portuguese East Cambridge, this Moroccan is more formal than other area Middle Easterns with white linens and interesting stone and wood walls; a number of tasting menus are offered, with the bold flavors of prunes, nutmeg, olives and preserved lemons predominating.

Mary Chung [S][M]≠ 21 | 9 | 15 | $16

464 Mass Ave. (Central Sq.), Cambridge, 617-864-1991

■ "You haven't lived until you've tried" this "fiery", "no-frills" Central Square Chinese "cult classic" where "famous dishes" like "chicken velvet" are raised to "an art form" and "worth the wait"; according to "die-hard locals", "if you don't like it, there must be something wrong with you."

Mass Bay Restaurant [S][M] 20 | 18 | 19 | $29

Sheraton Boston Hotel & Towers, 39 Dalton St. (Boylston St.), Boston, 617-236-6023

◩ Diners are divided on this Back Bay hotel dining room, with fans talking up "fine presentation" of "very good food" including "wonderful, innovative seafood" and foes finding the Cajun-Creole-German "menu strange" and the entire experience "not memorable"; yet, it's "good for a Sheraton."

Massimino's Cucina Italia [M] 22 | 14 | 19 | $23

207 Endicott St. (Commercial St.), Boston, 617-523-5959

■ "What it lacks in atmosphere", this "small", "noisy", "crowded" North End Italian "makes up for" with "excellent traditional cooking" ("best tripe"), a "good wine selection", "courteous service" and "fair prices"; no wonder the "wait is excruciating" if you don't "get there early."

MATT MURPHY'S PUB [S][M]⊄ 24 | 18 | 18 | $17

14 Harvard St. (Kent St.), Brookline, 617-232-0188

■ This "restaurant masquerading as a pub", where "you feel like you're in Dublin", is unanimously applauded as "another reason to live in Brookline"; expect "honest food" including "beef stew to die for", the "best shepherd's pie" and "fish 'n' chips better than in England" brought to table by a "superfriendly staff" and washed down with "incredibly reasonable drafts" in a "mellow, smokefree atmosphere"; not surprisingly, surveyors "wish it were bigger."

Maurizio's [S][M] 23 | 15 | 21 | $26

364 Hanover St. (Clark St.), Boston, 617-367-1123

■ "Brilliantly creative combinations of fresh ingredients" ("the ravioli floats off your plate"), an "intimate atmosphere" and "very friendly service" make this "cozy" North End Italian-Mediterranean "a jewel" and "great for a date"; voters "love everything about this place except for the small tables" and decor that "lacks character."

Medieval Manor [S][M] 9 | 19 | 16 | $27

246 E. Berkeley St. (bet. Albany St. & Harrison Ave.), Boston, 617-423-4900

◩ "The Middle Ages were not known for dining" and neither is this Medieval-themed South End dinner theater; as ratings attest, many lance the food, service and even the "mediocre entertainment", yet it's seen by a handful of party-goers as "a fun place for a night out" with "a big group."

Mediterraneo Bistro [M] 20 | 18 | 19 | $30

323 Turnpike St. (Rte. 138), Canton, 781-821-8881

■ "What a surprise in a strip mall" – an "overall fantastic" Mediterranean offering an "interesting and varied menu" of "superlative food" with an "undercurrent of North African flavors" in a "friendly" setting; a few feel it's "overpriced."

Mercury Bar   18 | 19 | 15 | $27
116 Boylston St. (Tremont St.), Boston, 617-482-7799

☑ Wear your best black duds, settle into a "puffy overstuffed booth" and check out the "beautiful people" (and "wanna-bes") at this "ultrahip, ultratrendy" Theater District International; those who "thought it might be more style than substance" grudgingly admit that the tapas are "tasty", but still say "everything is secondary to the scene."

METROPOLIS CAFE Ⓢ Ⓜ   25 | 18 | 20 | $30
584 Tremont St. (bet. Clarendon & Dartmouth Sts.), Boston, 617-247-2931

■ "After two years, they finally got it right" at this "intimate" South End French-Eclectic "bistro extraordinaire" boasting "delicious", "imaginative preparations" that are "reasonably priced" – "and they take reservations" – all of which explains why customers continue to come despite the "tiny, cramped" quarters and "attitude of the owners now that the place is popular."

Michael Sherlock's Ⓢ Ⓜ   15 | 13 | 16 | $18
99 Broad St. (Franklin St.), Boston, 617-350-7077

☑ The jury's still out on this Financial District "Irish pub with a down-home feel"; defenders deem it "good" and "fast for lunch" or "after-work" unwinding, while prosecutors claim it "gives Irish food a bad name"; your call, mate.

Michael's Waterfront Ⓢ Ⓜ   18 | 18 | 17 | $27
85 Atlantic Ave. (Commercial Wharf), Boston, 617-367-6425

☑ Longtime regulars regard this "reliable" Eclectic across from the Harbor as "an old favorite for a relaxing dinner" with "creative dishes", a "terrific wine list" and a "nice romantic feel", while more critical customers claim it's "old and tired" and "there are better in the area"; best bet: "go in the summer and eat outside."

Middle East ◕ Ⓢ Ⓜ   15 | 11 | 14 | $14
4 Brookline St. (Central Sq.), Cambridge, 617-354-8238
472 Mass Ave. (Brookline St.), Cambridge, 617-492-9181

☑ These "funky" Central Square Middle Easterns where you "don't have to fear the price tag" are also "smoky and noisy" rock 'n' roll nightclubs frequented by the "nipple ring crowd"; some applaud "good cheap eats", but others maintain "the music is the thing – the food is just there."

Midwest Grill Ⓢ Ⓜ   18 | 11 | 18 | $21
1124 Cambridge St. (Prospect St.), Cambridge, 617-354-7536

■ Carnivores come together at this "friendly", still somewhat "undiscovered" East Cambridge Brazilian for "awesome", "authentic rodizio" (aka "all you can eat meat on a skewer") backed by a buffet with more than a dozen daily changing entrees and side dishes; it's "fairly priced" and "crowded but worth it."

Mike's City Diner [S] [M] ⊄ ▽ 17 | 10 | 19 | $11

1714 Washington St. (Mass Ave.), Boston, 617-267-9393

■ A "homey" early morning to midafternoon urban diner near Boston City Hospital that's lauded by loyal locals for its "hearty breakfasts" and lunches ("great ham-on-the-bone and turkey") "served by waitresses who call you 'sugar' and 'hon'."

Milano's Italian Kitchen [S] [M] 15 | 15 | 16 | $20

47 Newbury St. (Berkeley St.), Boston, 617-267-6150

◪ There's much debate about this "bright" Back Bay eatery, with supporters finding the food "surprisingly good" and the atmosphere "pleasant" and adversaries complaining it "should be called McDonald's Italian Kitchen" and "could you dim the lights a little?"; still, it's "one of the few moderately priced restaurants on Newbury Street" "for a casual quick dinner."

Mildred's [S] [M] 11 | 14 | 12 | $13

552 Tremont St. (Clarendon St.), Boston, 617-426-0008

◪ This South End cafe with "no ovens" is more about "camp than cuisine" – so "go for coffee and dessert" and the "pretty boys inside."

Milk Street Cafe [M] 18 | 11 | 12 | $12

Post Office Sq. (bet. Franklin & Congress Sts.), Boston, 617-350-7275

50 Milk St. (Devonshire St.), Boston, 617-542-3663

◪ Some see this pair of "convenient" Financial District Koshers offering vegetarian specialties along with "soups, sandwiches and salads" as "good for a healthy lunch cafeteria-style", but dissenters find it "boring and too expensive for what it is"; perhaps a post-*Survey* menu expansion that will add wraps, Italian items and more will boost its appeal.

Mill Falls, The [M] 18 | 21 | 19 | $32

383 Elliot St. (Chestnut St.), Newton, 617-244-3080

◪ The "lovely location" on the banks of the Charles makes for a "nice atmosphere" at this Newton Falls Regional American, and though "it's been around for awhile", fans say "the quality is still there"; foes counter the "Wasp menu" is "bland as can be" and the place "needs a makeover"; still, "it keeps the over-60 set happy."

Ming Garden [S] [M] 15 | 13 | 15 | $18

1262 Boylston St. (opposite Star Market), Chestnut Hill, 617-232-4848

◪ "Fill up on the huge buffet table" at this Chestnut Hill Chinese that's deemed "solid" by most; they recommend the "good soups" and weekend "dim sum brunch that sure beats going to Chinatown"; but those who don't dig this garden call it "inconsistent" and "generic."

Miracle of Science Bar + Grill S M 19 17 15 $15
321 Mass Ave. (State St.), Cambridge, 617-868-2866
■ This "cool", "creative take on a college bar" is an "MIT hangout" near Central Square offering "basic" American fare that "proves delicious food doesn't have to cost a lot" (the "best roasted potatoes", a "burger that may win your heart"); even those who note it's "crowded" and "extremely loud" with "marginal service" concede "it's fun."

MISTRAL S M 23 25 23 $41
223 Columbus Ave. (Berkeley St.), Boston, 617-867-9300
☑ The long-awaited venture of chef Jamie Mammano (formerly of Aujourd'hui) and nightclub impresario Seth Greenberg, this South End Provençal has quickly impressed fans who say it's "soon to be the hottest spot" in town thanks to "very good food" from a menu with "excellent variety" and "beautiful" decor likened to the "Delano Hotel in South Beach"; even with what some see as "too much attitude" and inconsistency, it's "already a place to be seen."

Miyako S M 18 15 17 $26
279A Newbury St. (Exeter St.), Boston, 617-236-0222
☑ Loyalists like this "best treat on Newbury Street" Japanese with "traditional sushi and tempura" and "attentive service", advising "be sure to eat outside if you're a people-watcher"; however, cynics say "it's decent, but not worth the money" to eat "nothing new or exciting" in a "too bright" space that's in "need of updating."

Montien S M 21 15 19 $20
63 Stuart St. (bet. Tremont & Washington Sts.), Boston, 617-338-5600
■ An "overlooked" Theater District Thai near the Wang Center that's "good pre- and post-theater"; the food is "tasty" with "good curries and pad Thai" and "terrific fish dishes", so "sit in a booth and ignore the decor."

Moon Villa ● S M 14 8 14 $17
19 Edinboro St. (bet. Essex & Kingston Sts.), Boston, 617-423-2061
■ A "Chinese greasy spoon" in Chinatown with late hours that draw night-crawlers who confess "what makes this place so good is that it's usually 3 AM and you don't realize how bad it is"; even those who "eat here sober" report that it may be "very forgettable."

Moon Woman Cafe 21 17 19 $26
108 Oak St. (bet. Chestnut St. & Highland Ave.), Newton, 617-630-9569
■ "Newly expanded" and "not as noisy", this "delightful" Newton Italian under the same ownership as Stellina is "a best-kept secret" with "unique, imaginative food" served by a "knowledgeable staff"; sure, the "clientele is suburban", but where the heck do you think you are anyway?

MORTON'S OF CHICAGO [S] [M] 26 | 18 | 23 | $44

1 Exeter Plaza (Boylston St.), Boston, 617-266-5858

■ "Excellent steaks in a basement" sums up this Back Bay subterranean outpost of the Chicago chain; while the room doesn't thrill, it has the requisite "old boys club feel" plus "terrific meat", a "solid wine list" and "great service"; some feel there's too much noise and too little space between tables, but for most this is "what steak and potatoes ought to be" – "if your company pays."

Mother Anna's [S] [M] 21 | 15 | 20 | $25

211 Hanover St. (Cross St.), Boston, 617-523-8496

■ "An oldie but a goody", this 1931 North End Italian delivers "good basic cooking"; since it serves "mouthwatering lobster ravioli", fans ask "why go to any other place?"

Mr. & Mrs. Bartley's Burger Cottage [M] 🚫 20 | 12 | 15 | $11

1246 Mass Ave. (bet. Bow St. & Plympton Ave.), Cambridge, 617-354-6559

■ "The only place in Harvard Square that hasn't been Starbucked", this "institution" with an "endless" American menu offers "awesome burgers anyway you like them", plus "great onion rings", shakes and "classic fountain drinks like lime rickeys"; to the few who mutter "too much grease", the "mobs" of devotees reply "a must."

Mucho Gusto Cafe & Collectibles [S] 19 | 22 | 23 | $17

1124 Boylston St. (bet. Hemenway St. & Mass Ave.), Boston, 617-236-1020

■ The "kitschy" '40s–'60s decor (most everything is for sale), "friendly staff" and "unique dishes" have won fans for this "mucho fun" Cuban newcomer near the Berklee School of Music; while a few say the food "needs more seasoning", boosters insist that "it's cooked with heart."

Museum of Fine Arts Restaurant [S] 17 | 20 | 16 | $23

Museum of Fine Arts, 465 Huntington Ave. (Museum Rd.), Boston, 617-369-3474

◩ "The picture is beginning to improve" say optimists about this New American in the MFA, and the arrival of Jim Dodge to oversee the kitchen may change the minds of those who have found the food "overpriced" and just "ok"; "slow" service draws knocks, but the "surroundings are unsurpassed" (even more so with a post-*Survey* redo).

Nara [M] 17 | 9 | 15 | $21

85 Wendell St. (Broad St.), Boston, 617-338-5935

◩ While ratings are middling, a few fans note "very good sushi" at this "smallest of Japanese restaurants" in the Financial District; others who point out the "not great decor" still say it's "ok for lunch."

Narita Japanese Restaurant [S] [M] ▽ 19 13 18 $20

18 Elliot St. (JFK St.), Cambridge, 617-868-2226

◪ Many say "Cambridge's best new sushi" source is this "unpretentious" Harvard Square newcomer that provides a "calm, restful place for lunch"; although a few complain it's "not too cheap", the "genuine Japanese atmosphere" and "good" food have already established a following.

Neighborhood Restaurant & Bakery [S] [M] ⊄ 17 8 14 $14

25 Bow St. (Union Sq.), Somerville, 617-623-9710

■ "Go for breakfast and you won't need lunch or dinner" promise fans of this "friendly" Union Square Portuguese, a "great deal" notable for "huge portions" of "honest" eggs, home fries, waffles and other AM grub; though crowds may keep the "staff in a daze" and most agree the quality never rises above "standard", "quantities compensate."

New Asia [S] [M] 17 9 15 $15

194 Mass Ave. (Lake St.), Arlington, 781-643-6364
93 Trapelo Rd. (Common St.), Belmont, 617-484-7000
180 Endicott St. (opp. Liberty Tree Mall), Danvers, 978-774-8080
211 Mass Ave. (Park Ave.), Lexington, 781-862-9655
328 Somerville Ave. (Union Sq.), Somerville, 617-628-5533

■ It may be "boring", but this minichain delivers "basic Chinese the way it should be" making it a "safe bet for a simple meal"; most see them as "good family places" that are "convenient for takeout" if "nothing special."

New Bridge Cafe [S] [M] ⊄ 22 7 14 $15

650 Washington Ave. (Woodlawn Ave.), Chelsea, 617-884-0134

◪ An "unpretentious", "smoky" "local bar" in Chelsea near the Everett line where "crowds throng" "to eat not dine" on some of "Boston's best steak tips" and "great" ribs and chicken in "large portions"; critics dismiss it as "completely overrated by people who like lots of cheap food."

New Mother India [S] [M] 22 17 18 $19

336 Moody St. (Main St.), Waltham, 781-893-3311

■ While curry lovers praise nearly everything about this "consistent and friendly" "good choice" in Waltham's Little India, noting the "well-designed interior", "helpful service" and "excellent food", it's the "great beers" that seem to generate the most excitement; "thank heaven this is in Waltham or you'd never get in."

New Shanghai [S] [M] 22 15 18 $21

21 Hudson St. (bet. Beach & Kneeland Sts.), Boston, 617-338-6688

■ "Try the scallops in black pepper sauce" urge fans of this standout dish at "one of Chinatown's best", a favorite for its "accommodating" staff, "nice atmosphere" and "excellent food"; watch out for "long lines" at lunch.

New Yorker Diner S M ⌐⌐ — 15 11 16 $11
39 Mt. Auburn St. (Summer St.), Watertown, 617-924-9772
■ Whether you like your "solid breakfasts" "after a drinking binge" or after the sun rises, this "classic", "open late" Watertown American diner is reliable for "good omelets, eggs and French toast"; N.B. it closes at 2 PM daily, but reopens Thursday–Saturday from 10:30 PM– 4 AM.

Nicole Ristorante S — ▽ 19 16 21 $27
54 Salem St. (bet. Cross & Parmenter Sts.), Boston, 617-742-6999
■ The "gracious owner-hostess makes every meal a pleasant experience" at this "North End surprise" that earns bravos for the "great quality" and "good variety" of "real" Italian specialties; although not well known to our surveyors, it seems worth checking out.

Noble House S M — 19 18 17 $21
1306 Beacon St. (Harvard St.), Brookline, 617-232-9580
☑ "Gourmet Chinese food" and good service in a "tasteful" "modern" setting impress many reviewers of this "refined" Coolidge Corner spot offering "interesting" "delicious versions of Chinese standards"; although less enthused diners place the food "just a notch above routine" and say prices are "high for what you get", the majority insists it's "worth every penny."

No Name S M ⌐⌐ — 15 9 13 $18
15 Fish Pier (Northern Ave.), Boston, 617-338-7539
☑ According to its deck hands, there's a "good variety of really fresh seafood" at "decent prices" to be found at this "noisy", truly "no-frills" "waterfront classic" on the Boston Pier that's been serving "excellent chowder" since 1917; but mutineers growl: "mediocrity presides here – no wonder no one wants to put his name on it"; your call.

Noodles M — 19 12 16 $17
414 Washington St. (Beacon St.), Somerville, 617-492-1770
☑ "Excellent fresh pasta and sauces" are the draw at this "fun, funky and fast" Somerville Italian with a "pleasant" staff and "mushroom lasagna to die for"; many "wish they had a little more space" – "but a table outside on a summer night is a treat."

North East Brewing Co. S M — 18 19 16 $19
1314 Commonwealth Ave. (Harvard St.), Allston, 617-566-6699
☑ The "upscale" decor ("beautiful woodwork", "cozy fireplace", "windows that open onto the street") is a major hit at this "wonderful" "adult" "brew restaurant not brewpub" in Allston that's called "the best place to sample microbrews" in the Boston area; but reactions to the food vary ("impressive" vs. "average") and "forgetful service" has few defenders.

Norumbega Park S M   16 | 16 | 16 | $24 |
287 Auburn St. (Lexington St.), Newton, 617-558-7654
◪ Locals enjoy this "charming bistro" in an "interesting historical" "converted house" in "restaurant-poor Newton" and have warm words for the "friendly" owners who "try very hard"; but the "inconsistent" Eclectic kitchen and "slow service" lead some to conclude it's a "go back only if you are in the neighborhood."

OAK ROOM, THE S M   23 | 26 | 24 | $50 |
Fairmont Copley Plaza, 138 St. James Ave. (bet. Dartmouth & Trinity Sts.), Boston, 617-267-5300
◪ This "classy" traditional steakhouse in the Fairmont Copley Plaza is where an "older crowd" heads for "A-1" martinis and "very good steaks and chops"; expect to pay for the "ritzy" digs and "superb service", but also be warned that some say "cigar smoke permeates the room."

Oasis Cafe S   ▽ 19 | 13 | 15 | $20 |
176 Endicott St. (bet. Commercial & Thatcher Sts.), Boston, 617-523-9274
■ The "only non-Italian in the North End", this aptly named "American oasis" fulfills cravings for "excellent" and "inexpensive" burgers, roasts and other comfort fare including desserts that are "worth every calorie"; boosters say it "never fails to deliver."

Oceanic Chinese Seafood ◖ S M   19 | 11 | 16 | $17 |
91 Mass Ave. (bet. Commonwealth Ave. & Newbury St.), Boston, 617-353-0791
■ For "good Chinese near Symphony Hall", afishionados turn to this Back Bay rarity serving "interesting" and "consistent" multiregional fare including "good steamed fish"; food ratings have risen considerably since the last *Survey*, indicating it's worth a try.

Ocean Wealth ◖ S M   21 | 11 | 14 | $20 |
8 Tyler St. (Beach St.), Boston, 617-423-1338
◪ "After so many boring Chinese restaurants, a real find" is the main school of thought on this Chinatown "fish lovers' delight" that's "always an adventure"; although a few carp that it's "indistinguishable from dozens of others", more find it "most unusual and tasty" although the "atmosphere leaves a lot to be desired."

O'Fado S M   ▽ 20 | 12 | 19 | $26 |
72 Walnut St. (Harris St.), Peabody, 978-531-7369
■ Although some regulars of this "reasonably priced" "best Portuguese on the North Shore" lament the recent remodeling ("it's no longer a great neighborhood joint"), all agree that the chef "continues to turn out excellent food night after night" at this "hidden treasure" for ethnic specialties prepared in a "caring, loving" fashion.

OLIVES   28 | 22 | 22 | $43
10 City Sq. (bet. Main & Park Sts.), Charlestown, 617-242-1999
☑ With "gutsy", "extremely creative" food, Todd English's
Charlestown Eclectic is again Boston's Most Popular
restaurant; sure, there are "drawbacks" – "noise", crowds
and "nearly intolerable" waits due to no reserving except
for large groups – but most feel it's "worth the discomfort" to
enjoy "beautifully presented" food; dissenters who find
"too many tastes" on the plate and "rushed service" are
easily outvoted by those who say "everything works."

Omonia 🖫   17 | 16 | 19 | $24
75 S. Charles St. (Stuart St.), Boston, 617-426-4310
☑ Those with tickets may want to sample the "basic Greek
food" in a "quiet setting" "tucked away in the Theater
District"; it may be "behind the times", but supporters
counter that the "baklava is as good as in the Plaka" and
anyway, "in a city with few good Greek restaurants", it's a
"friendly" place for sunny memories and moussaka.

On The Park 🖫   20 | 15 | 19 | $23
1 Union Park (Shawmut Ave.), Boston, 617-426-0862
☑ You'll "want to linger by the warm windows" at this
New American–Eclectic "neighborhood" bistro in the
South End that turns out a "justifiably famous" Sunday
brunch as well as other "interesting and good food";
but fame exacts a price: this "charming hole-in-the-
wall" is "small" so "come prepared to wait."

Original Sports Saloon ◑🖫Ⓜ   16 | 13 | 14 | $18
*Copley Square Hotel, 47 Huntington Ave. (Exeter St.),
Boston, 617-536-1904*
☑ Despite middling ratings, BBQ cognoscenti insist the "ribs
are as good as they say" at this saloon in the Copley Square
Hotel that's also "known for sports memorabilia"; although a
few ask "what's the big deal?" and note "slow service",
the "great AYCE" special on Wednesdays is "a bargain."

Oskar's ◑🖫Ⓜ   16 | 21 | 16 | $30
107 South St. (Kneeland St), Boston, 617-542-6756
☑ "People usually go for the cool atmosphere" rather than
the "inconsistent" Eclectic fare at this Leather District haunt;
although "everything is great except the food – what a
shame", things may be on the upswing since some report
that under a new chef (ex Ritz-Carlton) "the food's improving."

Other Side Cosmic Cafe ◑🖫Ⓜ⊅   16 | 16 | 12 | $12
407 Newbury St. (Mass Ave.), Boston, 617-536-9477
☑ "Unless you have something pierced", you may feel out
of it at this "funky" "grunge chic" American in the Back Bay;
but for "the young set", this "artist hangout" is a "completely
fun place to eat amazing smoothies and sandwiches" even if
service may seem "nonexistent"; it's also one of the few
"cool places" in Boston that's "open late."

Pagliuca's [S][M] 20 | 13 | 20 | $21
14 Parmenter St. (Hanover St.), Boston, 617-367-1504
◪ The "old-fashioned" Southern Italian fare at this "friendly" North Ender suits traditionalists who enjoy "red sauce" pastas and "solid" standards such as "pork chops with vinegar peppers that are out of this world"; although critics grouse "the warmth of the staff does not compensate for insipid food", more are won over by "homestyle" appeal.

Palenque [S] – | – | – | M
300 Beacon St. (Eustais St.), Somerville, 617-491-1004
"Outstanding service" and "very good" "authentic" Mexican food earn a welcome from the few reviewers who know this "nice new neighborhood hangout" in Somerville; but the "cafeteria decor" leaves room for improvement.

Palm Restaurant [S][M] 20 | 17 | 20 | $42
Westin Hotel, 200 Dartmouth St. (bet. St. James Ave. & Stuart St.), Boston, 617-867-9292
◪ "Big beef, big lobsters, big tab" is the mantra for this Back Bay outpost of the NY "meat eaters' heaven" chain; its "boys' club" atmosphere that some find "delightful" makes it good for a "power dinner or bachelor party", but adamant foes insist it's "a cut below the tough Boston steak competition" and "too pricey" for the "antiseptic decor."

Pandan Leaf [S] – | – | – | M
250 Harvard St. (Coolidge Corner), Brookline, 617-566-9393
A Coolidge Corner Malaysian newcomer that has sizzled since opening thanks to exotica like barbecued skate wing, raw fish salad and curried fish head, along with mix and match curry dishes and plenty of noodle items that are popular at lunch; it's often noisy and crowded, but fast service makes the wait at the small bar tolerable.

Panda Palace ◐[S][M] ▽ 18 | 13 | 16 | $18
719 Broadway (Josephine St.), Somerville, 617-625-9441
■ If you're big on appetite and short on funds, head to this "solid neighborhood Chinese" in Somerville where the "all you can eat buffet" is "one of the best bargains around."

Pandorga's [S] ▽ 21 | 12 | 19 | $18
170 Willow St. (bet. Main & River Sts.), Waltham, 781-647-9270
◪ There's "extraordinary cuisine hidden away" in Waltham, according to enthusiasts of this Ecuadorian offering a "large selection of South American food in a tiny place"; its popularity may create weekend waits (so reserve ahead), but once seated there's "warm attention" and "good, cheap" meals; a few caution: "worth trying but uneven."

Papa Razzi [S][M] 16 | 16 | 16 | $22
271 Dartmouth St. (bet. Boylston & Newbury Sts.), Boston, 617-536-9200 ◐
Cambridgeside Galleria, 100 Cambridgeside Pl. (Memorial Dr.), Cambridge, 617-577-0009

Papa Razzi (Cont.)
Chestnut Hill Mall, 100 Boylston St. (Rte. 9), Chestnut Hill, 617-527-6600
768 Elm St. (Baker Ave.), Concord, 978-371-0030
16 Washington St. (Rte. 16), Wellesley, 781-235-4747
☑ Advocates of this "hip Italian" chain say it's "better than you'd expect" with a "consistent" menu focusing on "tasty pizza and pastas", while hard-liners counter that it's "not worth the price" for "formula food"; "not bad, but not a place to plan your evening around" is the consensus.

Parker's S M   19 22 22 $32
Omni Parker House, 60 School St. (Tremont St.), Boston, 617-227-8600
☑ While this legendary American in the Omni Parker House Hotel still draws praise for its "lovely old atmosphere", those who suggest it "needs upgrading" may be pleased to learn that at press time it was about to reopen after a renovation; it remains to be seen if this "home of the blue hairs" will still offer loyalists the "wonderful brunch" that some feel is one of Boston's "best-kept secrets."

Parrish Cafe ◖ S M   19 14 15 $17
361 Boylston St. (Arlington St.), Boston, 617-247-4777
☑ "Awesome sandwiches and a great deck" are the prime draws at this Back Bay American where the "creative, delicious" sandwiches "designed by some of Boston's best chefs", along with a "great beer selection" and "an alluring place to sit in warm weather", add up to one of the "the best lunch places" in town – with one caveat: many slam some of the "worst service in Boston."

Passage to India S M   17 12 16 $16
1900 Porter Sq., Cambridge, 617-497-6113
☑ "Standard Indian fare" (including "excellent breads") and "friendly management" make this "reasonably priced" Porter Square spot a "fine neighborhood" option; although tougher critics say it's still "not quite" there, "it's on the way."

Pat's Pushcart   – – – M
61 Endicott St. (Cross St.), Boston, 617-523-9616
"The ambiance is weak, but the specials are uniformly strong" at this long-standing "cheap", "quiet" North End Southern Italian; it's a "real surprise" that "makes a nice change", but call ahead since it's "often closed."

Peach Farm ◖ S M   22 9 15 $19
4 Tyler St. (Beach St.), Boston, 617-482-1116
☑ Surveyors draw swords over whether this Chinatowner is in fact a peach; advocates extol food that "sparkles", especially the "excellent" crab and clams in black bean sauce; but foes swear it's "very overrated", asking "why did this place get raves?"; still, critics must be a minority since it's "hard to get a table at peak times."

Peking Cuisine ⓈⓂ   ▽ 19 | 13 | 18 | $17
10 Tyler St. (Kneeland St.), Boston, 617-542-5857
870 Walnut St. (Beacon St.), Newton, 617-969-0888
■ They've added a Newton sib, but patrons confine their comments to the "very Chinese" second-floor walk-up in Chinatown, a source for "great scallion pancakes" and other "wonderful food"; a "welcome renovation" and staff that "could not be more accommodating" are further pluses.

Pellino's Ⓜ   – | – | – | E
261 Washington St., Marblehead, 781-631-3344
This chef-owned, second-floor Marblehead Italian with fresh flowers on every table offers modern dishes (like potato-crusted sea bass drizzled with red wine sauce) that all too often seem to be alien fare in the suburbs; of course, there are the usual suspects (rack of lamb, lobster fra diavolo) as well; interesting wines are a plus.

Penang ⓈⓂ   24 | 19 | 17 | $20
685 Washington St. (Kneeland St.), Boston, 617-451-6373
◨ "Interesting" is the word most often used to describe the Malaysian fare at "the new hip Asian hangout (lots of cell phones and cigars)", a "fascinating place to eat and watch people" with "creative food" and "different decor"; service is "so-so" and some worry that it's "a bit too authentic for Bostonian tastes", but ratings indicate otherwise.

Pentimento ⓈⓂ   17 | 18 | 14 | $14
69 Leonard St. (Moore St.), Belmont, 617-489-7295
◨ Devotees from its old days in Cambridge still argue the merits of this "funky", "nuts and berries" Eclectic's move to Belmont Center ("lost its charm" vs. "easily survived the move"), but it "still feels like the right thing to do on a Sunday morning" for "excellent waffles" and the "best French toast in history"; despite "slow service", "there's no place like it" for "good food for old hippies and vegetarians."

Pete's Bar & Grille ●Ⓜ   – | – | – | M
916 Commonwealth Ave. (St. Paul St.), Brookline, 617-566-0300
Same owners, but a new name and concept (Southwestern) for the former Caffe Lampara near BU; they still make a fine pizza, but now the house special appetizer is guacamole prepared tableside, and other offerings range from grilled fish with fruit salsas to big burgers and fries; in step with the casual ambiance, microbrews are the drink of choice.

Phoenicia ⓈⓂ   22 | 13 | 17 | $16
240 Cambridge St. (Garden St.), Cambridge, 617-523-4606
■ While the decor is "nothing fancy", there are "delicious, inexpensive" Lebanese specialties "on the less nice side of Beacon Hill" at this "warm, casual" "family-run" eatery; the "terrific" food has taken a leap in ratings since the last *Survey,* and locals rejoice that it's "in the neighborhood" – "it makes you realize how good Middle Eastern can be."

Pho Pasteur ⓈⓂ | 22 | 10 | 16 | $14 |

682 Washington St. (Beach St.), Boston, 617-482-7467
8 Kneeland St. (bet. Stuart & Washington Sts.), Boston,
617-451-0247
137 Brighton Ave., Allston, 617-783-2340
35 Dunster St. (Mt. Auburn St.), Cambridge, 617-864-4100
■ "Delicious and cheap" Vietnamese fare is offered at this
foursome where diners overlook the "atmosphere of a
paneled van" (except at the new, more attractive, liquor-
licensed Harvard Square site) and focus instead on the
large menu that includes "wonderful soups" and "great
fresh spring rolls."

Pho Republique ⓈⓂ | – | – | – | M |

468 Mass Ave. (Central Sq.), Cambridge, 617-576-2111
Didi Emmons (ex Delux Cafe) has opened this striking
French-Vietnamese bistro with a bamboo-covered ceiling
in the former Oh! Calcutta in Central Square; large banquet
tables make it easy for big groups to share highlights such
as bouillabaisse and other soups, plenty of vegetarian
choices, a cheese plate and lemongrass crème brûlée.

Piccola Venezia ⓈⓂ | 19 | 16 | 18 | $20 |

263 Hanover St. (bet. Cross & Richmond Sts.), Boston,
617-523-3888
☑ Look for "crispy light chicken cutlets" and "delicious
meatballs" at this North End Italian that's a "good value"
thanks to "generous portions" of "traditional" fare (like
"grandma's cooking") served by "warm, friendly" staff.

Piccolo Nido Ⓜ | 20 | 18 | 20 | $30 |

257 North St. (Lewis St.), Boston, 617-742-4272
☑ Admirers say this North End Italian offers "high-quality"
fare with "flair" in an "upscale" atmosphere; "great service"
is also commended, but a few find "nothing to distinguish it."

PIGNOLI ⓈⓂ | 24 | 24 | 22 | $41 |

79 Park Plaza (Arlington St.), Boston, 617-338-7500
☑ Lydia Shire's 'other' restaurant (besides Biba) brings
"refined" modern Italian dining and "sizzling decor" to
Park Square; to most the "electric atmosphere" is "cool"
and the menu is "different" and "bold", but some call it
"poshly sterile" and object to paying "big bucks for tiny
portions" of food that's "occasionally too weird."

Pillar House Ⓜ | 21 | 23 | 22 | $35 |

26 Quinobequin Rd. (bet. Rtes. 16 & 128), Newton, 617-969-6500
☑ This Newton pillar of "old-fashioned charm" set in a
"beautiful" "country house" turns out "surprisingly good"
American vittles and is perfect for "special occasions";
"despite the preponderance of blue hair, it takes its food
and wine seriously" and its new casual cafe is "a welcome
addition"; detractors carp about "slightly stuffy" atmosphere
and "expensive" prices, but they're outvoted; dinner only.

Pinardi's ⓈⓂ
17 | 13 | 17 | $14

711 Centre St. (Borough St.), Jamaica Plain,
617-524-0050

☑ A chorus of early birds sings the praises of the "delicious, bountiful pancakes", "best French toast in town" and other AM fare at this Jamaica Plain spot that doubles as an Italian restaurant; but few have much to say about lunch and dinner, declaring "breakfast is the best meal" here.

Pit Stop Bar-B-Q ◑⇄
– | – | – | I

888 Morton St. (Evan St.), Mattapan, 617-436-0485

"Great big yummy ribs" "come with all the trimmings" at this Mattapan BBQ pit stop; given that it's a "little joint" with "weird hours" (open Thursday–Saturday only) and decor and service that can be "lacking", some opt "for takeout."

Pizzeria Uno ◑ⓈⓂ
13 | 12 | 14 | $15

731 Boylston St. (Dartmouth St.), Boston, 617-267-8554
1 Brookline Ave. (Kenmore Sq.), Boston, 617-262-4911
Faneuil Hall, 22 Clinton St. (North St.), Boston,
617-523-5722
280 Huntington Ave. (Gainsborough St.), Boston,
617-424-1697
1230 Commonwealth Ave. (Harvard Ave.), Allston,
617-739-0034
250B Granite St. (93S, exit 6), Braintree, 781-849-8667
22 JFK St. (Harvard Sq.), Cambridge, 617-497-1530
820 Somerville Ave. (Porter Sq.), Cambridge, 617-864-1916

☑ Supporters of this Windy City–based, deep-dish pizza chain say if it's "not quite Chicago, it's a pretty good fake" with "tasty", "filling" pies; bashers say "not even close" and wish they'd "get the grease out of the crust" and do something about the "inattentive service"; but harried diners say they're "fine for a fast lunch."

Plaza III - The Kansas City Steakhouse ◑ⓈⓂ
– | – | – | E

101 S. Market Bldg. (Merchants Row), Boston, 617-720-5570

Expect high, well-marbled steaks, a very good but expensive wine list and a main dining room done up in rugged Western decor at this Faneuil Hall outpost of the legendary Kansas City steakhouse; downstairs is a more casual grill with live jazz and good burgers, but upstairs is where serious beef buffs head for meat flown in daily from KC and served by a very gracious staff.

Polcari's ◑ⓈⓂ
15 | 15 | 15 | $23

92 Broadway/Rte. 1N, Saugus, 781-233-3765

☑ "Huge family-style piles" of Southern Italian food are dished up at this Route 1 Saugus eatery; boosters laud the '50s "peppy decor" and call the chow "decent", while detractors say it "tastes more like a chain" than an authentic North End restaurant; the fact that it's "very busy" means it's doing something right.

POMODORO [S] [M] ⊄ — 25 | 13 | 18 | $28
319 Hanover St. (bet. Prince & Richmond Sts.), Boston, 617-367-4348
◪ A "hole-in-the-wall" Italian North Ender where "tight quarters" ("packed like sardines") and bathrooms two doors down don't deter those seeking "great, simple, fresh food", from seafood to "perfect pasta"; if the specials sometimes "try too hard", it's still "a cut above most in the North End", which explains the "long lines."

Ponte Vecchio [S] [M] — 23 | 18 | 21 | $37
435 Newbury St. (Topsfield Fairgrounds), Danvers, 978-777-9188
◪ A "best-kept secret" in the suburbs, this Danvers Italian might be "a bit pretentious for a restaurant in a strip mall" ("waiters in tuxes"), but few can resist its "great veal chop" and other "outstanding" (if "pricey") food; despite a solid service rating some report "snobby" staff.

Poppa & Goose [M] — 18 | 11 | 15 | $16
69 First St. (Spring St.), Cambridge, 617-497-6772
■ While there's "not much decor" at this "cafeteria-like" Cambridge Pan-Asian, the "really fresh" food (including "lots of veggie choices") at "unbelievably cheap prices" more than "makes up for it"; P.S. the "lunchtime buffet is fantastic" and convenience to the courthouse is a boon when "on jury duty."

Pranzare [S] [M] — ▽ 17 | 11 | 19 | $20
Howard Johnson, 1271 Boylston St. (near Fenway Park), Boston, 617-424-1441
◪ If on the way to Fenway Park, this Italian in a HoJo offers a convenient alternative to hot dogs and peanuts; predictably, the atmosphere's "awful", but you can have a "quick meal" of "good food" at "reasonable prices."

PROVIDENCE [S] — 24 | 21 | 21 | $39
1223 Beacon St. (St. Paul St.), Brookline, 617-232-0300
◪ Most surveyors "love Paul O'Connell's take" on New American cuisine at this "fairly formal but friendly" Brookliner with a "plain facade" that conceals a love-it vs. hate-it "baroque" interior of "columns and curtains"; a "great wine list" nicely complements the winning menu, and servers are as "witty" as the decor; nitpickers rate it "a notch below the best places" but still call it "a nice surprise."

Purple Cactus Burrito & Wrap Bar [S] [M] — 20 | 12 | 16 | $12
312 Shawmut Ave. (Union Park), Boston, 617-338-5675
2263 Mass Ave. (bet. Day & Dover Sts.), Cambridge, 617-354-5200
■ Increasingly popular Tex-Mex wrap/burrito bars prized for their "fresh", "healthy", "original", "filling" combos; while basically for takeout, "you can eat there, but there may not be room for anyone else."

Rangoli 🆂Ⓜ   23 | 15 | 20 | $18
129 Brighton Ave. (Harvard Ave.), Allston, 617-562-0200
■ Diners shout "hooray" for this "very popular" Allston eatery specializing in "brilliantly prepared", "light" South Indian dishes that are the perfect "antidote" to "cookie-cutter" standards; expect dosa to "dream about", plus "attentive service" and tasteful decor; the only drawback – "parking is a problem."

Rasol 🆂Ⓜ   19 | 16 | 18 | $19
308 Main St. (Rte. 60), Malden, 781-388-2448
☑ A "bit hard to find", this Malden Indian earns praise for its "outstanding" low-cost lunch buffet; the "fine" regular menu offers "good variety", though "nothing is exciting."

Rattlesnake Bar ◑🆂Ⓜ   12 | 11 | 13 | $17
382 Boylston St. (bet. Arlington & Berkeley Sts.), Boston, 617-859-8555
☑ "Abandon taste buds all ye who enter here" and "eat before you go" typify detractors' comments on this Back Bay Southwestern that's a popular "meet market" for the "after-work crowd"; still, "big portions" and "good appetizers" help draw "twentysomethings" who use the "cool patio roof deck" for people-watching.

Rebecca's 🆂Ⓜ   17 | 14 | 14 | $21
21 Charles St. (bet. Branch & Chestnut Sts.), Boston, 617-742-9747
☑ This "crowded" Beacon Hill American remains popular for its "great Sunday brunch" and lunches that have "the edge over regular sandwich places"; "fabulous cakes" also earn praise, however, a critical contingent calls the decor "worn out", service "indifferent" and the food "not what it used to be."

Redbones 🆂Ⓜ⊅   22 | 13 | 17 | $18
55 Chester St. (Elm St.), Somerville, 617-628-2200
☑ "Now I know why I'll never be a vegetarian" declare boosters of this "loud and chaotic", "down and dirty" BBQ joint in Somerville with "incredible" ribs in "lots of styles"; they caution "don't wear your nice clothes", "bring a towel" and "beware overintake"; if you can't stand the "long wait", remember it's a great choice "for takeout."

Red Herring Ⓜ   22 | 19 | 20 | $25
1 Columbus Ave. (bet. Arlington & Charles Sts.), Boston, 617-423-1581
■ A "brilliant new Theater District" spot is the consensus on this Salamander sib (same owner) with an "excellent" International tapas menu offering "serious bites" that are "great for noshing" pre- or post-show; surveyors applaud the "complex combinations of flavors" and "well-matched wine list" and say they "get the details right from terrific breads to real tea", but some feel "cramped."

RED RAVEN'S HAVANA [S] 24 | 22 | 23 | $31
90 Washington St. (bet. Church & Derby Sts.), Salem, 978-740-3888
RED RAVEN'S LOVE NOODLE
75 Congress St. (Derby St.), Salem, 978-745-8558
■ There's nothing Cuban on the menu although the dangling beads, black ceiling and deep red walls lend a sort of funky Caribbean feel to Red Raven's Havana, the newer, more upscale member of this "hip" Salem duo; the over-the-top ambiance segues into a "creative" Eclectic–New American menu ranging from crispy chicken livers to roast salmon and confit of duck as well as a spa menu.

Regina Pizzeria ◐ [S] [M] ≠ 22 | 11 | 15 | $14
11 ½ Thatcher St. (N. Margin St.), Boston, 617-227-0765
■ "The only place to eat pizza in the North End" say devotees of this long-standing "institution" that many think turns out "the best" pizza in Boston (and it tastes even better "after a Celtics game"); the "awesome" thin-crust pies are worth "fighting the traffic for", but "don't expect much else" because the decor has "no personality" and the staff can have too much ("attitude"); P.S. the "suburban Reginas do not compare."

Restaurant Clio [S] [M] ▽ 26 | 27 | 26 | $47
Eliot Hotel, 370 Commonwealth Ave. (Mass Ave.), Boston, 617-536-7200
■ "Destined to be a big star" is the word on this swank Parisian-style supper club in the Eliot Hotel, where a plush bar leads to the dining room decked out in banquettes and a leopard skin rug; Ken Oringer (ex Silks in San Francisco) uses big flavors to expand on New French fare; all in all, it's "somewhat expensive" but "superb."

Restaurant Zinc ◐ [S] 21 | 20 | 19 | $40
35 Stanhope St. (bet. Berkeley & Clarendon Sts.), Boston, 617-262-2323
◪ This Back Bay New French near the Mass Pike is a "happening", with all the pluses and minuses that implies; while most surveyors praise Nick Tischler's food ("crystal clear flavors", "good bistro fare like you'd find in Paris"), many report that "small portions", high prices and "large doses of attitude" and "noise" make it "less desirable"; "handsome decor" and a "sleek bar" are pluses.

Rhythm & Spice [S] [M] 17 | 14 | 15 | $19
315 Mass Ave. (State St.), Cambridge, 617-497-0977
◪ "Spice is the word" at this "fun" Caribbean joint outside Central Square in Cambridge cited as "the place for curried goat" and other "authentic" fare; while some find the food "uneven", it still makes for an "interesting" "change of pace", especially on Thursday–Saturday nights when live reggae and calypso music "rules."

RIALTO S M
27 | 26 | 25 | $46

Charles Hotel, 1 Bennett St. (Harvard Sq.), Cambridge, 617-661-5050

■ Jody Adams' "big, bold" Mediterranean fare is offered in a "swank" Harvard Square setting, making for an evening that's both "comforting and elegant"; "invigorating" and "intriguing" are typical comments on the seasonally changing menu, and though some cite "high-attitude staff", most consider it "one of the best, and getting better."

Ristorante Euno S
– | – | – | M

119 Salem St. (Cooper St.), Boston, 617-573-9406

The owners of a nearby cafe and pottery shop have opened this "beautifully decorated" North End Mediterranean with lovely ceramics on the walls; downstairs is more intimate, but up or down, expect dishes such as braised rabbit with olives and a "welcoming" staff; most Friday evenings find a tenor circulating the room singing arias.

Ristorante Marcellino M
▽ 18 | 16 | 18 | $27

16 Cooper St. (Pine St.), Waltham, 781-647-5458

▨ "Hidden in Waltham", this "very nice" Italian newcomer offers "high-quality" fare at "low prices"; while some think it needs "time to improve", the fact that it's already "crowded" suggests it's "worth" seeking out.

Ristorante Olivio S
– | – | – | E

(fka Bernardo's)

24 Fleet St. (Commercial St.), Boston, 617-723-4554

Recently remodeled and with an "excellent new menu", this "basic Italian" is a "sweet little place" in the North End that pleases the few surveyors who know it.

Ristorante Toscano S M
22 | 20 | 20 | $39

41-47 Charles St. (Chestnut St.), Boston, 617-723-4090

▨ "Very much like Italy" say admirers of this Beacon Hill Italian where "you're guaranteed a good meal" in a "romantic setting" (though "you pay for it"); however, critics insist the "tired" menu "needs a shot of inspiration."

Rita's Place ◖ M
20 | 10 | 17 | $31

31 Williams St. (Winnisimmet St.), Chelsea, 617-884-9010

▨ This "eccentric", "no ambiance" Chelsea Italian has been around a "long time" and has a "loyal following" based on its "dependable" fare and "friendly service."

Ritz Cafe ◖ S M
22 | 24 | 24 | $35

Ritz-Carlton, 15 Arlington St. (Newbury St.), Boston, 617-536-5700

▨ "You feel special eating" at this "elegant" Back Bay hotel cafe that's "a must for Boston Brahmins"; admirers call its "updated" New American menu a "real success" and applaud "gracious" service, recommending it for a "relaxing lunch" or weekend breakfast; a few say "ain't what it used to be", but for most it remains a "lovely" taste of "old Boston."

RITZ CARLTON DINING ROOM S   24   26   26 $52

Ritz-Carlton , 15 Arlington St. (Newbury St.), Boston, 617-536-5700

■ "Old-world charm", fine Classic French food courtesy of chef Mark Allen (ex Ritz Cafe) and "gracious service" await diners at this classy hotel's second-floor dining room overlooking the Public Garden; perhaps the kitchen "isn't the ultimate, but the elegance is", and though it may be "a bit stuffy" and more than a bit pricey, surveyors agree it's "worth it" – after all, "this is the Ritz."

Road Trip M   15   19   16 $26

54 Canal St. (bet. Causeway & New Chardon Sts.), Boston, 617-720-2889

☑ The "great atmosphere", "cool bar" and wine list are "strong points" at this "trendy" North Station American offering regional fare ranging from New England to the Pacific Northwest; however, naysayers skip this trip 'cause the "inconsistent" food is "all over the map."

Rod Dee ●SM⇄   21   6   13 $12

1430 Beacon St. (Summit Ave.), Brookline, 617-738-4977

■ This Brookline Thai has some reviewers raving that it's the "best around", with "authentic flavors" happily teamed with "cheap prices" and "very fast" service; although "smaller than a dorm room" and "always packed", it "can't be beat for takeout."

Roggie's ●SM   16   13   16 $15

356 Chestnut Hill Ave. (bet. Beacon St. & Commonwealth Ave.), Brighton, 617-566-1880

☑ Brighton American grill and pizza joint that's a "college crowd" "hangout" near BC, where the "great beer" is complemented by "fall-off-the-bone ribs and great sauces" along with televised sports; a "wacky atmosphere" and "noise" come with the territory.

Roka SM   20   16   17 $23

1001 Mass Ave. (bet. Central & Harvard Sqs.), Cambridge, 617-661-0344

☑ Although it "needs a face-lift", this downstairs Cambridge Japanese between Harvard and Central Squares is a "sentimental favorite" for "reliable", "authentic" dishes including "great sushi and tempura"; although dissenters dub it "generic", they're outvoted.

Rosebud Diner ●SM   16   17   17 $14

381 Summer St. (Elm St.), Somerville, 617-666-6015

■ A "cute", "retro" Somerville diner that's "a step above the rest", offering "suprisingly good" food from a "creative menu" in a "welcoming, spotless" environment; at press time, a more formal, expanded seating area was under construction in the back of the restaurant.

ROWES WHARF 🆂Ⓜ | 25 | 26 | 24 | $47 |
Boston Harbor Hotel, 70 Rowes Wharf (Atlantic Ave.),
Boston, 617-439-3995
■ "Fabulous views" across the Harbor enhance Daniel
Bruce's "imaginative", modern New England cooking at
this "elegant" hotel dining room; his "seasonal" menus
are "daring but never silly", and though opinions on the
service vary ("pleasant and not aloof" vs. "stiff"), all like
the "beautiful decor" and "luscious Sunday brunch."

Royal East 🆂Ⓜ | 21 | 12 | 18 | $18 |
792 Main St. (Windsor St.), Cambridge, 617-661-1660
☑ "MIT's chow house", this East Cambridge Chinese
provides "good, dependable" food at "low prices" with
especially "great lunch values"; but while insiders say
"off the menu dishes can be wonderful" and "the owner
is charming", the consensus is "decent" but "not great."

R PLACE | 25 | 15 | 22 | $34 |
53 Prospect St. (Main St.), Waltham, 781-893-8809
■ "Innovative cooking" from a New American menu
with Southwestern accents earns raves for this "small
but yummy" Waltham "winner" where the "scrumptious
grilled Caesar salad" and "good wine list" earn special
mention; a few feel the "lack of decor" hurts, but the
majority begs "please don't put out the word" on this "gem."

Rubin's 🆂Ⓜ | 20 | 8 | 15 | $15 |
500 Harvard St. (bet. Beacon St. & Commonwealth Ave.),
Brookline, 617-731-8787
☑ "The only real deli in town", this Brookline glatt kosher
spot is known for "piled-high" corned beef sandwiches and
"very good" matzo ball soup; although "it's not NY" and "they
charge an arm and a leg", most conclude "it's the best
Boston has to offer": "forget cholesterol – go and enjoy."

Ruby's 🆂Ⓜ | ▽ 12 | 7 | 14 | $12 |
280 Cambridge St. (opp. Mass General), Boston, 617-367-3224
☑ Located across the street from Mass General is what
some see as a "fine neighborhood diner" that's reliable for
good, cheap breakfasts; but beyond eggs the feeling is
"big appetites are satisfied, but taste buds are not."

Rudy's Cafe 🆂Ⓜ | 17 | 12 | 16 | $14 |
248 Holland St. (Broadway), Somerville, 617-623-9201
■ This "solid" Tex-Mex in Somerville near Tufts serves
"decent" fare, including BBQ, "for little money" to a "college
crowd"; "great margaritas" help block out the "bland decor."

Ruggieri's Happy Haddock 🆂Ⓜ | 16 | 12 | 16 | $19 |
491 Riverside Ave. (Wellington Circle), Medford, 781-395-6785
☑ A long-lived Medford Italian-American fish house with
"family-style" food and the "best clam chowder"; while it
may be "nothing special", realistic respondents counter
that it's "good for what it is – a neighborhood restaurant."

Rustica S
20 | 18 | 16 | $22
30 Leonard St. (Moore St.), Belmont, 617-489-6333
☑ "At last a place to eat in Belmont" enthuse locals over this "consistently good" Mediterranean storefront with "some divine dishes" such as "yummy risotto cakes", "superb pizza" and "great grilled chicken"; on the down side, many gripe about "snooty" service and think it's "overpriced", although "lunch is a special bargain."

R. Wesley's ●S
22 | 16 | 19 | $31
31 Cambridge St. (Sullivan Sq. Rotary), Charlestown, 617-242-7202
■ Chef Robert Wesley's Charlestown Eclectic scores with a "creative" menu of "amazing food" that not only comes in "huge portions" but in "marvelous presentations"; the "vibrant", "festive" atmosphere and "fabulous desserts" are other reasons converts insist "you've got to go."

Sablone's
18 | 13 | 17 | $26
107A Porter St. (Chelsea St.), E. Boston, 617-567-8140
☑ This classic (circa 1947) East Boston Italian known for "always great veal" and clown decor still draws praise from loyalists for its "consistent" cooking and "casual atmosphere" ("hasn't changed in years and I hope it never does"); but critics sneer that it's a "stopped in time" "inspiration for tourist traps"; your call.

Sabra S M
13 | 9 | 13 | $16
45 Union St. (Langley Rd.), Newton, 617-964-9275
☑ Despite the "no-frills" setting, regulars like this Newton Middle Eastern's "inexpensive", "decent" lunch buffet and advise "try the sampler plate"; but scores lend support to critics who claim the "boring" food tastes "mass-produced" and that the whole operation "could be better all around."

Sage S M
24 | 18 | 21 | $32
69 Prince St. (bet. Hanover & Salem Sts.), Boston, 617-248-8814
■ This "innovative" Italian–New American "jewel" "tucked away" in the North End offers a "creative menu" that's an "excellent alternative to red sauce" ("lots of truffle oil, unusual ingredients" and "spectacular risottos"); a "cozy", "romantic" ambiance and "warm service" are more reasons "these people deserve fame"; reservations recommended.

Saigon Vietnamese Cuisine S M ⊅
23 | 14 | 22 | $14
431 Cambridge St. (Harvard Ave.), Allston, 617-254-3373
■ A "very friendly", "minimalist" Vietnamese in Allston where the cooking is done "with loving care", creating "breathtakingly good food" at "incredibly low prices"; both the kitchen and dining area have expanded to accommodate the crowds that flock nightly to "the bargain spot of Boston."

Sakurabana 🇸🇲　　　22 | 13 | 18 | $22
57 Broad St. (Milk St.), Boston, 617-542-4311
■ This "reliable" Downtown Japanese provides "consistent high quality", including "great box lunches", which keeps it "packed at lunch" with hungry financial types; some warn "go on weeknights if you want to hear yourself think."

SALAMANDER 🅜　　　26 | 24 | 23 | $42
1 Athenaeum St. (1st St.), Cambridge, 617-225-2121
☑ "Zesty" describes both the food and open kitchen setting at this Cambridge Asian-Eclectic where Stan Frankenthaler's "unthought-of food combinations" provide "a festival of tastes" "bursting with good ideas"; while most enjoy his "party on a plate" creations, critics feel they can be "too busy", but "creative" is the key word and fans only wish that the "limited menu" offered more choice.

Salty Dog Seafood　　　12 | 11 | 12 | $19
Grill & Bar 🇸🇲
206 Faneuil Hall Marketplace (bet. Congress & North Sts.), Boston, 617-742-2094
■ Though critics claim you will "overpay" for food that's merely "acceptable", there's "great people-watching on the patio" at this Faneuil Hall seafooder and tourist haunt; too bad the patio is only open April 1–October 31.

Sami's 🇸🇲　　　17 | 6 | 16 | $9
Holyoke Ctr., 1350 Mass Ave. (Harvard Sq.), Cambridge, 617-497-5051 ♿
384 S. Main St., Sharon, 781-793-0042
Vanderbilt Cafe 🇸🇲 🅜 ♿
107 Louis Pasteur Ave. (Longwood Ave.), Boston, 617-432-0402
■ Convenient lunch spots providing "fast food but better", these Middle Easterners earn kudos for "great baba ghanoush and hummus", "good value" and "friendly, efficient service" that offset the "no-frills" atmosphere.

Samuel Adams Brewhouse 🌑🇸🅜 12 | 13 | 14 | $16
Lenox Hotel, 710 Boylston St. (Exeter St.), Boston, 617-536-2739
☑ Foes suggest it's best to "eat before" visiting this "small", "smoky" brewpub in the Lenox Hotel "relying on a name for the tourist dollar" and serving "mediocre" Traditional American pub grub; it may be a "good place to drink", but some note "it's owned by the hotel and prices back it up."

Sandrine's 🅜　　　19 | 18 | 18 | $33
8 Holyoke St. (Mass Ave.), Cambridge, 617-497-5300
☑ "The gourmands of Harvard Square thank God for this bistro" where Raymond Ost's (ex Julien) Alsatian cooking provides "large portions" of "remarkably good" and "satisfying" food amid a "dynamite ambiance"; a few sniff about the "uneven" and "extremely limited menu" and occasional service lapses, but they're outweighed by optimists who predict they'll "work the kinks out" soon.

S&S Restaurant & Deli [S][M]≠ 17 | 12 | 15 | $15
1334 Cambridge St. (Inman Sq.), Cambridge, 617-354-0777
◪ "The best breakfast in town" (served all day long) and a "great Sunday brunch" make this Inman Square "institution" "the queen of Boston delis" (and the "huge menu" of "diner food" also makes it a good "late-night nosh place"); but a few can't see "what all the fuss is about", citing "ludicrous lines" that form for "so-so" food and service.

Santa Barbara Cafe [M] ▽ 18 | 11 | 20 | $11
1 Arrow St. (bet. Bar St. & Mass Ave.), Cambridge, 617-547-5508
◪ Most agree this Harvard Square cafe is the "closest thing to California-style cuisine you can get in the area"; but some aren't convinced that the "laid-back" service ("I was traumatized just ordering a frozen mochaccino") and "low-fat" menu can be transplanted onto Cambridge soil.

Santarpio's Pizza ☾[S][M]≠ 21 | 7 | 13 | $13
111 Chelsea St. (Porter St.), E. Boston, 617-567-9871
◪ "A great place for a slice and a bar fight", this East Boston pizza joint near Logan Airport draws fearless crowds through the tunnel for pies that are some of the "best around"; although the "seedy" atmosphere and "trademark surly service" "may not be for everyone", "go prepared to wait."

SAPORITO'S [S] 27 | 19 | 24 | $33
11 Rockland Circle (George Washington Blvd.), Hull, 781-925-3023
◪ "Creative but not annoyingly trendy", this husband-and-wife-run Tuscan in Hull offers "Boston quality" at "Hull prices"; one diner's "cozy", "casual" decor is another's "no atmosphere", but quibbles over "plain booths" and "uncomfortable chairs" fade in the face of "inventive" fare that "gets better and better"; "friendly staff" is another plus at this "quirky spot" that's "worth the drive."

Saraceno [S][M] 21 | 18 | 21 | $30
286 Hanover St. (bet. Parmenter & Prince Sts.), Boston, 617-227-5353
◪ The "very good", "fresh food" at this North End Italian earns accolades, and the "excellent" staff that "will do anything to make you happy" is another standout; but many complain about "overpricing" and warn that "friendly, casual suggestions for extras" can quickly "up the bill."

Savoy ☾[M] ▽ 18 | 20 | 17 | $25
174 Lincoln St. (South St.), Boston, 617-451-7289
■ This new Leather District entry offers Mediterranean, Asian and American cuisine in an eclectic spirit that chef Peter Laspia may have inherited from his previous position as executive sous chef for Lydia Shire at Biba; the few surveyors who've tried it praise the "surprisingly good food" and "cool room" – "hope it does well."

Sawasdee Thai Restaurant [S][M] 20 | 16 | 19 | $19
320 Washington St. (Holden St.), Brookline, 617-566-0720
■ "One of the better Thais in town", this Brookline Village stalwart earns applause for "delicious" "high-quality food", an "upbeat" atmosphere and "great service" all of which adds up to a "nice date restaurant"; while a handful grouse that it's "expensive", the majority maintains "you get what you pay for here."

Sazarac Grove Bar & Grill [S][M] 13 | 11 | 10 | $17
1 Kendall Sq. (Hampshire St.), Cambridge, 617-577-7850
◪ "The pool table seems to be the big deal" at this "funky", "inexpensive" Kendall Square Eclectic that draws a "loud", "young crowd" "for the scene, not the food"; older folks who grumble about "sloppy service", "uncomfortable seats" and "mediocre" fare say it "survives because of its location."

Scandia [S][M] 21 | 18 | 19 | $32
25 State St. (bet. Pleasant & Water Sts.), Newburyport, 978-462-6271
■ "A small but excellent restaurant in a great little riverport city" is how one surveyor sums up this storefront Newburyport New American where the "consistently wonderful" meals focus on New England–style seafood; "very friendly service" is another reason it's "a favorite."

Schroeder's [M] 16 | 15 | 18 | $28
8 High St. (Summer St.), Boston, 617-426-1234
◪ Although "perhaps not as freshly peppered as other places", this "staid" Continental-German "business classic" in the Financial District maintains the loyalty of longtime regulars who note approvingly that "nothing shocks the senses but nothing disappoints either"; foes who find it too "old-line" leave it to those "over 65 or in a suit."

Scullers Grille [S][M] 16 | 18 | 17 | $28
Doubletree Guest Suites, 400 Soldiers Field Rd. (River St.), Allston, 617-783-0090
■ Just about everyone agrees you "don't go for the food" to this Allston New American in the Doubletree Guest Suites; despite a "comfortable ambiance" overlooking the Charles, it's "strictly for convenience if going to a jazz show" at Scullers' Jazz Club next door; otherwise, "it's hotel food – what do you expect?"

Seaside [S][M] 13 | 11 | 16 | $21
Faneuil Hall Marketplace, 188 S. Market Bldg. (State St.), , 617-742-8728
◪ For best results, "get a table outside" at this Faneuil Hall American where most agree that "people-watching is the big bonus"; the "basic seafood" is acceptable, though "nothing jumps off the menu."

SEASONS 🆂Ⓜ   25 | 24 | 24 | $46
Regal Bostonian Hotel, 9 Blackstone St. N. (North St.),
Boston, 617-523-4119
☑ A "comfortable" yet "truly elegant" "dining experience" is
what most enjoy at Michael Taylor's New American with a
"lovely view" of Faneuil Hall; it offers "fancy food" and
"fancy service" at "fancy prices", but supporters say "you
get your money's worth"; if "not quite as good as it was",
it's still a "special" spot for a "celebratory" meal.

Sevens Ale House 🆂Ⓜ⇩   14 | 18 | 16 | $15
77 Charles St. (bet. Mt. Vernon & Pinckney Sts.), Boston,
617-523-9074
■ "A great bar with a good sandwich", this "Pickwickian"
Beacon Hill hangout is "famous with the college crowd for
its cheap pitchers" of beer; it's been around since 1933 and
loyalists are "hoping it never closes."

Shalimar of India 🆂Ⓜ   19 | 13 | 16 | $16
546 Mass Ave. (Central Sq.), Cambridge, 617-547-9280
☑ This Central Square Indian inspires debate: boosters
swear it's been the "best for years running" with a "very
affordable lunch buffet" and "excellent tandoori", but
critics complain about the service and "forgettable" fare;
food ratings tend to bolster the ayes.

Shalom Hunan 🆂Ⓜ   14 | 11 | 15 | $18
92 Harvard St. (School St.), Brookline, 617-731-9760
☑ "Surprisingly edible" damns with faint praise this
Brookline kosher Chinese; a few maintain the food is "good
even if you don't care about kosher", but others find no peace
with a kitchen where "everything tastes the same" – "bland."

Sherborn Inn 🆂Ⓜ   18 | 22 | 19 | $28
33 N. Main St. (Rtes. 16 & 27), Sherborn, 508-655-9521
☑ "Like a country club but with better food", this "picture-
perfect" eclectic Sherborn American offers both a "beautiful
dining room" and very popular tavern; although many find
the food "inconsistent", the "Sunday brunch is one of the
best" and the "quiet", "colonial" ambiance wins many
admirers who consider it "wonderful for social affairs."

Shilla ◗🆂Ⓜ   16 | 9 | 13 | $21
57 JFK St. (Winthrop St.), Cambridge, 617-547-7971
☑ A newly relocated Harvard Square Korean-Japanese
whose "late-night hours", "cheap sushi" and "good Korean"
fare draw "lots of students"; more demanding critics find the
food "uninteresting" and warn "beware karaoke night."

Shogun 🆂   21 | 14 | 17 | $22
1385 Washington St. (Elm St.), W. Newton, 617-965-6699
■ "You can't get fresher sushi anywhere for such a low
price" is only part of the praise locals bestow on this West
Newton Japanese; it's "always reliable" for "beautiful
raw fish, delicious hot food" and "honorable service."

Siam Cuisine [S][M] 23 | 17 | 18 | $18
961 Commonwealth Ave. (Gaffney St.), Allston, 617-254-4335
◪ An "old reliable Thai choice" on the outskirts of the BU campus that pleases with its "good selections of fish" and "terrific beef"; while a few budget-minded surveyors prefer lunch, claiming "prices double for dinner", it's recommended by many as a "tasty" option "in the neighborhood."

Siam Garden [S][M] 18 | 14 | 15 | $18
45½ Mt. Auburn St. (Harvard Sq.), Cambridge, 617-354-1718
◪ "Friendly service, authentic decor, efficient preparation and decent flavors" generate a positive response to this Harvard Square Thai; while some suggest "you can do better" elsewhere in the Square, most call it reliably "good."

Sichuan Garden [S][M] 21 | 17 | 17 | $17
295 Washington St. (Beacon St.), Brookline, 617-734-1870
■ New Brookline Szechuan offering "the real thing", meaning plenty of "hot and spicy" specialties; those who have tried it say it's an "excellent surprise."

SILKS [S][M] 24 | 26 | 23 | $46
Stonehedge Inn, 160 Pawtucket Blvd. (Rte. 113), Tyngsboro, 978-649-4400
■ This "stylish" restaurant/inn "in Tyngsboro of all places" is "worth the ride from Boston" (45 minutes) for "fine" New French dining enhanced by an "outstanding wine list"; its brand of "European country elegance" comes with fireplaces, good service and extras like wine tasting dinners; though this "sleeper" can be a bit sleepy, it's a "charming" place to take "that special someone."

Sindibad [M] ▽ 18 | 6 | 14 | $11
145 First St. (Binney St.), Cambridge, 617-492-2421
■ The few surveyors who comment on this cavernous Middle Eastern near the Cambridgeside Galleria say the food is "delicious", "authentic" and "cheap"; just don't expect an elegant atmosphere at these prices.

Siros [S][M] 20 | 19 | 16 | $29
307 Victory Rd. (Boardwalk), N. Quincy, 617-472-4500
■ This Marina Bay Med-Italian in a "lively" waterfront setting draws bravos for "generous" portions of "well-made" fare including "innovative dishes"; though "in the land of big hair", don't let it obscure the "great" bay view.

Skewers, The [S][M] 15 | 7 | 11 | $11
92 Mt. Auburn St. (JFK St.), Cambridge, 617-491-3079
◪ Supporters say "don't let the outside fool you": this Harvard Square Middle Eastern is a "worthwhile" option for "cheap, good food"; but cynics skewer "cafeteria"-quality fare, claiming it's "neither as good or as cheap" as others of its ilk; even some fans suggest it's "best to take out", considering the surroundings.

Skipjack's S M   19 | 15 | 17 | $25
199 Clarendon St. (St. James Ave.), Boston, 617-536-3500
2 Brookline Pl. (Brookline Ave.), Brookline, 617-232-8887
◪ "Solid", "very fresh" fish dishes are found at these "comfortable", "fairly priced" seafooders, according to afishionados who call them "Legal's only competition", offering "excellent rolls", "early dinner bargains" and an annual crab fest that's "a must"; a dissenting school insists the "fish swim in butter rather than the ocean" and "quality has declined."

Small Planet Bar & Grill ◐ S M   16 | 17 | 15 | $19
Copley Sq., 565 Boylston St. (bet. Clarendon & Dartmouth Sts.), Boston, 617-536-4477
◪ "Better for people-watching than food" is how some view this "funky" Back Bay Eclectic with "wooden jungle" decor and "live music"; while fans say the "concept" kitchen turns out some "real winners", others say it's best if you "stick to appetizers" and enjoy the "good bar scene" and "reasonable prices."

Sol Azteca S M   19 | 17 | 18 | $21
914A Beacon St. (bet. Park Dr. & St. Mary's St.), Brookline, 617-262-0909
75 Union St. (Beacon St.), Newton, 617-964-0920
◪ The "best white-collar Mexican food around" satisfies most surveyors, who call these south of the border veterans "good standbys" for "authentic" cooking, "must-have sangria" and "beautiful" decor; even critics who find them "tired" admit "for Boston it's about as good as Mexican gets" and if you're "outside on the patio under the trees" (at the Newton Centre branch) it's even better.

Sonsie ◐ S M   19 | 20 | 16 | $29
327 Newbury St. (bet. Hereford St. & Mass Ave.), Boston, 617-351-2500
◪ An "egregiously hip", "loud" Newbury Street International that's "still the place to be seen in Boston", where the big "surprise" to fans is the "great food, considering most patrons don't care"; foes dismiss it as a shrine to "plastic faces, tight Lycra and overpriced mashed potatoes", but if it's for you, "don't forget your sunglasses and Gitanes."

Sorento's ◐ S M   20 | 15 | 17 | $20
86 Peterborough St. (behind Star Market), Boston, 617-424-7070
◪ Loyalists relish this "quiet", "hidden" Fenway Northern Italian whose "delicious", "interesting" pizzas (and "large portions of pasta") can be slowly savored "outside in the candlelight" on the patio or squeezed in "before a Red Sox game"; either way, most agree it's the "only pie worth considering" if you're in the area.

Sorrela's [S] [M] ⊘ ▽ 21 | 12 | 19 | $11

388 Centre St. (Perkins St.), Jamaica Plain, 617-524-2016

■ Though few voters know it, insiders say "huge, cheap breakfasts and lunches" are hits at this "funky" Jamaica Plain American with a "variety of omelets, pancakes and French toast" and waitresses apt to "call you 'honey.'"

Sound Bites [S] [M] ⊘ 23 | 12 | 19 | $11

708 Broadway (Boston Ave.), Somerville, 617-623-8338

■ This "earthy", "inexpensive" and "inventive" Somerville cafe is "one of Boston's best for breakfast and brunch" ("awesome muffins", "incredible fruit pancakes") and there are "excellent Middle Eastern dishes" as well; while the "small" space makes a few feel "squeezed", devotees depart feeling "magically restored."

Spasso [S] [M] 17 | 16 | 16 | $23

160 Commonwealth Ave. (Dartmouth St.), Boston, 617-536-8656

◪ "Great" "romantic" outdoor dining is the main asset at this Back Bay Italian serving "ok but nothing special" food; although some find it "relaxing", "slow" service irks others.

SPINNAKER ITALIA [S] [M] 16 | 25 | 18 | $28

Hyatt Regency Cambridge, 575 Memorial Dr. (Amesberry St.), Cambridge, 617-492-1234

◪ Amazing city panoramas await at this revolving Italian atop the Hyatt on Memorial Drive, but some fear the "chef has been revolving too long" since the "view is much more appealing" than the food; still, for "frozen drinks" or "dessert on a clear night" it can be "surprisingly awesome."

Sports Depot ◐ [S] [M] 10 | 13 | 13 | $14

353 Cambridge St. (Harvard Ave.), Allston, 617-783-2300

◪ A "jock's paradise" in Allston sporting "big food" and "TVs at every turn" ("this is why they invented satellite dishes"); "it's a great place to watch a game" even if it bats out basic "bar grub" that's "nothing special" – though we hear no complaints about the onion rings and "cold beer."

Stars [S] [M] 18 | 13 | 17 | $19

24 Otis St./Rte. 3A (North St.), Hingham, 781-749-3200

■ If you pine "to hang out with the jocks you hated in high school", this "noisy", "friendly" "diner plus" in Hingham will fill the bill, offering "solid American fare" and the "best beer list"; there's no decor, but it can be "fun" at times.

STELLINA [S] [M] 23 | 17 | 20 | $28

47 Main St. (Rtes. 16 & 20), Watertown, 617-924-9475

■ "Homey and delicious", this "wonderful" Watertown Italian combines "fresh ingredients" and an "innovative" style to produce "terrific cuisine"; while many complain about the "sense of chaos" that pervades the small dining room and advise "eat on the patio", most also agree the "imaginative" seasonal menus and "great value" "more than compensate for the noise and crowded tables."

Stephanie's on Newbury [S][M] — 18 | 17 | 15 | $26

190 Newbury St. (Exeter St.), Boston, 617-236-0990

◪ "A great location for people-watching" is the most popular feature of this Newbury Street American that otherwise takes hits for "very uneven" food, "high prices" and "unprofessional service"; but it's a "casual" place where "yuppie shoppers can take a break."

Stockyard [S][M] — 16 | 13 | 16 | $21

135 Market St. (N. Beacon St.), Brighton, 617-782-4700

◪ An "icon of an age gone by", this Brighton steakhouse offers "good value for slightly above-average food" that "hits the spot" for carnivores; a few feel it's "outdated" and the service "needs improving", but you may "see the mayor or your plumber" at this "dependable" "standby" for "huge portions" and "reasonable prices."

Sultan's Kitchen [M] — 22 | 10 | 15 | $12

72 Broad St. (bet. Franklin & Milk Sts.), Boston, 617-338-7819

■ "Rich", "authentic Turkish cuisine" crafted from "high-quality ingredients" makes this a "healthy", "innovative" Financial District "lunch treat"; it's "short on atmosphere" and not open for dinner, but "fans line up at the door" in an area "sorely lacking ethnic choices."

Sunset Cafe [S][M] — 19 | 15 | 17 | $20

851 Cambridge St. (Inman Sq.), Cambridge, 617-547-2938

■ Newcomers find this East Cambridge Portuguese a "pleasant surprise" with its "big portions" of "very good food in a nice atmosphere"; the live fado music on Friday and Saturday is another plus.

Sunset Grill and Tap ◐ [S][M] — 16 | 15 | 14 | $16

130 Brighton Ave. (Harvard Ave.), Allston, 617-254-1331

■ "The food definitely plays second fiddle" at this "beer drinker's paradise", an Allston American offering over 100 taps and 400 microbrews; it's "jammed with college kids" who are generally satisfied with the "basic" "football-watching" grub, but foodies forage elsewhere.

Tables of Content [S][M] — 17 | 12 | 15 | $28

Midtown Hotel, 220 Huntington Ave. (Mass Ave.), Boston, 617-262-2122

◪ "Upscale, uptown with upbeat food" is how partisans describe this New American BYO "meal deal" "convenient to the symphony"; though malcontents mutter the "drab" "locker room" decor is a "turnoff", others say that if they served wine and had "sharper service, it could be a winner."

Tacos El Charro [S][M] — 21 | 11 | 16 | $14

349 Centre St. (Jackson Sq.), Jamaica Plain, 617-983-9275

■ There's "simple", "yummy", "authentic" Mexican food at this affordable Jamaica Plain "hole-in-the-wall"; it's "good for a group" and on weekends the "fun mariachi band" helps distract diners from the utter lack of decor.

Tacqueria Mexicana ◖🅂🅼 19 | 11 | 14 | $13
24 Charles St. (bet. Main & Murray Sts.), Waltham, 781-647-0166
☒ Fans so appreciate the "very cheap, plentiful" Mexican fare at this "favorite" Waltham eatery (now in larger but still "bare-bones" quarters) that they plead "don't let the secret out"; but critics counter "you can take a siesta while waiting for your meal" and "everything is starting to look and taste the same."

Takeshima 🅂🅼 22 | 14 | 19 | $23
308 Harvard St. (Beacon St.), Brookline, 617-566-0200
■ This "popular" Brookline Japanese rolls "great sushi" and offers "innovative specials" in a pleasant setting with "lovely service"; it even gets a few votes as "best in Boston", though for most it's basically a "dependable" choice for a "solid" meal.

Tallulahs ◖🅂🅼 16 | 15 | 15 | $19
65 Holland St. (Davis Sq.), Somerville, 617-628-0880
☒ The "interesting fare", "relaxing environment" and "fantastic beer sampler" at this Davis Square Traditional American score with some who consider it "a new friend"; however, another contingent knocks "clueless staff" and calls it a "trendy food wanna-be" – the "ideas are there, the execution is not."

Tam O'Shanter ◖🅂🅼 17 | 12 | 15 | $19
299 Harvard St. (Beacon St.), Brookline, 617-227-0982
☒ A "good gathering place" offering "hearty food" and jazz is how admirers view this Coolidge Corner American, but doubters cite "growing pains" after a recent move shook up the kitchen and stripped the decor of its "Irish pub" "funky charm"; now the ambiance is likened to a "Bennigan's" and even a few longtime fans sigh "it's not the same."

Tandoor House 🅂🅼 20 | 11 | 15 | $16
569 Mass Ave. (bet. Essex & Norfolk Sts.), Cambridge, 617-661-9001
■ Supporters say a "good selection" of "properly made" food puts this Central Square Indian "a step above the rest" (literally – it's located upstairs); while a few critics find the setting "plastic" and claim service can be "inattentive", they're outvoted by those who consider this house "a gem."

Tapeo 🅂🅼 22 | 21 | 20 | $26
266 Newbury St. (bet. Fairfield & Gloucester Sts.), Boston, 617-267-4799
■ With its "exciting" tapas and "affordable wine list", this Newbury Street Spaniard is the "perfect grazing spot" ("just like Madrid"); whether or not it's up to its Somerville sister Dali is debated, but for its many fans there's no question that "summer equals tapas and sangria on the patio."

Taqueria la Mexicana S M ⌀   ▽ 20 | 6 | 14 | $10
247 Washington St. (Union Sq.), Somerville, 617-776-5232
■ "Piping hot tamales" and "great nachos" are offered at this Somerville Mexican, but insiders insist the burritos are the "best buy"; with "no atmosphere" (unless you count noise), it's clear that this hole-in-the-wall has survived on "consistent quality and quantity" at wallet-friendly prices.

Tasca S M   20 | 19 | 21 | $22
1612 Commonwealth Ave. (Washington St.), Brighton, 617-730-8002
■ An "ambitious" Brighton Spaniard specializing in "terrific tapas" with "plenty of garlic", "superb bread" and sangria; "good music" (Spanish guitar), "knowledgeable" service and "reasonable prices" add to the appeal.

Taste of India S M   19 | 12 | 19 | $16
91 Bigelow Ave. (Mt. Auburn St.), Watertown, 617-926-1606
■ This "quiet" Watertown Indian wins the respect of its patrons with "basic" but "consistently good" cuisine; maybe it's not a "star place", but the "sweet" staff makes dining here a "pleasant" experience.

Tatsukichi S M   23 | 18 | 17 | $27
189 State St. (Atlantic Ave.), Boston, 617-720-2468
■ "Superb sushi" along with "nice box lunches" make this Financial District Japanese "one of the best traditional places in town"; "helpful staff", "authentic decor" and a "comforting" ambiance are more reasons fans return.

Tavern on the Water S M   10 | 20 | 11 | $19
1 Pier 6 (8th St., Charlestown Navy Yard), Charlestown, 617-242-8040
◩ Respondents give high marks to the "spectacular Boston view" and "neat location on the water" but little else at this "noisy" Navy Yard Traditional American with a seafood and BBQ focus; the menu doesn't get much comment.

Ten Center St. S M   19 | 20 | 20 | $33
10 Center St. (bet. Liberty & Water Sts.), Newburyport, 978-462-6652
■ "Charming decor" and "elegant table settings" are paired with "consistently decent food" at this "rustic" American in a 1790s Newburyport building; a "great Sunday brunch" and working fireplaces are other pluses.

TERRAMIA S M   26 | 18 | 21 | $31
98 Salem St. (Parmenter St.), Boston, 617-523-3112
■ Surveyors are uniform in their praise for Mario Nocera's "simple, upscale gourmet Italian" fare at this North Ender that seems to be "outside the [North End] mold"; though "small and noisy", its food "stands above the rest", even if the "lack of coffee and dessert" (typical in the North End) strikes some as "a real pain."

T.G.I. Friday's ◐ⓢⓂ   12 | 13 | 14 | $17 |
26 Exeter St. (Newbury St.), Boston, 617-266-9040
49 Newbury St. (Rte. 1), Danvers, 978-777-7483
285 Washington St. (Rte. 53), Norwell, 617-659-1581
☑ "A no-brainer when you just want to chow down", this "raucous" chain serves "mass-produced" American fare; they're "reasonable" and "good" for "a basic burger", but critics cry "thank God there are other restaurants."

Thai Basil ⓢⓂ   20 | 14 | 18 | $19 |
132 Newbury St. (bet. Clarendon & Dartmouth Sts.), Boston, 617-424-8424
■ In the "wide field" of Boston Thais, this Newbury Street eatery "stands out" for its "rich, interesting" fare and "fast, attentive service"; despite the "bland setting" with "too much tile", for many it remains a "favorite."

Thai House ⓢⓂ   21 | 15 | 16 | $18 |
1033 Commonwealth Ave. (Babcock St.), Brighton, 617-787-4242
☑ At this "fast and easy" Thai near BU's West Campus, fans feast on "consistently excellent" food including "tasty pad Thai" and "delicious garlic chicken"; however, a few dissenters who find the fare "routine" declare that "the search" for the ultimate Asian "continues."

Thai's ⓢⓂ   17 | 17 | 16 | $19 |
1 Kendall Sq. (bet. B'way & Hampshire St.), Cambridge, 617-577-8668
☑ Loyalists like the "delicious spring rolls and satays", "lovely", "moderately upscale" ambiance and "excellent service" at this Kendall Square Thai, but it's not quite unanimous: "run-of-the-mill", "overpriced."

1369 Coffee House ⓢⓂ⇄   15 | 14 | 14 | $10 |
1369 Cambridge St. (bet. Hampshire & Springfield Sts.), Cambridge, 617-576-1369
757 Mass Ave. (bet. Inman & Prospect Sts.), Cambridge, 617-576-4600
■ "Everyone seems to be writing a novel" at this "relaxed" Cambridge duo with "great coffee, muffins, scones" and the "best selection of teas"; it's "what a coffeehouse should be" except "they close far too early" (3 PM).

Thyme's on the Square ⓢⓂ   – | – | – | M |
197 E. Main St. (Plum St.), Gloucester, 978-282-4426
The few surveyors who know this Gloucester New American count themselves lucky to have made such a "find" and say they'll "try it again"; hours are seasonal, so call to check.

Tim's Tavern Ⓜ⇄   19 | 6 | 13 | $12 |
329 Columbus Ave. (Dartmouth St.), Boston, 617-437-6898
■ The "biggest, cheapest", "best burgers around" ("you'll be extremely full") plus noteworthy ribs are the draws at this "no-frills" South End American; it's "loud, greasy, cozy" and "a great place to talk to your neighbors."

Tokyo [S] [M] 19 17 16 $25

307 Fresh Pond Pkwy. (Lakeview St.), Cambridge, 617-876-6600

◪ A West Cambridge Japanese that earns plaudits for its "excellent" "traditional fare" including "the freshest sushi", a good "Sunday brunch" and "dishes not found elsewhere"; outvoted critics carp that it's "overpriced" and that the "menu hasn't changed in years."

Tom Shea's [S] [M] 20 19 19 $27

122 Main St. (Rte. 133), Essex, 978-768-6931

◪ This Essex seafooder offers "reliable" New England dining with "great fried clams" and a splash of "panache" that comes from its location "overlooking the river"; but skeptics insist that "anything would taste good with this view", advising "get a window table or it's just another joint."

TOP OF THE HUB [S] [M] 21 26 21 $38

Prudential Ctr., 800 Boylston St. (Huntington Ave.), Boston, 617-536-1775

■ The real "surprise" at this renovated, "romantic" New American with a "tremendous" view from atop the Prudential Tower landmark isn't the "great new decor" but rather the "beautifully presented", "delicious" food; most diners can't get over how much the cuisine has improved and are wowed that it's "risen to its potential."

Tosca [S] [M] 24 23 22 $35

14 North St. (Rte. 3A), Hingham, 781-740-0080

■ There's "big city dining in the 'burbs" at this "civilized" Hingham Northern Italian that wins bravos for "imaginative" cuisine, "excellent wine", "upbeat service" and its "busy but romantic" ambiance; devotees "can't get enough" and say the "seasonal menus demand repeat visits" to this "little bit of Italy on the South Shore."

Towne Lyne House [S] [M] 15 17 17 $27

Rte. 1S (Newbury St.), Lynnfield, 781-592-6400

◪ "Old-fashioned" meals, "accommodating staff" and a "pleasant" lake setting are found at this 1936 American in Lynnfield; but many find the ambiance "better than the food" and insist the "menu needs updating."

Trattoria A Scalinatella [S] [M] 22 20 21 $33

253 Hanover St., 2nd fl. (bet. Cross & Richmond Sts.), Boston, 617-742-8240

■ "A hidden gem" that's "the closest you can come to being in a trattoria in Italy" sigh admirers of this "authentic" North End Sicilian; the "wines are good value" and the setting "romantic", especially by "the fireplace in winter."

Trattoria Il Panino [S] 20 16 17 $25

120 S. Market St. (Faneuil Hall), Boston, 617-573-9700 [M]

295 Franklin St. (Broad St.), Boston, 617-338-1000 [M]

(Continues)

Trattoria Il Panino (Cont.)
11 Parmenter St. (Hanover St.), Boston, 617-720-1336 Ⓜ⊟
126 Washington St. (Pleasant St.), Marblehead, 781-631-3900
◼ The "chaos might raze a romantic dinner", but "great pastas" ("try the lobster ravioli") make these "noisy", upscale Italians "fun for large groups"; however, bashers find their "popularity inexplicable", saying the "food is satisfactory but not stellar" and "the staff has an attitude."

Trattoria Pulcinella ⓈⓂ⊟ 22 | 16 | 20 | $38
147 Huron Ave. (Concord Ave.), Cambridge, 617-491-6336
◼ Locals consider this "tiny", "very tasty" West Cambridge Italian their "best-kept secret"; there's an "imaginative menu" and "beautifully prepared and served food" in "a romantic" setting; just note they don't take plastic and it can be "surprisingly expensive", particularly the specials.

Tremont 647 Ⓢ 22 | 19 | 20 | $32
647 Tremont St. (W. Brookline St.), Boston, 617-266-4600
◼ Andy Husbands' "superb" Eclectic is a "hot", "happening South End gathering place" where diners begin with "the best martinis in town" and move on to "exciting" food from an open kitchen; doubters say it sometimes "tries a little too hard" and complaints are aimed at "noise" and "attitude with a capital A", yet most consider it a "nice new find."

Truc Ⓢ – | – | – | E
560 Tremont St. (Clarendon St.), Boston, 617-338-8070
With a French name that roughly means 'thingamajig', this subterranean South End French is an inviting spot with a spiffy tin roof and vintage chairs; chef/co-owner Corinna Mozo (ex Chez Henri) offers a small menu of rustic, updated bistro fare including a cheese course; Sunday brunch is also served, but alas, no reservations are accepted.

Tullio's Restaurant & Grotto ⓈⓂ 19 | 17 | 17 | $21
150 Hancock St. (½ mi. from Neponset Circle), N. Quincy, 617-471-3400
◼ This Quincy Italian earns praise for "consistent", "fresh" fare including "flavorful seafood pasta" and "crisp pizza"; while critics claim "there's something missing and we can't put our finger on it", most maintain this "joint" is "fine" for "good food at everyday prices."

Turner Fisheries of Boston ⓈⓂ 21 | 18 | 19 | $33
Westin Hotel, Copley Pl., 10 Huntington Ave. (Stuart & Dartmouth Sts.), Boston, 617-424-7425
◼ "Seafood presented with a touch of class" sums up this "elegant" hotel restaurant; while a few cite "fancy prices" for a "standard fishing hole", more are reeled in by the likes of the "great Sunday buffet brunch" and "best clam chowder in the universe"; jazz in the lounge Tuesday–Saturday is a plus; N.B. David Filippetti (ex Ambrosia) is now at the stoves.

TUSCAN GRILL S
25 17 21 $35

361 Moody St. (bet. Spruce & Walnut Sts.), Waltham, 781-891-5486

◨ "Fabulous hearty dishes" that "evolve with the seasons" and are "grilled to perfection" make this informal yet highly rated Northern Italian worth the trip to Waltham; despite reports of "high decibels", "cramped tables" and "pressure to eat quickly and be gone", most put up with any hassles to enjoy "wonderful rustic country fare."

29 Newbury S M
19 17 16 $30

29 Newbury St. (bet. Arlington & Berkeley Sts.), Boston, 617-536-0290

◨ Best if you're "very young, thin and chic" or "an aging lothario" sneer cynics about this Newbury Street New American with a "lively" bar scene; despite solid food scores, most agree it's more a "place to be seen than to eat", but a new chef and new management may change that.

224 Boston Street S M
22 17 20 $28

224 Boston St. (Andrews Sq. & Mass Ave.), Dorchester, 617-265-1217

■ This "cozy", "funky", "gay-friendly" Dorchester "gem" turns out New American "homestyle fare with flair" from a "great open kitchen"; a few complain about the "noise, smoke" and "wait for a table", but most appreciate the "warm space" and "campy staff."

Uncle Pete's Hickory Ribs S M ⊘ ▽
23 10 20 $17

309 Bennington St. (Chelsea St.), E. Boston, 617-569-7427

◨ Despite "dreary" decor, this East Boston BBQ joint "feels like home" to those who say it has the "best ribs in town"; critics claim that like "all Boston BBQ, it's a mediocre copy" of the real thing, but to the majority it's "finger-licking good."

Union Square Bistro S M
20 17 19 $27

16 Bow St. (Union Sq.), Somerville, 617-628-3344

■ This "amiable" Somerville American boasts "delicious", "inventive" food and a casually "elegant" atmosphere that feels like "dining with friends"; while some say the "uneven" cooking veers from "excellent to mediocre", for most the "attentive" service, "incredible" deck and "exceptionally nice owner" make it worth it.

Union Street ◗ S M
14 13 14 $17

107R Union St. (bet. Beacon & Centre Sts.), Newton, 617-964-6684

◨ With live music and a pleasant patio, this "cheap", "casual" Newton American draws a hefty student crowd that's "more concerned with drinking and meeting people" than dining; it's a "good place to kick back and relax", but critics sniff "don't bother" unless you're an undergrad.

UPSTAIRS AT THE PUDDING S M 24 | 22 | 22 | $39

10 Holyoke St. (Mass Ave.), Cambridge, 617-864-1933

■ For many, the "best alfresco dining in Boston" is found on the "magical" roof garden at this Harvard Square New American offering "superb food" in an "elegant" setting; while a few feel it's "a bit stuffy" and "overpriced", most say the "creative" cuisine, "romantic" ambiance and fine service are "worth the splurge."

Uva M 19 | 17 | 18 | $28

1418 Commonwealth Ave. (bet. Harvard & Washington Sts.), Brighton, 617-566-5670

☑ All agree that this Brighton Cal-Italian has "an awesome wine list that's priced right" and served in a "wonderfully homey" setting; it's the "mix and match" food (patrons pick the ingredients and sauce for their pizza and pasta) that stirs debate: some call it "inventive and tasty", while others opine "overpriced", "not remarkable."

Vadopazzo ● S M 19 | 22 | 19 | $26

241 Hanover St. (Richmond St.), Boston, 617-248-6800

■ "Don't go if you're expecting standard Italian" because this "new-style North End joint" serves the "best risotto in Boston" and "great appetizers"; even though the room is "beautifully decorated", a few feel it's too "upscale" for the area and "missing some of its charm."

Vault, The M – | – | – | E

105 Water St. (Liberty Sq.), Boston, 617-292-9966

Dark wood, shiny brass and tall ceilings set the scene at this Financial District New American tucked behind Le Meridien Hotel; at first glance it may seem like just another Brahmin outpost, but chef Rebecca Esty (ex Dakota's) leaves tradition behind with dishes such as hazelnut-crusted chicken livers and, for dessert, a 'goat cheesecake'; wine lovers will appreciate the tasting flights.

Verona S ▽ 18 | 9 | 17 | $18

18 Mt. Auburn St. (Main St.), Watertown, 617-926-0010

☑ Fans claim that for "a cheap Italian meal" this sterile but "reliable" Watertown "family restaurant can't be beat", while critics counter "it depends on who is cooking – some days the food is so-so, other days it's to die for"; the ayes have a slight edge, but it's your call.

Veronique S 19 | 23 | 21 | $31

Longwood Towers, 20 Chapel St. (Longwood Ave.), Brookline, 617-731-4800

☑ With its "great hall", "leather booths", "live harp" music and "elegant woodwork", this Brookline French reminds respondents of dining "in a castle"; while loyalists cite "surprisingly wonderful" food and "excellent service", calling it a "nice place to celebrate", others insist it's the "atmosphere that makes the food tolerable."

Victoria ◐ⓈⓂ ▽ 14 10 17 $16
1024 Mass Ave. (New Market Sq.), Boston, 617-442-5965
■ Your "basic diner", this New Market Square spot is populated by "cops" and "hardworking waitresses"; the food comes in "huge portions", but as ratings attest, not everyone finds the kitchen victorious.

Vidalia's Truck Stop ⓈⓂ 12 15 13 $15
13 Central St. (Abbot St.), Wellesley, 781-431-0011
■ "Another upscale 'concept' diner" that brings its "cute" truck stop theme to Wellesley; those who say hop aboard feel it's a "good family alternative to chains", but others who cite "pedestrian food" and poor service would rather push on to the next exit.

Viet Foods Ⓢ 20 10 20 $13
617 Main St. (Elm St.), Waltham, 781-894-9783
■ This popular Waltham Vietnamese provides "simple" but "lovely" meals — "try the half-stuffed chicken and the crêpes"; the new, expanded location, "wonderful" owner and "low cost" make it a local "staple."

Viet Hong Ⓢ⇗ ▽ 23 6 20 $14
182 Brighton Ave. (Allston St.), Allston, 617-254-3600
■ "A friendly place", this Allston Vietnamese is an "amazing hole-in-the-wall" with "huge portions" and "cheap prices"; communal tables and bright lights explain the low decor score; while most feel the food is "authentic" and "tasty", we also hear "too many dishes taste the same."

Villa Francesca ◐ⓈⓂ 20 16 17 $24
150 Richmond St. (bet. Hanover & North Sts.), Boston, 617-367-2948
■ "The garlic stays for days" after a meal at this crowded, classic North Ender serving "large portions" of hearty Northern Italian fare including some of "Boston's best calamari"; it's "worth the wait" to fans, even if a few foes label it "overpriced" and claustrophobic; there's an opera singer some nights, so call if you're not into serenades.

Village Fish, The ⓈⓂ⇗ 20 12 15 $22
22 Harvard St. (Brookline Village), Brookline, 617-566-FISH
■ This Brookline Village Italian-style seafooder offers big helpings of "excellent" fish and "good pasta" in a "crowded", "no-frills" setting; but what some consider "straightforward", "simply cooked" fare, others brand "bland", and most agree the no credit card policy is "a drag."

Village Smokehouse ◐ⓈⓂ 17 12 15 $19
1 Harvard St. (Rte. 9), Brookline, 617-566-3782
■ Some BBQ buffs shout "yahoo" for this Brookline Village rib joint with a "laid-back" "Texas atmosphere"; they like its "huge portions" and advise "don't miss the beans"; but bashers say the food is "not even in the running for best 'cue", suggesting "fly south" if you want the real thing.

Vin & Eddie's 🆂   21 16 20 $27
1400 Bedford St./Rte. 18 (bet. Rtes. 58 & 139), Abington,
781-871-1469
■ A "pleasant alternative to in-town dining" is the majority
opinion on this Abington Italian, a "solid" suburban veteran
with a "wonderful wine list" to enhance its "consistent"
food; "great service" helps make it "good for kids" too.

Vinny's at Night 🅼   ▽ 19 15 19 $16
76 Broadway (Hawthorne St.), Somerville, 617-628-1921
■ The few voters who know this Somerville Italian
"treasure" say there are "huge portions" of "very good"
pastas and other homestyle Sicilian specialties along with
"fabulous service and prices"; in sum, a real "find."

Vinny Testa's Bar Ristorante 🆂🅼   13 13 17 $19
1700 Beacon St. (Washington Sq.), Brookline, 617-277-3400
Comfort Inn, 320 Elm St. (Rte. 1), Dedham, 781-320-8999
20 Waltham St. (Mass Ave.), Lexington, 781-860-5200
801 Worcester Rd. (Rte. 9), Natick, 508-655-8787
1114 Beacon St. (Walnut St.), Newton, 617-332-6767
☑ "Rivers" of "red sauce" flow at these Southern Italian
"temples of excess" where the "humongous" helpings are
spiked with garlic galore; while many revel in the "crowded"
"circus" ambiance and claim the quality is "better than
you expect", critics say "bigger ain't always better."

V. Majestic 🆂🅼⊅   20 4 18 $12
164 Brighton Ave. (Harvard Ave.), Allston, 617-782-6088
■ "One of the first Vietnamese" restaurants in Allston
"opens up a new world" of "fresh, clean tastes"; regulars
overlook the decor (or lack thereof) and focus on the "good,
solid food", "gracious host" and "cheap" prices.

Walden Grille 🆂🅼   16 13 14 $27
24 Walden St. (Main St.), Concord, 978-371-2233
☑ Opinions split on the new menu and decor at this
Concord Eclectic near Thoreau's Walden Pond; some cite
"improvement" and call it a "creative", "upscale" addition;
but others report "average" food and at times "rude" staff.

Warren Tavern 🆂🅼   16 21 16 $20
2 Pleasant St. (Main St.), Charlestown, 617-241-8142
■ This circa-1780 Charlestown American is a "historic site
with colonial flair" and a "fun" place for brunch or to grab a
"decent" burger on a "cold winter night"; as ratings show,
the "authentic" atmosphere "is a big part" of its appeal.

Watch City Brewing Co. 🆂🅼   13 16 15 $17
256 Moody St. (Pine St.), Waltham, 781-647-4000
☑ While some see potential in the "good" housemade beers,
"personable bartenders" and "serviceable" pub fare at
this "noisy" Waltham American, others call it "generic" with
"just ok" food, saying this watch has "sprung its springs."

Wayside Inn [S] [M] | 19 | 24 | 21 | $29 |
Wayside Inn, Wayside Inn Rd., Sudbury, 978-443-1776
◪ "Immortalized by Longfellow", this "rustic" Sudbury American offers "Revolutionary charm", a "nostalgic" dining room and "beautiful grounds" so it's nice for "older" "visitors from out of town"; while foes dismiss the "plentiful" "Yankee" fare as "heavy and boring", most think that "for a historic landmark, the food, service and decor are excellent."

West Street Grille [M] | 17 | 18 | 16 | $25 |
15 West St. (bet. Tremont & Washington Sts.), Boston, 617-423-0300
◪ Foes may complain of "mediocre, trend-driven" food and "snobby" staff at this Downtown Crossing New American, but that doesn't faze fans who report "surprisingly good fare" in a "great location", making it "good" for "business lunches" and "after-work drinks and "perfect for a date."

Weylu's [S] [M] | 15 | 18 | 15 | $21 |
Rte. 1N, Saugus, 781-233-1632 🌙
288 Mishawum Rd. (Washington St.), Woburn, 781-937-3700
◪ The Saugus branch of this Chinese duo has "astonishing" decor ("impressive" vs. "hideously ornate"), but critics say "kitschy surroundings can't give personality to ho-hum food"; still, the "respectable" lunch buffet has its adherents.

Whiskey's [S] [M] | 13 | 13 | 13 | $16 |
885 Boylston St. (Gloucester St.), Boston, 617-262-5551
■ Cynics say if you "drink enough you won't notice" the "uninspired" food and service at this Back Bay BBQ joint; but fans praise the ribs and pulled pork sandwich, and "half-price appetizers at happy hour" make it a "frat boy hangout."

WHITE RAINBOW [S] | 26 | 22 | 25 | $41 |
65 Main St. (Rogers St.), Gloucester, 978-281-0017
■ "Gloucester's best", this Continental–New American in a "historic" building offers outstanding food and wines in a "fantastic setting" with a "quiet ambiance"; it's "unique" and the "new owner seems to be maintaining consistency", so while it may be "hard to find", it's well worth the effort.

Willow Pond Kitchen [S] [M] 🚫 | 13 | 12 | 13 | $16 |
745 Lexington Rd./Rte. 9A (1 ½ mi. from Concord Ctr.), Concord, 978-369-6529
◪ Your "basic roadhouse", this Concord American dishes up "tempting fried treats", frogs' legs and lobster specials that "can't be beat"; while a few find it "more worn out than cute", most call it a "diamond in the really rough."

Wonder Bar 🌙 [S] [M] | 16 | 20 | 14 | $18 |
186 Harvard Ave. (bet. Brighton & Commonwealth Aves.), Allston, 617-351-2665
■ This "posh" Allston International offers "tasty" tapas and a "trendy" bar with "brilliant jazz"; no wonder most find it "hip" and "fun", although more "for drinks" than dinner.

Woo Chun [S][M] ▽ 22 | 14 | 19 | $20

290 Somerville Ave. (Cambridge St.), Somerville, 617-623-3313

■ Aficionados cherish this "welcoming" Union Square Korean; the helpful staff teaches the uninitiated "how to eat" "authentic"; a few bemoan the fact that there's "no liquor license", but the varied menu brings most back.

Woodman's [S][M]⊘ 21 | 11 | 11 | $17

121 Main St. (Rte. 133), Essex, 978-768-6057

◩ "Allegedly the fried clam was invented" at this 1914 "quintessential" Essex seafooder that also offers "lobsters in the rough", fried shrimp and onion rings; detractors insist it's nothing more than "overpriced" "grease, butter and beer in a shack" that's "resting on its reputation", but tell that to the hordes in the "long lines."

Woody's ☾[S][M] – | – | – | M

58 Hemenway St. (Westland Ave.), Boston, 617-375-9663

This American on the Fenway also offers Italian specialties like "consistently tasty" brick-oven pizza; a good selection of microbrews also makes this newcomer a welcome addition.

Wrap Culture [S][M]⊘ 16 | 16 | 13 | $10

Cleveland Circle, 1940 Beacon St., Brighton, 617-739-0340
71 Mt. Auburn St. (Holyoke St.), Cambridge, 617-354-5838

◩ Wraps, smoothies and local music meet at this "colorful" Harvard Square newcomer; while pros find the rolled-up sandwiches "creative" and "filling", cons call them "soggy bombs" filled with "too many flavors" and served by a sometimes "spacey" staff.

Yama [S][M] 21 | 18 | 19 | $22

245 Washington St., Wellesley, 781-431-8886

■ "Excellent sushi" "served with flair" makes this Japanese "a refreshing alternative" for Wellesley locals; most have no complaints about the "tasty food" or "super service", though some say they "need a liquor license" – meanwhile, BYO.

Yangtze River [S][M] 17 | 14 | 16 | $18

25 Depot Sq. (Mass Ave.), Lexington, 781-861-6030

◩ This Lexington Chinese may be "unremarkable", but supporters consider it a "dependable" source of "good old-fashioned" food, with special praise for the daily lunch and dinner buffet.

Yenching Palace [S][M] 13 | 7 | 13 | $19

671 Boylston St. (Copley Sq.), Boston, 617-266-9367
1326 Mass Ave. (Harvard Sq.), Cambridge, 617-547-1130

◩ Though some surveyors have kind words for "nice service" that's "great with kids", that doesn't appease critics who knock this Back Bay Chinese and its Harvard Square sibling for "greasy" food and "no atmosphere"; still, they can be useful for takeout.

Ye Olde Union Oyster House ⓈⓂ 16 | 20 | 15 | $26
41 Union St. (bet. North & W. Hanover Sts.), Boston, 617-227-2750
☑ "Truly ye olde", this "venerable" circa-1826 Quincy Market seafooder is "a bit of Boston lore" and wows out-of-towners with its "atmosphere" and "charm", if not its "uneven" food and service; though many feel it's "coasting on tourist traffic", loyal locals say "stick to the raw bar" for "great oysters" and beer and you'll enjoy this "institution."

Yerardi's ⓈⓂ 16 | 12 | 19 | $18
418 Watertown St. (Rte. 16), Newton, 617-965-8310
☑ The food may be "basic", ditto the decor, but this Newton Italian strikes supporters as a "reasonably priced", "good local dining" option; it's "upstairs from a loud bar", which presumably gets even louder on live music nights.

Yokohama ⓈⓂ ▽ 18 | 14 | 19 | $22
238 Washington St. (Harvard St.), Brookline, 617-734-6465
☑ "They know what they're doing" when it comes to sushi according to admirers of this Brookline Village Japanese-Korean; while that opinion isn't unanimous ("not my first choice", "portions on the small side"), even doubters concede that it's "small, quiet and good enough."

Zaatar's Oven ⓈⓂ 19 | 13 | 13 | $11
242 Harvard St. (Coolidge Corner), Brookline, 617-731-6836
■ The "next trend in noshing", this Coolidge Corner Middle Eastern serves "fresh, tasty, cheap" "fast food with flair" in the form of "delicious" flatbreads with a "variety" of toppings and fillings, plus "excellent salads" and such; though it takes some knocks for "surly service" and "no atmosphere", most consider it a welcome "change of pace."

Zaftigs Eatery ⓈⓂ _ | _ | _ | I
335 Harvard St. (Coolidge Corner), Brookline, 617-975-0075
This Coolidge Corner New American deli lives up to its name in looks – bold Rubenesque images and deli scenes on the walls – as well as taste, offering rich chicken soup, hefty potato pancakes and more; it also appeals to a more thin-thinking crowd with items like leaner corned beef and grilled salmon; in a breakfast-poor city, they shine early on with strong coffee and good pancakes.

Zuma Tex-Mex Cafe ⓈⓂ 14 | 13 | 16 | $17
Faneuil Hall, 7 N. Market St. (Clinton St.), Boston, 617-367-9114
☑ "Decent" Tex-Mex food that's "fairly priced for Faneuil Hall" is what most find at this "friendly, casual" cafe, but it's the "neon margaritas" that really make it a "fun" "Friday after work" kind of place; dissenters shrug "ok", "touristy."

Top Restaurants in Cape Cod, Martha's Vineyard, Nantucket, Rhode Island, New Hampshire and Maine

CAPE COD

F	D	S	C

Abbicci 🅂🅼
24 | 23 | 22 | $36

43 Main St. (bet. Railroad Ave. & Willow St.), Yarmouth Port, 508-362-3501

■ For fans who feel this "always pleasant" Yarmouth place is the "best Italian on the Cape", the setting is "very stylish" and the food is "wonderful", "classy" and "a nice change from the ubiquitous fried seafood"; while it can be "pricey", if you "go before 6 PM" or "for lunch" you'll find it's "an exceptional value" as well.

Adrian's 🅂🅼
17 | 15 | 14 | $22

Outer Reach Motel, 535 Rte. 6, N. Truro, 508-487-4360

◪ "Satisfactory" Truro Italian where the "food and service can be spotty" and the "decor needs work"; while surveyors wish the cooking were as "spectacular as the sunset view", it's still a "great spot for brunch."

Aesop's Tables 🅂🅼
21 | 20 | 18 | $34

316 Main St. (next to Town Hall), Wellfleet, 508-349-6450

■ This "charming" "big old mansion" offers "an excellent atmosphere" in which to enjoy "delicate" New American cooking including "great desserts" and "delightful outdoor luncheons"; it's "a little expensive but worth every penny" – "a must when in Wellfleet" and "summer heaven."

Bubala's by the Bay 🅂🅼
16 | 14 | 16 | $23

183 Commercial St., Provincetown, 508-487-0773

◪ Fans of this P-town seafooder that offers a "good breakfast", "great views", "reasonable prices" and "martinis that are worth the trip" say it's swell for "people-watching" and definitely "part of the scene"; but critics say it's "touristy", "the food has gone downhill" and the staff has "attitude"; so, bubala, it's your call on this one.

Cafe Edwige 🅂🅼
23 | 16 | 18 | $26

333 Commercial St., Provincetown, 508-487-2008

■ Proffering "French toast that's better than sex", this Provincetown American-Eclectic wins "the best breakfast in town" award; the "small" "upstairs" spot serves "creative", "excellent" food and "great salads" in a "sweet , romantic" setting, leading loyalists to sigh there's "nothing like" it.

Cape Sea Grille 🅂🅼
▽ 23 | 23 | 22 | $34

31 Sea St. (Rte. 28), Harwich Port, 508-432-4745

◪ The few voters who've visited this "preppy" Eclectic seafooder in Harwich Port praise the "excellent" food and service and "pretty" decor, advising "get a window table"; wallet watchers say "overpriced" for "small portions."

Chillingsworth 27 25 25 $53
2449 Main St. (Rte. 6A), Brewster, 508-896-3640
■ "Sit back and enjoy the three-hour culinary ride" say admirers of this Brewster New French; "amazing" food, "knowledgeable" service and a "sublime setting" earn it votes as "best on the Cape" and the place to make a special occasion "an event to remember"; "high prices" for the main dining room's prix fixe menu give some pause, but the more casual bistro's à la carte offerings are a welcome option.

Dancing Lobster [S] 25 16 18 $28
463 Commercial St. (Bangs St.), Provincetown, 508-487-0900
■ Praised by partisans as "the best of P-town", this Mediterranean recently moved into a "more mainstream" site, and those who've visited report that the "inventive" food is "as good as ever" and they now "take reservations and credit cards"; on the downside, "erratic service" seems to have made the move from the pier.

Flume, The [S] [M] 19 12 15 $24
13 Lake Ave. (Rte. 130), Mashpee, 508-477-1456
◪ There are two currents of thought on this "old standby" American near Falmouth: "keep this gem a secret", "no place like it" for "down-home" "delicious dinners" vs. "too basic" and "ordinary" with "brusque service"; still, it's "always busy."

Front Street [S] [M] 26 19 22 $37
230 Commercial St. (Masonic St.), Provincetown, 508-487-9715
■ "Fabulous food, year after year" is what most find at this "Provincetown institution"; besides a "well-rounded menu" of Eclectic fare with Mediterranean-Italian accents, it has "a wonderful wine list" and "waiters who actually know what they're talking about"; the only discord is over the setting: "terribly romantic" vs. "cave-like."

Gallerani's Cafe [S] [M] 20 15 18 $26
133 Commercial St. (Montello St.), Provincetown, 508-487-4433
◪ "The ambiance is in the people, not the decor" at this "small", "friendly", "always crowded" Provincetown American with an Italian slant; you'll "eat with the locals" in a "boisterous", "easygoing" ambiance, enjoying food that most find "good" if "basic"; as one loyalist put it, "eat at Gallerani's and all's right with P-town, if not the world."

High Brewster [S] [M] 25 24 24 $42
High Brewster Inn, 964 Satucket Rd. (Stony Brook Rd.), Brewster, 508-896-3636
■ The quintessential New England experience can be had at this 1738 Brewster farmhouse/inn serving "absolutely delicious" Traditional American food in an "antique" atmosphere; "great service" and "beautiful gardens" add to the appeal.

Martin House [S][M] 24 | 24 | 22 | $37

157 Commercial St. (Atlantic St. Landing), Provincetown, 508-487-1327

■ There's "delightful" dining at this "soothing" P-town New American set "in an old house on the harbor" with "small, rickety rooms" and "nice nooks and crannies"; enthusiasts enjoy "exceptional service" and "inspired" and "inventive" cuisine by the "fireplaces in winter" and rave about "outdoor dining in the summer."

Nauset Beach Club [S][M] 21 | 16 | 18 | $30

222 Main St. (Beach Rd.), E. Orleans, 508-255-8547

◩ "In a great spot close to the beach" in Orleans, this Italian attracts "huge crowds" of "young people" and families in search of "well-prepared" food that "won't disappoint"; a few feel it's "gone downhill" with "middle of the road" eats, but most still appreciate the "nice ambiance" that "puts you in a beachy mood."

Paddock [S][M] 20 | 18 | 20 | $33

W. Main St. Rotary, 20 Scudder Ave., Hyannis, 508-775-7677

■ For "casual dining on the Cape", this "consistently good" Hyannis Continental draws an "older crowd" and gets "very busy in season" partially because of its "nice location" "convenient to the Melody Tent"; although there are "no surprises", "good pricing", "gracious service", "pretty decor" and an interesting wine list make this "old standby" "worthy of a trip."

Penguins Sea Grill [S][M] 22 | 18 | 21 | $31

331 Main St. (Ocean St.), Hyannis, 508-775-2023

◩ Fin fanciers feel this Hyannis seafooder is "the perfect place to enjoy a good dinner"; though some find it only "ok for a quick meal", the "location" and "very good" service make it a standout considering there are "not too many choices Downtown."

Purple Cactus Burrito & Wrap Bar [S][M]⊄ 20 | 12 | 16 | $12

215 Commercial St., Provincetown, 508-487-4432

See review in Boston Directory.

Regatta of Cotuit at the Crocker House [S][M] 25 | 23 | 24 | $43

4631 Falmouth Rd. (Rte. 28), Cotuit, 508-428-5715

◩ Set in "a magnificent old mansion" in Cotuit, this "gourmet" New American seafooder may be "expensive", but for many it's "worth it" for the "unbelievable" food, "charming" atmosphere and "dependable" service"; only a small contingent claims it's "pretentious" and has "fallen a bit behind the times."

Regatta of Falmouth by the Sea §M
| 23 | 22 | 23 | $40 |

217 Clinton Ave., Falmouth, 508-548-5400

☑ A "lovely" "on the water" location makes this "relaxed" sibling of the Cotuit Regatta a "must while in Falmouth"; despite scattered reports that the New American fare is only "ok", admirers consider it "an island of quality in an ocean of mediocrity" and the "only drawback is the price."

Sal's Place §M
| 19 | 15 | 15 | $32 |

99 Commercial St. (bet. Cottage & Mechanic Sts.), Provincetown, 508-487-1279

☑ Delight in "outdoor dining by candlelight" at this popular, "family-owned", "old-fashioned Southern Italian" in P-town proffering "large portions" of "average to good food"; however, "service can be lethargic" and be sure to "ask for a table outside" because indoors can be "cramped and stuffy"; P.S. "reserve early on summer weekends."

MARTHA'S VINEYARD

Black Dog Tavern §M
| 20 | 17 | 17 | $25 |

Beach St. Ext., Vineyard Haven (Vineyard Haven Harbor), Martha's Vineyard, 508-693-9223

☑ BYO American "on the water's edge" that inspires "a love it or hate it" reaction: while supporters cite the "can't be beat for sunsets" setting, "awesome breakfasts" and "fresh fish specials", detractors call it a "big tourist trap" with "food that's nothing special"; the consensus is the cuisine "doesn't match the mystique, but it's fun anyway" and remains a "required part of the Vineyard experience" even if you "go just for the T-shirts."

Homeport §M
| 19 | 17 | 18 | $29 |

North Rd., Menemsha, Martha's Vineyard, 508-645-2679

■ "Get a reservation in time for the unbelievable sunset" at this Martha's Vineyard BYO seafooder; since it offers "a beautiful view" but the food strikes some as "basic", the soundest advice may be to head to the "fresh seafood bar outside" and take in nature's spectacle.

Le Grenier §M
| ▽ 21 | 17 | 20 | $39 |

96 Main St., Vineyard Haven, Martha's Vineyard, 508-693-4906

☑ Admirers of this "old-fashioned", "traditional" French on the Vineyard serving the likes of shrimp Pernod and sweetbreads applaud the "very good" "rich food" and call the veteran "a keeper"; but faultfinders feel there are "too many offerings" on the menu and "there's better French around – even on the Vineyard."

L'Etoile [S][M] 28 | 28 | 27 | $54

Charlotte Inn, 27 S. Summer St., Edgartown, Martha's Vineyard, 508-627-5187

■ "What fine dining is all about", this "high-level", "class act" French in the Charlotte Inn boasts an "extremely romantic" atmosphere including "a garden that will make your date swoon"; while it may be "a bit expensive", most feel the "outstanding food" is "excellent at any price" and advise "make it a point to go" if you're on the island.

Main Street Diner [S][M] ▽ 22 | 19 | 21 | $19

65 Main St. (Summer St.), Edgartown, Martha's Vineyard, 508-627-9337

■ A "great deal for the overpriced Vineyard", this '50s diner with "art deco" decor is a "wonderful place to eat"; it's where locals go to gobble gossip and three-squares a day.

Savoir Fare [S][M] 27 | 21 | 22 | $45

Old Post Office Square, Edgartown, Martha's Vineyard, 508-627-9864

■ Many call this "pricey" New American with a strong Italian influence "exceptional" and "the best of the Vineyard", with "superb food, beautifully presented dishes and excellent service"; despite a few complaints about "snooty" staff, for the vast majority it's a "romantic" "oasis" that's a "must try."

NANTUCKET

American Seasons [S][M] 25 | 22 | 22 | $42

80 Centre St. (W. Chester St.), Nantucket, 508-228-7111

◪ "Popular", "romantic" Nantucket New American with an "unusual menu" and "well-presented imaginative" food; there's a sense that the kitchen is "sometimes overly dramatic in its use of ingredients", but overall "very creative" cooking and "knowledgeable service" make it "worth going to"; P.S. you "need reservations."

Black Eyed Susan's [S][M]🚫 23 | 14 | 19 | $21

10 India St. (Centre St.), Nantucket, 508-325-0308

■ "Small, crowded" and "casual" Nantucket International that's seen as a "best value" for dinner partly due no doubt to the BYO policy; there's a frequently changing "gourmet" menu with "very creative food" plus "marvelous" breakfasts featuring "great omelets"; N.B. closed for lunch.

Boarding House 23 | 21 | 22 | $46

12 Federal St. (India St.), Nantucket, 508-228-9622

■ Expect "fresh, well-prepared" fare (including "excellent pecan scrod") as well as a "fun bar" at this "unusual" New American with Asian and Mediterranean accents "in the heart of Nantucket"; the "basement" setting may be a "bit cramped", but it's "quiet" and there's also a patio.

Chanticleer, The S
25 | 27 | 24 | $53

9 New St. (Siasconset Ctr.), Nantucket, 508-257-6231

■ "A special place on a special island" is the verdict on this Nantucket Classic French; offering "terrific" food in a "lovely" setting, it's "one of the most romantic restaurants ever", especially "in the garden"; a very few find it "snooty" and of course it's "expensive", but devotees say if you're on Nantucket you must dine here "at least once."

Club Car, The S M
21 | 20 | 19 | $44

1 Main St. (S. Water St.), Nantucket, 508-228-1101

■ For "classic" Continental cuisine, partisans swear by this Nantucket "old-style bar" with a "stopped in time" feel and "very eager to please owner"; accolades such as "best swordfish steak ever", "three words – rack of lamb" explain why most don't mind if it can be "expensive."

Le Languedoc S
24 | 22 | 22 | $43

24 Broad St. (Centre & Federal Sts.), Nantucket, 508-228-2552

☑ This Nantucket French features two different dining options – a "fun bar/cafe menu downstairs" and a Continental menu and "more formal setting upstairs"; while a few cite a "not kid-friendly" atmosphere as a reason why it "does not hit the mark", others enjoy the "very romantic" setting and "consistently good" cuisine.

Ropewalk S M
18 | 21 | 17 | $29

1 Straight Wharf (end of Straight Wharf), Nantucket, 508-228-8886

■ The "good" seafood at this Nantucket New American is best enjoyed "outdoors on the dock" because "you can't beat the view"; it also offers "one of the best bars" on the island – "certainly all the bartenders think so."

Straight Wharf S
24 | 23 | 23 | $39

Straight Wharf (Harbor Sq.), Nantucket, 508-228-4499

■ The "good food" and "rich Nantucket feel" at this "wonderful" seafooder are complemented by "a great view" and a "fun" atmosphere; but the "terrific fried clams" don't come cheap – "you pay for the location."

Summer House S M
23 | 26 | 23 | $42

17 Ocean Ave., Siasconset, Nantucket, 508-257-9976

■ A place where "Gatsby couldn't have been happier", this Nantucket New American pleases patrons with a "romantic setting" and "great food"; "beautiful decor" makes the experience "even more wonderful" and "worth the price."

Toppers S M
26 | 27 | 26 | $57

Wauwinet Inn, 120 Wauwinet Rd., Nantucket, 508-228-8768

■ A "fantastic" New American in Nantucket's Wauwinet Inn, with "excellent food and service", an award-winning wine list and a "gorgeous" setting that includes the "best sunset in New England"; while a few find it "overpriced", there's no denying that Toppers is still on top.

21 Federal [S][M] | 25 | 24 | 23 | $44

21 Federal St. (India St.), Nantucket, 508-228-2121

◪ With "excellent food", an "elegant" "old Nantucket house" setting and a "lively bar" scene, it's no wonder this New American frequented by "money types" is "tough to get into on weekends"; cynics sniff "too formal", "expensive" and "has seen better days", but they're in the minority.

RHODE ISLAND

Adesso [S][M] | 23 | 19 | 19 | $31

161 Cushing St. (bet. Brook & Thayer Sts.), Providence, 401-521-0770

■ "The only place in RI where Californians feel at home" is this "excellent" Cal-Italian, a "hip" Providence destination where "creative" food, a "cordial staff", "superb decor" and a "relaxing atmosphere" add up to a "winner"; it's "always packed", so expect long "waits."

Agora [M] | 24 | 24 | 24 | $47

Westin Providence, 1 W. Exchange St. (bet. Francis & Sabin Sts.), Providence, 401-598-8011

■ "Elegant" fare including "excellent seafood", "a lovely setting", "tremendous service" and "attention to details" are the pluses at this "pampering" New American in the Westin Hotel in Downtown Providence; even the few who call it "pricey" and "pretentious" admit it's "delicious."

Al Forno | 27 | 22 | 25 | $40

577 S. Main St. (Wickendin St.), Providence, 401-272-7980

■ "Nobody does it better" than this "world-famous" Providence Northern Italian; "consistently delicious" and "creative" cuisine, "the best pizzas" and "heavenly made to order desserts" give it the "reputation it deserves" and make it "worth the drive from Boston"; a few who "were expecting the sun, moon and stars and didn't get it" find the "tight quarters", "long waits" and no reserving a "bummer", but most contend you'll have "a meal to dream about."

Black Pearl [S][M] | 21 | 20 | 19 | $34

Bannister's Wharf, Newport, 401-846-5264

■ A "classic" and "popular" New England haunt that "captures the feeling of Newport"; the casual tavern and patio offer "great outdoor dining" and American seafood, while the formal Commodore Room (jacket required at dinner) serves Continental cuisine; a handful of critics cry "crowded", "noisy" and "overrated", but they're drowned out by loyalists who claim "a chowder and a beer outside and you're in heaven."

Cafe Nuovo Ⓜ　　　25　25　23　$38
*1 Citizens Plaza (bet. Canal & Steeple Sts.), Providence,
401-421-2525*
■ This "hot", "trendy" Providence International with
"outdoor seating on the river" is the "place to see and be
seen" where "every meal is an adventure" – from the
"wonderfully inventive" entrees to the "tremendous desserts
that are truly artworks"; it's "pricey", but delighted devotees
don't seem to mind.

Capital Grille Ⓢ Ⓜ　　　25　24　24　$42
1 Cookson Pl. (Francis St.), Providence, 401-521-5600
■ "Superb food in a clubby, wood-paneled inner sanctum
brings the power crowd" to this Providence steakhouse, a
classic "red meat, red wine" establishment offering "enough
food for a king" washed down with "excellent bar drinks";
still, most commoners reserve it "for special occasions"
due to "the fortune they charge."

Caserta Pizzeria Ⓢ ⧰　　　19　10　12　$13
121 Spruce St. (Acorn St.), Providence, 401-272-3618
■ Enthusiasts insist this Federal Hill pizza joint's "cheap",
"old-fashioned", "reliably delicious" pies "rock" and are
"definitely worth the trip" from Boston; but some surveyors
say they're "best for takeout" because the dining room
offers "zero atmosphere."

Clarke Cooke House Ⓢ Ⓜ　　　20　23　18　$40
26 Bannister's Wharf, Newport, 401-849-2900
☑ The "antique elegance" of this Newport American-
Mediterranean satisfies "contemporary tastes" and draws a
crowd of "beautiful people" who enjoy "marvelous dining"
"on the dock"; while there can be "too long a wait" in
season and service has "seen better days", most praise
this "peaceful" place.

Davio's Ⓢ　　　21　18　19　$30
*Biltmore Hotel, 11 Dorrance St. (Washington St.),
Providence, 401-274-4810*
See review in Boston Directory.

Florentine Grille　　　26　22　24　$35
*1195 Douglas Ave. (bet. Branch & Mineral Spring Aves.),
N. Providence, 401-354-8411*
■ A "superb synthesis of an American steakhouse and an
Italian restaurant" with "huge portions" of "super", "fresh
food" at "fair" prices; "mouthwatering" dishes, a "fabulous
atmosphere" and "excellent service" lead surveyors to say
this "very in" spot in North Providence "can give Boston a
run for the money."

Gatehouse S M
21 25 23 $40
4 Richmond Square (Waterman St.), Providence, 401-521-9229
■ Enthusiasts enjoy the "excellent food, atmosphere and service" at this Providence Regional American with a New England and Cajun-Creole slant, a "pretty place" for a "special get together"; foes feel they "try hard", but it's "not consistent."

Hemenway's M
20 22 20 $31
1 Old Stone Square (bet. S. Main & S. Water Sts.), Providence, 401-351-8570
■ This legendary Providence seafooder, "a fishy version of Capital Grille", reels in afishionados with "excellent", "reasonably" priced fin fare that just may be the "freshest in RI"; from another angle, however, it's "expensive" and "nothing special" and service is "spotty"; the net result seems to be "always dependable but not exciting."

L'Epicureo
25 22 24 $41
238 Atwells Ave. (bet. Dean & DePasquale Sts.), Providence, 401-454-8430
■ An "elegant", "expensive" Federal Hill Italian that's very popular with locals who dub it "the best of Providence" – "as good as Al Forno but without the wait"; our reviewers' only concern about giving this "great" but "too small" spot "such high ratings" is that it may inspire "all those Boston people to come down on weekends"; N.B. a recent expansion should help it accommodate the crowds.

New Rivers
25 20 24 $37
7 Steeple St. (bet. Canal & Main Sts.), Providence, 401-751-0350
■ Despite a "tiny dining room" that "lacks atmosphere" and a limited menu, this Providence New American "gem" receives high marks for using "only the best ingredients" in "truly innovative" dishes with "wonderful flavors"; the "excellent" food ranges from "great salads" to the "best homemade cookies."

Pizzico S M
▽ 23 16 22 $33
762 Hope St. (Rochambeau Ave.), Providence, 401-421-4144
■ Lauded as the "next best thing to being in Italy", this "delightful" Italian near Brown University offers "one of the best bowls of pasta anywhere" along with winning pizza and focaccia; expect a "relaxing atmosphere" that will allow you time to work through the "generous portions."

Pot au Feu S M
23 21 21 $36
44 Custom House St. (Weybosset St.), Providence, 401-273-8953
■ "In the shadow of grim, gray 19th-century skyscrapers" stands this "top-notch" Downtown Providence French with a "cozy", "romantic" bistro downstairs and a more formal dining room upstairs; in both locations the "staff is great" as are the lamb chops, leading loyalists to hope their own personal "steady favorite" remains a "secret."

Raphael Bar Risto 🅂   ▽ 23 | 21 | 22 | $36

345 S. Water St. (Division), Providence, 401-421-4646
■ People come from afar ("50 minutes of well-rewarded driving") to eat at this "very trendy, very noisy" Providence Italian that's like "a small Venice"; surveyors say the "food and service are excellent" and the "hip" experience is "everything I expected, including the high price."

Spain 🅂🅜   23 | 22 | 23 | $31

1073 Resevoir Ave., Cranston, 401-946-8686
■ "The staff is always singing" *Happy Birthday* at this "busy" Cranston Continental-Iberian in an "open, loud", "European"-looking setting; foodies single out the paella and double pork chops for kudos, adding that whatever you order it'll come in "mammoth portions"; in sum – a "great special evening out."

White Horse Tavern 🅂🅜   24 | 26 | 25 | $40

26 Marlborough St. (Farewell St.), Newport, 401-849-3600
■ For a "true Newport" experience there's nothing like dining in this circa 1673 "classic tavern" among "soothing", "dignified" and "authentic surroundings" ("tall persons must beware of ceiling beams"); the staff provides "superb personal attention" and the "quality and preparation" of the American food "continues to surprise", especially on Sunday when there's a "champagne brunch that's worth the drive from Boston"; P.S. don't worry, "it's definitely not a tourist trap."

NEW HAMPSHIRE AND MAINE

Arrows 🅂   27 | 27 | 27 | $53

Berwick Rd. (2 mi. west of Rte. 1), Ogunquit, ME, 207-361-1100
■ "Summer doesn't arrive until you visit" this seasonal Ogunquit New American in a "romantic", "private" setting that's most "stunning when the garden is in bloom"; chef-owners Mark Gaier and Clark Frasier turn out "outstanding, inventive cuisine" (including vegetables plucked from the garden) backed up by "excellent" service, making for "vibrant" dining that's "well worth" the cost and the drive.

Barnacle Billy's 🅂🅜   20 | 17 | 16 | $25

Perkins Cove, Ogunquit, ME, 207-646-5575
Oarweed Cove Rd., Ogunquit, ME, 207-646-5575
◪ "Sit on the deck and watch the boats" at this seasonal, self-serve seafood veteran in Ogunquit (the newer Barnacle Billy's Etc. next door has table service and an expanded menu); it may look like "an old shack" and some call it an "overpriced" "tourist trap", but fans swear by it for "New England's sweetest lobster" and "heavenly" clam chowder.

DiMillo's Floating Restaurant S M | 14 | 17 | 17 | $28 |
25 Long Wharf, Portland, ME, 207-772-2216
▨ The food may not make waves, but this Portland Italian set on a "large, crowded" boat certainly has a "great setting" and "fair prices", making it "justifiable on a meteorologically good day" and a "fun place to go with tourists."

Fore Street   – | – | – | M |
288 Fore St. (Franklin St.), Portland, ME, 207-775-2717
The brainchild of former Harraseeket Inn chef Sam Heyward, this Portland New American set in a large, open room turns out lusty grilled dishes from an open kitchen; while fairly new, it's quickly become as cool a scene as you're likely to find in Portland; N.B. try the rack of pork.

Harraseeket Inn S M   23 | 23 | 24 | $38 |
Harraseeket Inn, 162 Main St. (Rte. 1N), Freeport, ME, 207-865-1085
▨ A "great place to collapse" after shopping L.L. Bean and the outlets, this Freeport New American offers "quiet respite" in an "almost luxurious atmosphere" along with "superb local food"; while a few feel it "suffers from the loss of chef Sam Heyward", ratings suggest they're a minority.

Hooch & Holly's Seaside Bistro ▽ 23 | 24 | 25 | $26 |
131 Rte. 1, Ogunquit, ME, 207-646-4662
▨ Boston caterer Dan Mathieu has opened this large, hip Ogunquit New American–Eclectic to positive early notices; the few surveyors who have visited report "excellent food" ("try the pork chop") and great ambiance with "retro" decor.

Pond View S M   20 | 21 | 20 | $33 |
Rte. 125, Kingston, NH, 603-642-5556
▨ No one argues with the "beautiful pond view", but beyond that diners don't see eye to eye on this Kingston Continental; supporters love the "wonderful prime rib" and "the charm" of its "crooked, squeaky floors and nonmatching china"; but foes find it "dark" and "stuffy" with "garish table settings" and "boring food"; your view?

Promises To Keep   20 | 22 | 22 | $36 |
199 Rockingham Rd. (Rte. 28), Derry, NH, 603-432-1559
▨ An "elegant Derry tradition" in a "beautiful" glass-enclosed setting, this American-Continental has loyal followers who say it keeps its promise with "lovely food and service to match"; hard to please critics say "nice decor, but the food is not spectacular."

Street & Company S M   23 | 19 | 23 | $28 |
33 Wharf St. (bet. Dana & Union Sts.), Portland, ME, 207-775-0887
▨ Fans say this waterfront Mediterranean seafooder has the "best fish in Portland", making it "a great place to stop" on the way to or from Boston; some praise the "lovely" setting with an open kitchen, others find the tables "too small" and the room "crowded", but few fault the "simple, good food."

Walter's Cafe [S] [M] 24 | 18 | 21 | $27

15 Exchange St. (Fore St.), Portland, ME, 207-871-9258

■ An "eclectic menu" that "works" makes this "trendy", "noisy" Portland New American "very popular" with fans who call it one of the "best restaurants outside greater Boston"; look for "innovative seafood and pasta dishes" and "great salads" at "reasonable prices."

White Barn Inn [S] [M] 27 | 28 | 27 | $55

White Barn Inn, 37 Beach St, Kennebunkport, ME, 207-967-2321

■ "I could write a full page about this one" gush surveyors dazzled by this Kennebunkport standout's "world-class" New England food, "gorgeous", "pristine" flower-filled room and "impeccable" "black tie service" (though a few find the waiters so serious they "make you tense"); all agree it makes for "very memorable" dining that's up to "the best of Relais & Châteaux standards"; prix fixe only.

Indexes to Restaurants

Special Features and Appeals

TYPES OF CUISINE*

Afghan
Helmand

American (New)
Aesop's Tables/C
Agora/RI
American Seasons/N
Anago
Arrows/ME
Audubon Circle
Aujourd'hui
Back Bay
Bay Tower Rm.
Biba
Blue Wave
Boarding House/N
Botolph's
Brew Moon
Bristol
Cafe Edwige/C
Cafe Promenade
Cafe Soho
Cafe 300
Clarke Cooke Hse./RI
Copley's
Cranebrook Tea Rm.
Daddy-O's
David's
Fava
Fire & Ice
Flora
Fore Street/ME
Franklin Cafe
Gallerani's Cafe/C
Gargoyles
Glenn's Rest./Cool Bar
Grand Canal
Grapevine
Grille at Hobbs Brook
Hamersley's Bistro
Harraseeket Inn/ME
Hill Tavern
Hooch & Holly's/ME
Icarus
Isabella
Julia's
Landing
Lyceum B&G
Marquee
Martin House/C
Mildred's
Milk St. Cafe

Miracle of Science
Museum of Fine Arts Rest.
New Rivers/RI
On The Park
Other Side Cosmic
Pete's B&G
Providence
Rebecca's
Red Raven's Havana
Red Raven's Love
Regatta of Cotuit/C
Regatta of Falmouth/C
Ritz Cafe
Ropewalk/N
R Place
Sage
Savoir Fare/M
Scandia
Scullers Grille
Seasons
Summer House/N
Tables of Content
Thyme's on Square
Top of the Hub
Toppers/N
29 Newbury
21 Federal/N
224 Boston St.
Upstairs at Pudding
Vault
Walter's Cafe/ME
West St. Grille
White Rainbow
Woody's
Zaftigs Eatery

American (Regional)
Blue Ribbon BBQ
Cranebrook Tea Rm.
Dodge St. B&G
Finally Michael's
Flume/C
Gatehouse/RI
Hampshire House
Henrietta's Table
House of Blues
Last Hurrah
Mill Falls
North East Brewing
Pillar House
Road Trip
Rowes Wharf
Savoy

---

* All restaurants are in the greater Boston area unless otherwise
noted (C=Cape Cod; ME=Maine; M=Martha's Vineyard;
N=Nantucket; NH=New Hampshire; RI=Rhode Island).

Scandia
Towne Lyne Hse.
White Barn Inn/ME

American (Traditional)

Amelia's
Anchovies
Andover Inn
Atlas B&G
Aurora
Baker's Best
Barker Tavern
Barking Crab
Barrett's
Bennigan's
Black Dog Tavern/M
Black Pearl/RI
Black Rose
Blossoms Cafe
Boodle's
Boston Beer Garden
Boston Beer Works
Boston Sail Loft
Brandy Pete's
Bull & Finch Pub
Cambridge Brewing Co.
Cambridge Common
Capital Grille
Charley's Saloon
Charlie's Sandwich
Chart House
Cityside at Circle
Claddagh
Clarke's
Colonial Inn
Commonwealth Brew.
Coolidge Corner
Copley's
Dakota's
Dick's Last Resort
Division Sixteen
Dockside
Durgin Park
57 Rest.
Florentine Grille/RI
Flume/C
Frank's Steak Hse.
Gallerani's Cafe/C
Good Life
Green Dragon
Grill 23 & Bar
Halfway Cafe
Hard Rock Cafe
Harry's
Harry's Too
Hartwell House
Harvard Gardens
Harvey's
High Brewster/C

Hill Tavern
Hi-Rise Bread Co.
Hi-Rise Pie Co.
Houlihan's
Jacob Wirth
J.C. Hillary's Ltd.
Jimbo's Fish Shanty
Joe's American B&G
John Harvard's
Johnny's Luncheonette
Library Grill
Maddie's Sail Loft
Ma Glockner's
Marcella's
Mike's City Diner
Mr. & Mrs. Bartley's
New Bridge Cafe
New Yorker Diner
Oak Room
Oasis Cafe
Original Sports Saloon
Palm
Parker's
Parrish Cafe
Pillar House
Promises To Keep/NH
Roggie's
Rosebud Diner
Rowes Wharf
Ruggieri's
Salty Dog
Samuel Adams
S&S Rest.
Seaside
Sevens Ale Hse.
Sherborn Inn
Sorrela's
Sound Bites
Sports Depot
Stars
Stephanie's
Stockyard
Sunset Grill
Tallulahs
Tam O'Shanter
Tavern on Water
Ten Center St.
T.G.I. Friday's
Tim's Tavern
Tom Shea's
Towne Lyne Hse.
Union Sq. Bistro
Union Street
Victoria
Vidalia's
Warren Tavern
Watch City
Wayside Inn
White Horse Tavern/RI
Willow Pond Kit.

Asian/Fusion
Ambrosia
Billy Tse
Bok Choy
Buddha's Delight
Elephant Walk
Golden Temple
Jae's Cafe
Poppa & Goose
Salamander
Savoy

Bakeries
Hi-Rise Bread Co.
Hi-Rise Pie Co.

Bar-B-Q
Bison County BBQ
Blue Ribbon BBQ
Bob the Chef
East Coast Grill
Jake's Boss BBQ
M&M Bar-B-Q
M&M Station II
Original Sports Saloon
Pit Stop Bar-B-Q
Redbones
Rudy's Cafe
Uncle Pete's
Village Smokehse.
Whiskey's

Brazilian
Buteco
Café Brazil
Midwest Grill

Cajun/Creole
Dixie Kitchen
Gatehouse/RI
Johnny D's Uptown
Mass Bay Rest.

Californian
Adesso/RI
Blossoms Cafe
Blue Wave
Boca Grande
Santa Barbara Cafe
UVA

Cambodian
Elephant Walk

Caribbean
Green St. Grill
Legal C Bar
Rhythm & Spice

Chinese
Aku-Aku
Bernard's
Billy Tse
Cafe China
Carl's Pagoda
Changsho
Chau Chow
Chau Chow City
Chef Chang's Hse.
Chef Chow's Hse.
China Pearl
Dong Khanh
Ducky Wok
Dynasty
Eastern Pier
East Ocean City
Ginger Tree
Golden Palace
Golden Temple
Grand Chau Chow
Grand China
Hanmiok
Ho Yuen Ting
Hsin-Hsin
Imperial Seafood
Joyce Chen
Kong Luh
Kowloon
Lei Jing
Lotus Blossom
Lucky Garden
Mary Chung
Ming Garden
Moon Villa
New Asia
New Shanghai
Noble House
Oceanic Chinese
Ocean Wealth
Panda Palace
Peach Farm
Peking Cuisine
Royal East
Shalom Hunan
Sichuan Garden
Weylu's
Yangtze River
Yenching Palace

Coffeehouses
Cafe de Paris
Caffe Vittoria
Cybersmith
1369 Coffee Hse.

Coffee Shops/Diners
Blue Diner
Charlie's Sandwich

142

Harry's
Johnny's Luncheonette
L St. Diner
Main St. Diner/M
Mike's City Diner
New Yorker Diner
Rosebud Diner
Ruby's
Victoria
Vidalia's

Colombian
El Cafetal

Continental
Andover Inn
Black Pearl/RI
Cafe Budapest
Cafe Escadrille
Cafe Suisse
Club Car/N
57 Rest.
Hartwell House
Le Languedoc/N
Locke-Ober Cafe
Paddock/C
Pond View/NH
Promises To Keep/NH
Schroeder's
Spain/RI
White Rainbow

Cuban
Chez Henri
Mucho Gusto Cafe

Delis
B & D Deli
Manhattan Sammy's
Marcella's
Other Side Cosmic
Rubin's
S&S Rest.
Zaftigs Eatery

Dim Sum
Bernard's
Chau Chow City
China Pearl
Dynasty
Ginger Tree
Golden Palace
Grand China
Imperial Seafood
Lei Jing
Ming Garden

Eclectic/International
Biba
Black Crow Caffe

Black Eyed Susan's/N
Blue Room
Brew Moon
Cafe Edwige/C
Cafe Nuovo/RI
California Pizza Kit.
Cape Sea Grille/C
Centre St. Café
Cheesecake Factory
Christopher's
Claremont Cafe
Club Cafe
Delux Cafe
Duckworth Lane
East Coast Grill
eat
Fire King Bistro
Fraser's on Ave.
Front Street/C
Geoffrey's Cafe
Grendel's
Hooch & Holly's/ME
Jasmine Bistro
Johnny D's Uptown
La Bettola
Mercury Bar
Metropolis Cafe
Michael's Waterfront
Norumbega Park
Olives
On The Park
Oskar's
Pentimento
Purple Cactus
Purple Cactus/C
Red Herring
Red Raven's Havana
Red Raven's Love
R. Wesley's
Salamander
Sazarac Grove
Small Planet
Sonsie
Tremont 647
Walden Grille
Wonder Bar
Wrap Culture

English
Cornwall's
Medieval Manor

Ethiopian
Addis Red Sea

French
Chanticleer/N
Du Barry
Le Grenier/M

Le Languedoc/N
Le Lyonnaise
L'Espalier
Maison Robert
Mistral
Pot au Feu/RI
Ritz Carlton Din. Rm.
Truc

French Bistro
Ambrosia
Cafe Celador
Cafe de Paris
Cafe Fleuri
Chanterelle
Chez Henri
Hamersley's Bistro
Les Zygomates
Metropolis Cafe
Pho Republique
Pot au Feu/RI
Restaurant Zinc
Sandrine's

French (New)
Cafe Japonaise
Cafe Louis
Chillingsworth/C
Elephant Walk
Exchange
Hungry i
Jasmine Bistro
Julien
Le Bocage
L'Etoile/M
Restaurant Clio
Restaurant Zinc
Silks
Veronique

German
Jacob Wirth
Mass Bay Rest.
Schroeder's

Greek
Demo's
Omonia

Hamburgers
Charley's Saloon
Clarke's
Commonwealth Brew.
Coolidge Corner
Fuddruckers
Hard Rock Cafe
Mr. & Mrs. Bartley's
Tim's Tavern

Health Food
Five Seasons

Hungarian
Cafe Budapest
Jasmine Bistro

Indian
Akbar India
Bawarchi
Bombay Bistro
Bombay Cafe
Bombay Club
Delhi Darbar
India House
Indian Cafe
Indian Club
India Pavilion
India Quality
India Samraat
Kashmir
Kebab-N-Kurry
Maharaja's
New Mother India
Passage to India
Rangoli
Rasol
Shalimar of India
Tandoor House
Taste of India

Indonesian/Malaysian
Andover Inn
Bangkok Basil
Pandan Leaf
Penang

Irish
Amrheins
Black Rose
Burren
Claddagh
Doyle's Cafe
Finnegans Wake
Grafton St. Pub
Grand Canal
Green Dragon
Matt Murphy's
Michael Sherlock's

Italian
(N=Northern; S=Southern;
N&S=Includes both)
Abbicci/C (N&S)
Abbondanza (N&S)
Adesso/RI (N&S)
Adrian's/C (N&S)
Al Dente (S)
Al Forno/RI (N)

Alloro (N)
Anchovies (N&S)
Angelo's (N&S)
Angelo's Seafood (N&S)
Antico Forno (S)
Antonio's (N&S)
Appetito (N)
Armani Cafe (N&S)
Armida's (S)
Artu (N&S)
Arturo's (N&S)
Assaggio (N&S)
Bella's (S)
Bertucci's (N)
Black Goose (N&S)
Botolph's (N&S)
Cafe Celador (N&S)
Cafe Marliave (N&S)
Cafe Paradiso (N&S)
Caffe Lampara (N&S)
Caffe Luna (N)
Caffe Vittoria (N&S)
Cantina Italiana (N&S)
Carla's (N)
Carlo's (S)
Ciao Bella (N&S)
Daily Catch (S)
Davide Rist. (N)
Davio's (N)
Davio's/RI (N)
De Pasquale's (N&S)
DiMillo's/ME (N&S)
Dom's (N&S)
Donatello Rist. (N&S)
Enzo's on Charles (N&S)
Felicia's (N&S)
Figs (N&S)
Filippo Rist. (N&S)
Five North Sq. (N&S)
Florence's (S)
Florentina (N&S)
Florentine Cafe (N&S)
Florentine Grille/RI (N)
Gallerani's Cafe/C (N)
Galleria Italiana (N&S)
Galleria Umberto (S)
Giacomo's (N&S)
Giannino's (N)
Greg's (N&S)
G'Vanni's (N)
Harvard Gardens (N&S)
Ida's (N&S)
Il Baccio (N)
Il Capriccio (N)
Il Giardino Cafe (N&S)
Il Moro (N)
Joe Tecce's (S)
La Bettola (N)
La Famiglia Giorgio (N&S)

La Groceria (N&S)
La Summa (S)
L'Epicureo/RI (N&S)
L'Osteria (N&S)
Lucia's Rist. (N&S)
Mamma Maria (N&S)
Marcuccio's (N)
Marino Rist. (N&S)
Massimino's (N&S)
Maurizio's (N&S)
Milano's (N)
Moon Woman Cafe (N&S)
Mother Anna's (N&S)
Nauset Beach Club/C (N&S)
Nicole Rist. (N&S)
Noodles (N&S)
Pagliuca's (S)
Papa Razzi (N)
Pat's Pushcart (S)
Pellino's (N)
Piccola Venezia (N&S)
Piccolo Nido (N&S)
Pignoli (N&S)
Pinardi's (N)
Pizzico/RI (N&S)
Polcari's (S)
Pomodoro (N&S)
Ponte Vecchio (N&S)
Pranzare (N)
Raphael Bar-Risto/RI (N)
Ristorante Marcellino (S)
Ristorante Olivio (N&S)
Ristorante Toscano (N)
Rita's Place (N&S)
Ruggieri's (N&S)
Sablone's (N&S)
Sage (N&S)
Sal's Place/C (S)
Saporito's (N)
Saraceno (N&S)
Savoir Fare/M (N&S)
Siros (N)
Sorento's (N)
Spasso (N)
Spinnaker Italia (N&S)
Stellina (N&S)
Terramia (N&S)
Tosca (N)
Trattoria A Scalinatella (S)
Trattoria Il Panino (N&S)
Trattoria Pulcinella (N&S)
Tullio's (N&S)
Tuscan Grill (N)
UVA (N&S)
Vadopazzo (S)
Verona (N&S)
Villa Francesca (N)
Village Fish (N&S)
Vin & Eddie's (N&S)

Vinny's at Night (N&S)
Vinny Testa's (S)
Woody's (N&S)
Yerardi's (S)

Japanese
Bisuteki
Cafe Japonaise
Cafe Sushi
575
Ginza
Goemon
Gyuhama
Hanmiok
Jae's Cafe
JP Seafood Cafe
Kaya
Kyoto
Maluken
Miyako
Nara
Narita
Roka
Sakurabana
Shilla
Shogun
Takeshima
Tatsukichi
Tokyo
Yama
Yokohama

Jewish
(* kosher)
B & D Deli
Cafe Shiraz*
Jerusalem Cafe*
Manhattan Sammy's
Milk St. Cafe*
Rubin's*
S&S Rest.*
Shalom Hunan*

Korean
Arirang House
Hanmiok
Jae's Cafe
JP Seafood Cafe
Kaya
Korea House
Koreana
Shilla
Woo Chun
Yokohama

Lebanese
Phoenicia

Mediterranean
Aigo Bistro
Alloro
Cafe Celador
Caffe Bella
Casablanca
Clarke Cooke Hse./RI
Dalya's
Dancing Lobster/C
David's
575
Gardner Museum Cafe
Il Moro
Maurizio's
Mediterraneo
Mistral
Rialto
Ristorante Euno
Rustica
Savoy
Siros
Street & Company/ME

Mexican/Tex-Mex
Andale!
Anna's Taqueria
Baja Betty's
Baja Mexican
Boca Grande
Border Cafe
Cactus Club
Casa Elena
Casa Mexico
Casa Romero
Fajitas & 'Ritas
Forest Cafe
Iguana Cantina
Jose's
La Paloma
Palenque
Purple Cactus
Rudy's Cafe
Sol Azteca
Tacos El Charro
Tacqueria Mexicana
Taqueria la Mexicana
Zuma Tex-Mex

Middle Eastern
Bishop's
Cafe Barada
Cafe Jaffa
Jerusalem Cafe
Kareem's
Karoun
Lala Rokh
Middle East
Phoenicia
Sabra

Sami's
Sindibad
Skewers
Sound Bites
Sultan's Kitchen
Zaatar's Oven

Mongolian
Kong Luh

Moroccan
Marrakesh

Noodle Shops
Goemon

Persian
Cafe Shiraz
Lala Rokh

Pizza
Bertucci's
Bini Vini
Bluestone Bistro
California Pizza Kit.
Caserta Pizzeria/RI
Circle Pizza
Figs
Florentina
Galleria Umberto
Harvard Gardens
Papa Razzi
Pizzeria Uno
Regina Pizzeria
Roggie's
Santarpio's Pizza

Polynesian
Aku-Aku

Portuguese
Atasca
Casa Portugal
Neighborhood Rest.
O'Fado
Sunset Cafe

Russian
Aurora
Cafe St. Petersburg
Karoun

Seafood
Angelo's Seafood
Anthony's Pier 4
Atlantic Fish Co.
Bangkok Seafood
Barker Tavern
Barking Crab
Barnacle Billy's/ME

Black Pearl/RI
Boston Sail Loft
Bubala's by Bay/C
Cape Sea Grille/C
Captain's Wharf
Chart House
Chau Chow
Chau Chow City
Court Hse. Seafood
Daily Catch
Dino's Sea Grille
Dolphin
East Coast Grill
Eastern Pier
East Ocean City
Fishery
Five Seasons
Giacomo's
Grand Chau Chow
Grillfish
Grill 23 & Bar
Harry's
Harry's Too
Hemenway's/RI
Homeport/M
Ho Yuen Ting
Jimbo's Fish Shanty
Jimmy's Harborside
Jonah's
JP Seafood Cafe
Landing
Legal C Bar
Legal Sea Foods
Maddie's Sail Loft
Mass Bay Rest.
Michael's Waterfront
No Name
Oceanic Chinese
Ocean Wealth
Penguins/C
Providence
Regatta of Cotuit/C
Ropewalk/N
Ruggieri's
Salty Dog
Scandia
Seaside
Skipjack's
Straight Wharf/N
Street & Company/ME
Tavern on Water
Tom Shea's
Turner Fisheries
Village Fish
Walter's Cafe/ME
Woodman's
Ye Olde Union

South American
Blue Room
Café Brazil
Casa Elena
Pandorga's

Southern/Soul
Blue Ribbon BBQ
Bob the Chef
House of Blues
Magnolias
M&M Bar-B-Q
M&M Station II

Southwestern
Cottonwood Cafe
Kokopelli Chili Co.
Pete's B&G
Rattlesnake Bar
R Place

Spanish
Casa Elena
Dali
Iruna
Spain/RI
Tapeo
Tasca

Steakhouses
Bisuteki
Black Rose
Boodle's
Bugaboo Creek
Callahan's
Capital Grille
Capital Grille/RI
Chart House
Florentine Grille/RI
Frank's Steak Hse.
Grill 23 & Bar
Hilltop Steak Hse.
Jimmy's Steer Hse.
Jonah's
Ken's Steak Hse.
Morton's of Chicago
Oak Room
Palm
Plaza III
Stockyard

Tapas
Dali
Mercury Bar

Red Herring
Tapeo
Wonder Bar

Thai
Amarin/Thailand
Amarin II
Bangkok Basil
Bangkok Bistro
Bangkok Blue
Bangkok Cuisine
Bangkok House
Bangkok Seafood
Brown Sugar
Chiengmai
Erawan of Siam
Green Papaya
House of Siam
King & I
Kowloon
Lemon Grass
Montien
Rod Dee
Sawasdee Thai
Siam Cuisine
Siam Garden
Thai Basil
Thai House
Thai's

Turkish
Sultan's Kitchen

Vegetarian
(Most Chinese, Indian and
Thai restaurants)
Centre St. Café
Christopher's
Country Life
Five Seasons
Grapevine
Milk St. Cafe

Vietnamese
Dong Khanh
Ducky Wok
Pho Pasteur
Pho Republique
Saigon Vietnamese
Viet Foods
Viet Hong
V. Majestic

NEIGHBORHOOD LOCATIONS

BOSTON

Allston/Brighton

Bangkok Bistro
Bluestone Bistro
Café Brazil
Cafe Japonaise
Cafe Shiraz
Carlo's
Chef Chow's Hse.
Cityside at Circle
Ducky Wok
El Cafetal
Enzo's on Charles
Hanmiok
Jasmine Bistro
Julia's
Korea House
North East Brewing
Pho Pasteur
Pizzeria Uno
Rangoli
Roggie's
Saigon Vietnamese
Scullers Grille
Siam Cuisine
Sports Depot
Stockyard
Sunset Grill
Tasca
Thai House
UVA
Viet Hong
V. Majestic
Wonder Bar
Wrap Culture

Back Bay

Ambrosia
Anago
Angelo's
Armani Cafe
Arturo's
Atlantic Fish Co.
Aujourd'hui
Back Bay
Bangkok Blue
Biba
Blue Wave
Boodle's
Bristol
Cactus Club
Cafe Budapest
Cafe de Paris
Cafe Jaffa
Cafe Louis

Cafe Promenade
California Pizza Kit.
Capital Grille
Casa Romero
Chanterelle
Charley's Saloon
Ciao Bella
Copley's
Cottonwood Cafe
Davio's
Dick's Last Resort
Division Sixteen
Du Barry
575
Grill 23 & Bar
Gyuhama
Hard Rock Cafe
House of Siam
Hsin-Hsin
India Samraat
J.C. Hillary's Ltd.
Joe's American B&G
Kashmir
Kaya
Kebab-N-Kurry
La Famiglia Giorgio
Legal C Bar
Legal Sea Foods
L'Espalier
Mass Bay Rest.
Milano's
Miyako
Morton's of Chicago
Oak Room
Oceanic Chinese
Original Sports Saloon
Palm
Papa Razzi
Parrish Cafe
Pignoli
Pizzeria Uno
Rattlesnake Bar
Restaurant Clio
Restaurant Zinc
Ritz Cafe
Ritz Carlton Din. Rm.
Samuel Adams
Skipjack's
Small Planet
Sonsie
Spasso
Stephanie's
Tapeo
T.G.I. Friday's

Thai Basil
Top of the Hub
Turner Fisheries
29 Newbury
Whiskey's
Yenching Palace

Beacon Hill

Antonio's
Artu
Bangkok Seafood
Black Goose
Bull & Finch Pub
Figs
Hampshire House
Harvard Gardens
Hill Tavern
Hungry i
King & I
Lala Rokh
Lemon Grass
Library Grill
Rebecca's
Ristorante Toscano
Ruby's
Sevens Ale Hse.

Chelsea/East Boston/ Revere

Angelo's Seafood
Bisuteki
New Bridge Cafe
Rita's Place
Sablone's
Santarpio's Pizza
Uncle Pete's

Chinatown/Leather Dist.

Buddha's Delight
Carl's Pagoda
Chau Chow
Chau Chow City
China Pearl
Dong Khanh
Dynasty
East Ocean City
Ginza
Golden Palace
Grand Chau Chow
Grand China
Ho Yuen Ting
Imperial Seafood
Lei Jing
Les Zygomates
Moon Villa
New Shanghai
Ocean Wealth
Oskar's
Peach Farm

Peking Cuisine
Penang
Pho Pasteur
Savoy

Downtown Boston/ Financial District

Bay Tower Rm.
Blossoms Cafe
Blue Diner
Brandy Pete's
Cafe Fleuri
Cafe Marliave
Cafe Suisse
Commonwealth Brew.
Country Life
Dakota's
Fajitas & 'Ritas
Good Life
Julien
Last Hurrah
Locke-Ober Cafe
Maison Robert
Marquee
Michael Sherlock's
Milk St. Cafe
Nara
Parker's
Sakurabana
Schroeder's
Sultan's Kitchen
Tatsukichi
Trattoria Il Panino
Vault
West St. Grille

Faneuil Hall

Bertucci's
Black Rose
Clarke's
Durgin Park
Exchange
Green Dragon
Houlihan's
Pizzeria Uno
Plaza III
Salty Dog
Seaside
Seasons
Trattoria Il Panino
Ye Olde Union
Zuma Tex-Mex

Jamaica Plain/ West Roxbury

Bertucci's
Black Crow Caffe
Centre St. Café
Doyle's Cafe

Five Seasons
Jake's Boss BBQ
JP Seafood Cafe
Pinardi's
Sorrela's
Tacos El Charro

Kenmore Square/Fenway

Atlas B&G
Audubon Circle
Bawarchi
Bombay Cafe
Boston Beer Works
Brown Sugar
Buteco
Cornwall's
Elephant Walk
Gardner Museum Cafe
Goemon
Il Giardino Cafe
India Quality
Maluken
Museum of Fine Arts Rest.
Other Side Cosmic
Pizzeria Uno
Pranzare
Sorento's
Vanderbilt Cafe
Woody's

North End/No. Station

Al Dente
Alloro
Antico Forno
Armida's
Artu
Assaggio
Billy Tse
Cafe Paradiso
Caffe Vittoria
Cantina Italiana
Circle Pizza
Daily Catch
Davide Rist.
Dom's
Felicia's
Filippo Rist.
Five North Sq.
Florence's
Florentine Cafe
Galleria Umberto
Giacomo's
Grand Canal
G'Vanni's
Ida's
Il Baccio
Joe's American B&G
Joe Tecce's
La Famiglia Giorgio

La Summa
L'Osteria
Lucia's Rist.
Mamma Maria
Marcuccio's
Massimino's
Maurizio's
Mother Anna's
Nicole Rist.
Oasis Cafe
Pagliuca's
Pat's Pushcart
Piccola Venezia
Piccolo Nido
Pomodoro
Regina Pizzeria
Ristorante Euno
Ristorante Olivio
Road Trip
Sage
Saraceno
Terramia
Trattoria A Scalinatella
Trattoria Il Panino
Vadopazzo
Villa Francesca

South End/Roxbury/
Dorchester/Mattapan

Addis Red Sea
Anchovies
Appetito
Baja Mexican
Bertucci's
Bob the Chef
Botolph's
Charlie's Sandwich
Claddagh
Claremont Cafe
Club Cafe
Delux Cafe
Franklin Cafe
Geoffrey's Cafe
Giacomo's
Grillfish
Hamersley's Bistro
Harvey's
Icarus
Jae's Cafe
La Bettola
M&M Bar-B-Q
M&M Station II
Medieval Manor
Metropolis Cafe
Mike's City Diner
Mildred's
Mistral
On The Park
Pit Stop Bar-B-Q

Purple Cactus
Tim's Tavern
Tremont 647
224 Boston St.
Victoria

Symphony
Arirang House
Bangkok Cuisine
Dixie Kitchen
Mucho Gusto Cafe
Tables of Content

Theater District
Bennigan's
Brew Moon
David's
57 Rest.
Fuddruckers
Galleria Italiana
Jacob Wirth
Jae's Cafe
Kyoto
La Famiglia Giorgio

Mercury Bar
Montien
Omonia
Red Herring

Waterfront/South Boston
Amrheins
Anthony's Pier 4
Aurora
Barking Crab
Boston Beer Garden
Boston Sail Loft
Cafe 300
Chart House
Daily Catch
Eastern Pier
Jimbo's Fish Shanty
Jimmy's Harborside
Joe's American B&G
L St. Diner
Michael's Waterfront
No Name
Rowes Wharf

CAMBRIDGE

Central Square
Akbar India
Atasca
Bisuteki
Cafe Soho
Fishery
Green St. Grill
India Pavilion
Koreana
La Groceria
Mary Chung
Middle East
Midwest Grill
Miracle of Science
Pho Republique
Rhythm & Spice
Roka
Royal East
Shalimar of India
Spinnaker Italia
Tandoor House

Fresh Pond
Aku-Aku
Hi-Rise Bread Co.
Joyce Chen
Tokyo

Harvard Square
Bangkok House
Bertucci's
Boca Grande

Bombay Club
Border Cafe
Brew Moon
Cafe Celador
Cafe Paradiso
Cafe Sushi
Cambridge Common
Casablanca
Casa Mexico
Chez Henri
Cybersmith
Delhi Darbar
Fire & Ice
Forest Cafe
Fraser's on Ave.
Giannino's
Grafton St. Pub
Grendel's
Henrietta's Table
Hi-Rise Pie Co.
House of Blues
Iruna
John Harvard's
Jonah's
Jose's
Lucky Garden
Mr. & Mrs. Bartley's
Narita
Phoenicia
Pho Pasteur
Pizzeria Uno
Rialto

Sami's
Sandrine's
Santa Barbara Cafe
Shilla
Siam Garden
Skewers
Trattoria Pulcinella
Upstairs at Pudding
Wrap Culture
Yenching Palace

Inman Square

Cafe China
Casa Portugal
Court Hse. Seafood
Daddy-O's
East Coast Grill
Jae's Cafe
Magnolias
S&S Rest.
Sunset Cafe
1369 Coffee Hse.

Kendall Square

Bertucci's
Blue Room
Boca Grande
Boston Sail Loft
Cambridge Brewing Co.
Cheesecake Factory

Davio's
Florentina
Helmand
Legal Sea Foods
Manhattan Sammy's
Marrakesh
Papa Razzi
Poppa & Goose
Salamander
Sazarac Grove
Sindibad
Thai's

Porter Square

Changsho
Christopher's
Cottonwood Cafe
Dolphin
Finnegans Wake
Frank's Steak Hse.
Indian Club
Jose's
Kaya
Maharaja's
Marcella's
Marino Rist.
Passage to India
Pizzeria Uno
Purple Cactus

NEARBY SUBURBS

Arlington/Winchester/ Belmont

Cafe Barada
Flora
Jimmy's Steer Hse.
Kong Luh
Lucia's Rist.
New Asia
Pentimento
Rustica

Brookline/Chestnut Hill

Anna's Taqueria
Baja Betty's
B & D Deli
Bangkok Basil
Bernard's
Bertucci's
Bini Vini
Bok Choy
Bombay Bistro
Buddha's Delight
Cafe St. Petersburg
Caffe Luna
Capital Grille
Captain's Wharf
Charley's Saloon
Cheesecake Factory

Chef Chang's Hse.
Chef Chow's Hse.
Coolidge Corner
Daily Catch
Duckworth Lane
Fajitas & 'Ritas
Figs
Ginger Tree
Ginza
Golden Temple
India House
Indian Cafe
Jae's Cafe
Jerusalem Cafe
Kokopelli Chili Co.
Legal Sea Foods
Matt Murphy's
Ming Garden
Noble House
Pandan Leaf
Papa Razzi
Pete's B&G
Providence
Rod Dee
Rubin's
Sawasdee Thai
Shalom Hunan
Sichuan Garden

Skipjack's
Sol Azteca
Takeshima
Tam O'Shanter
Veronique
Village Fish
Village Smokehse.
Vinny Testa's
Yokohama
Zaatar's Oven
Zaftigs Eatery

Charlestown

Barrett's
Duckworth Lane
Figs
Olives
R. Wesley's
Tavern on Water
Warren Tavern

Newton/Needham

Amarin/Thailand
Appetito
Baker's Best
Bertucci's
Blue Ribbon BBQ
Caffe Lampara
Callahan's
Chiengmai
Duckworth Lane
Fava
Johnny's Luncheonette
Karoun
Mill Falls
Moon Woman Cafe
Norumbega Park
Peking Cuisine
Pillar House
Sabra
Shogun
Sol Azteca
Union Street
Vinny Testa's
Yerardi's

Quincy/Dedham

Amelia's
Halfway Cafe
Isabella
J.C. Hillary's Ltd.
La Paloma
Tullio's
Vinny Testa's

Somerville/Medford

Andale!
Bertucci's
Burren
Dali
De Pasquale's
eat
Elephant Walk
Gargoyles
Johnny D's Uptown
Neighborhood Rest.
New Asia
Noodles
Palenque
Panda Palace
Redbones
Rosebud Diner
Rudy's Cafe
Ruggieri's
Sound Bites
Tallulahs
Taqueria la Mexicana
Union Sq. Bistro
Vinny's at Night
Woo Chun

Watertown/Waltham

Bertucci's
Bison County BBQ
Bugaboo Creek
Casa Elena
Demo's
Dino's Sea Grille
Erawan of Siam
Green Papaya
Greg's
Grille at Hobbs Brook
Halfway Cafe
Iguana Cantina
Il Capriccio
Joe's American B&G
Kareem's
Le Bocage
New Mother India
New Yorker Diner
Pandorga's
Ristorante Marcellino
R Place
Stellina
Tacqueria Mexicana
Taste of India
Tuscan Grill
Verona
Viet Foods
Watch City

OUTLYING SUBURBS

North of Boston

Abbondanza
Andover Inn

Angelo's
Bertucci's
Bishop's

Border Cafe
Brew Moon
Bugaboo Creek
Dockside
Dodge St. B&G
Donatello Rist.
Glenn's Rest./Cool Bar
Grapevine
Hilltop Steak Hse.
Il Moro
J.C. Hillary's Ltd.
Kowloon
Landing
Legal Sea Foods
Lyceum B&G
Maddie's Sail Loft
New Asia
O'Fado
Pellino's
Polcari's
Ponte Vecchio
Rasol
Red Raven's Havana
Red Raven's Love
Scandia
Ten Center St.
T.G.I. Friday's
Thyme's on Square
Tom Shea's
Towne Lyne Hse.
Trattoria Il Panino
Weylu's
White Rainbow
Woodman's

Ma Glockner's
Mediterraneo
Pizzeria Uno
Sami's
Saporito's
Siros
Stars
T.G.I. Friday's
Tosca
Vin & Eddie's
Vinny Testa's

South of Boston

Barker Tavern
Bella's
Bertucci's
Brew Moon
Bugaboo Creek
Caffe Bella
Carla's
Cranebrook Tea Rm.
Fire King Bistro
Hilltop Steak Hse.
La Paloma

West of Boston

Aigo Bistro
Amarin II
Bertucci's
Bugaboo Creek
Cafe Escadrille
California Pizza Kit.
Colonial Inn
Dalya's
Dolphin
Figs
Finally Michael's
Harry's
Harry's Too
Hartwell House
Iguana Cantina
J.C. Hillary's Ltd.
John Harvard's
Ken's Steak Hse.
Legal Sea Foods
Le Lyonnaise
Lemon Grass
Lotus Blossom
New Asia
Papa Razzi
Sherborn Inn
Silks
Vidalia's
Vinny Testa's
Walden Grille
Wayside Inn
Willow Pond Kit.
Yama
Yangtze River

FAR OUTLYING AREAS

Cape Cod

Abbicci
Adrian's
Aesop's Tables
Bubala's by Bay
Cafe Edwige
Cape Sea Grille
Chillingsworth
Dancing Lobster

Flume
Front Street
Gallerani's Cafe
High Brewster
Martin House
Nauset Beach Club
Paddock
Penguins
Purple Cactus

Regatta of Cotuit
Regatta of Falmouth
Sal's Place

Maine

Arrows
Barnacle Billy's
DiMillo's
Fore Street
Harraseeket Inn
Hooch & Holly's
Street & Company
Walter's Cafe
White Barn Inn

Martha's Vineyard

Black Dog Tavern
Homeport
Le Grenier
L'Etoile
Main St. Diner
Savoir Fare

Nantucket

American Seasons
Black Eyed Susan's
Boarding House
Chanticleer
Club Car
Le Languedoc

Ropewalk
Straight Wharf
Summer House
Toppers
21 Federal

New Hampshire

Pond View
Promises To Keep

Rhode Island

Adesso
Agora
Al Forno
Black Pearl
Cafe Nuovo
Capital Grille
Caserta Pizzeria
Clarke Cooke Hse.
Davio's
Florentine Grille
Gatehouse
Hemenway's
L'Epicureo
New Rivers
Pizzico
Pot au Feu
Raphael Bar-Risto
Spain
White Horse Tavern

SPECIAL FEATURES AND APPEALS

Breakfast

(All hotels and the
following standouts)
Black Eyed Susan's/N
Charlie's Sandwich
Claremont Cafe
Davio's/RI
Mike's City Diner
Ruby's
Sorrela's
Sound Bites
Victoria
Zaftigs Eatery

Brunch

(Best of many)
Aujourd'hui
Biba
Bob the Chef
Bristol
Cafe Fleuri
Cafe 300
Charley's Saloon
Cheesecake Factory
Claremont Cafe
Club Cafe
Cottonwood Cafe
Cranebrook Tea Rm.
Davio's
East Coast Grill
Ginger Tree
Golden Palace
Hamersley's Bistro
Hampshire House
Harvey's
Henrietta's Table
Hungry i
Icarus
Johnny D's Uptown
Library Grill
Matt Murphy's
Metropolis Cafe
Pentimento
Rowes Wharf
Rustica
Sherborn Inn
Sound Bites
Spasso
Stephanie's
Tam O'Shanter
Tremont 647
Turner Fisheries
Zaftigs Eatery

Buffet Served

(Check prices, days
and times)
Abbicci/C
Aku-Aku
Amrheins
Andover Inn
Arturo's
Aujourd'hui
Baja Mexican
Barrett's
Blue Room
Bob the Chef
Bristol
Cafe Suisse
Cambridge Common
Casa Romero
Changsho
Club Cafe
Colonial Inn
Country Life
Davio's
Delhi Darbar
Dick's Last Resort
Enzo's on Charles
Galleria Italiana
Ginger Tree
Grille at Hobbs Brook
Harraseeket Inn/ME
House of Blues
India House
Indian Cafe
Indian Club
India Pavilion
Jimmy's Harborside
Jonah's
Jose's
Joyce Chen
Julia's
Kashmir
La Paloma
Le Bocage
Library Grill
Midwest Grill
Ming Garden
Museum of Fine Arts Rest.
New Mother India
Pinardi's
Poppa & Goose
Rattlesnake Bar
Ritz Carlton Din. Rm.
Roggie's
Rowes Wharf
Saporito's
Scandia
Scullers Grille

Shalimar of India
Small Planet
Spasso
Spinnaker Italia
Stephanie's
Sunset Grill
Tokyo
Turner Fisheries
Vinny's at Night
Weylu's
Yangtze River

Business Dining
Ambrosia
Anthony's Pier 4
Bay Tower Rm.
Bristol
Cafe Fleuri
Capital Grille/RI
Chillingsworth/C
Davio's
Davio's/RI
Donatello Rist.
Exchange
Filippo Rist.
Grapevine
Grille at Hobbs Brook
Grill 23 & Bar
Icarus
Il Capriccio
Jimmy's Harborside
Legal Sea Foods
L'Espalier
Library Grill
Locke-Ober Cafe
Maison Robert
Mamma Maria
Morton's of Chicago
Plaza III
Ponte Vecchio
Restaurant Clio
Salamander
Sandrine's
Schroeder's
Seasons
Turner Fisheries
Upstairs at Pudding
Vault

BYO
Angelo's
Anna's Taqueria
Bertucci's
Black Dog Tavern/M
Black Eyed Susan's/N
Country Life
Dong Khanh
Ducky Wok
Homeport/M

Jake's Boss BBQ
M&M Bar-B-Q
Narita
Neighborhood Rest.
Pentimento
Rustica
Sami's
Skewers
Yama

Caters
(Best of many)
Aigo Bistro
Angelo's
Antico Forno
Artu
Aurora
B & D Deli
Bangkok Basil
Bernard's
Billy Tse
Blossoms Cafe
Blue Ribbon BBQ
Blue Room
Bob the Chef
Boca Grande
Bombay Bistro
Bombay Club
Brew Moon
Brown Sugar
Carla's
Carlo's
Casablanca
Casa Mexico
Casa Portugal
Chez Henri
Chillingsworth/C
Claremont Cafe
Club Cafe
Cottonwood Cafe
Ducky Wok
East Coast Grill
Elephant Walk
Fava
Five Seasons
Flora
Gargoyles
Golden Temple
Green St. Grill
Gyuhama
Hampshire House
Hi-Rise Bread Co.
Hi-Rise Pie Co.
Iguana Cantina
Il Moro
Isabella
Jae's Cafe
Jake's Boss BBQ
Jasmine Bistro

Kashmir
Kebab-N-Kurry
La Bettola
La Paloma
Legal Sea Foods
Lotus Blossom
Maison Robert
Marcella's
Massimino's
Maurizio's
Mediterraneo
Milk St. Cafe
Mill Falls
Providence
Rangoli
Redbones
Rita's Place
R Place
Rustica
R. Wesley's
Sablone's
Seasons
Sherborn Inn
Small Planet
Sultan's Kitchen
Tables of Content
Tasca
Tatsukichi
Tosca
Woodman's
Zaatar's Oven

Dancing/Entertainment

(Check days, times and
performers for entertainment;
D=dancing)
Aesop's Tables/C (varies)
Andover Inn (D)
Aurora (varies)
Barrett's (D)
Bay Tower Rm. (D/piano)
Black Crow Caffe (jazz)
Black Rose (Irish)
Blue Room (jazz/piano)
Bob the Chef (gospel/jazz)
Brew Moon (jazz)
Bristol (jazz)
Bull & Finch Pub (D)
Burren (D/Irish)
Buteco (Brazilian)
Café Brazil (Brazilian)
Cafe Budapest (piano/violin)
Cafe Escadrille (D/bands)
Cafe Louis (Brazilian)
Cafe Soho (varies)
Cafe St. Petersburg (Russian)
Cambridge Common (bands)
Christopher's (jazz)
Clarke Cooke Hse./RI (D)

Club Cafe (piano/vocals)
Club Car/N (piano)
Colonial Inn (folk/jazz)
Commonwealth Brew. (D/bands)
Dakota's (piano)
Dockside (D/bands/karaoke)
Dodge St. B&G (bands)
Durgin Park (bands/piano)
Enzo's on Charles (D/jazz)
Exchange (jazz)
57 Rest. (piano)
Finnegans Wake (Irish)
Fire & Ice (music)
Fishery (piano)
Frank's Steak Hse. (piano)
Gargoyles (jazz)
Gatehouse/RI (jazz)
Glenn's Rest./Cool Bar
   (blues/jazz)
Good Life (jazz)
Grand Canal (bands)
Grand China (karaoke)
Green Dragon (varies)
Grille at Hobbs Brook (piano)
Hard Rock Cafe (bands)
Hartwell House (piano)
Houlihan's (DJ)
House of Blues (blues)
Icarus (jazz)
Jacob Wirth (piano)
J.C. Hillary's Ltd. (blues)
Jimbo's Fish Shanty (bands)
John Harvard's (bands)
Johnny D's Uptown (D/varies)
Jonah's (piano)
Julia's (jazz)
Julien (D/jazz/piano)
Karoun (belly dancer)
Ken's Steak Hse. (singer)
Koreana (karaoke)
Kowloon (D/bands/comedy)
La Famiglia Giorgio (jazz)
Last Hurrah (D/DJ)
Lei Jing (D/karaoke)
Les Zygomates (jazz)
Library Grill (D/jazz)
Lyceum B&G (piano)
Maluken (karaoke)
Marquee (bands/DJ)
Matt Murphy's (Irish)
Medieval Manor (theater)
Mercury Bar (D)
Michael Sherlock's (D/Irish)
Middle East (D/belly dancer)
Mill Falls (piano)
Moon Woman Cafe (jazz)
Mucho Gusto Cafe (Latin)
North East Brewing (varies)
Oak Room (jazz)

Paddock/C (D/piano)
Plaza III (jazz)
Pond View/NH (piano)
Pranzare (jazz)
Promises To Keep/NH (D/jazz/piano)
Regatta of Cotuit/C (piano)
Rhythm & Spice (D/Caribbean)
Ritz Cafe (harp)
Ritz Carlton Din. Rm. (piano)
Road Trip (D/varies)
Sazarac Grove (bands)
Scullers Grille (jazz)
Seaside (singer)
Seasons (jazz)
Sherborn Inn (jazz)
Silks (piano)
Siros (piano)
Skipjack's (jazz)
Spinnaker Italia (D/DJ)
Summer House/N (piano)
Sunset Cafe (guitar)
Tacos El Charro (mariachi band)
Tallulahs (blues/jazz)
Tam O'Shanter (D/varies)
Tasca (guitar)
Tavern on Water (guitar)
Towne Lyne Hse. (piano)
Trattoria Il Panino (D/jazz)
Turner Fisheries (jazz)
Union Street (D/bands)
Upstairs at Pudding (cabaret)
Veronique (harpist)
Villa Francesca (opera)
Warren Tavern (guitar)
Watch City (acoustic)
Weylu's (karaoke)
White Barn Inn/ME (piano)
Wonder Bar (jazz)
Yerardi's (blues)

Delivers*/Takeout

(Nearly all Asians, coffee shops, delis, diners and pasta/pizzerias deliver or do takeout; here are some interesting possibilities; D=delivery, T=takeout; * call to check range and charges, if any)
Addis Red Sea (T)
Aigo Bistro (T)
Akbar India (D,T)
Amelia's (T)
Amrheins (T)
Anna's Taqueria (T)
Appetito (D,T)
Armani Cafe (D,T)

Arturo's (D,T)
Atasca (T)
Baja Betty's (T)
Baja Mexican (D,T)
Baker's Best (T)
Barking Crab (T)
Barnacle Billy's/ME (T)
Bernard's (D,T)
Bini Vini (D,T)
Bishop's (T)
Bison County BBQ (T)
Black Crow Caffe (D,T)
Black Goose (T)
Blossoms Cafe (D,T)
Blue Ribbon BBQ (T)
Blue Room (T)
Bluestone Bistro (D,T)
Blue Wave (D,T)
Bob the Chef (T)
Boca Grande (D,T)
Bok Choy (T)
Bombay Bistro (D,T)
Bombay Cafe (D,T)
Bombay Club (D,T)
Border Cafe (T)
Boston Beer Garden (T)
Boston Beer Works (D,T)
Boston Sail Loft (T)
Botolph's (D,T)
Brandy Pete's (T)
Brew Moon (T)
Bugaboo Creek (T)
Bull & Finch Pub (T)
Burren (T)
Buteco (T)
Cafe Barada (T)
Café Brazil (T)
Cafe Celador (T)
Cafe Jaffa (T)
Cafe Marliave (T)
Cafe Shiraz (D,T)
Cafe Soho (T)
Caffe Lampara (D,T)
Caffe Vittoria (T)
Callahan's (T)
Cambridge Common (T)
Capital Grille/RI (T)
Captain's Wharf (T)
Carla's (T)
Carlo's (T)
Casablanca (T)
Casa Mexico (D,T)
Casa Romero (T)
Centre St. Café (T)
Christopher's (T)
Cityside at Circle (T)
Claddagh (T)
Claremont Cafe (T)
Clarke's (T)

Club Cafe (T)
Commonwealth Brew. (T)
Cottonwood Cafe (D,T)
Country Life (T)
Court Hse. Seafood (T)
Cybersmith (T)
Daddy-O's (T)
Dakota's (D,T)
Dalya's (T)
David's (T)
Delhi Darbar (D,T)
Delux Cafe (T)
Demo's (T)
Dick's Last Resort (T)
Dino's Sea Grille (T)
Dixie Kitchen (T)
Doyle's Cafe (T)
Duckworth Lane (T)
East Coast Grill (T)
eat (T)
El Cafetal (T)
Elephant Walk (D)
Enzo's on Charles (D,T)
Fajitas & 'Ritas (D,T)
Fava (T)
Filippo Rist. (T)
Fire King Bistro (T)
Fishery (T)
Five Seasons (T)
575 (T)
Florentina (D,T)
Forest Cafe (D,T)
Frank's Steak Hse. (T)
Fraser's on Ave. (T)
Gallerani's Cafe/C (D,T)
Gargoyles (T)
Geoffrey's Cafe (T)
Good Life (T)
Grand Canal (T)
Grendel's (T)
Grillfish (D,T)
Halfway Cafe (T)
Hamersley's Bistro (T)
Harry's (T)
Hill Tavern (T)
Hooch & Holly's/ME (T)
House of Blues (T)
Iguana Cantina (D,T)
India House (T)
Indian Cafe (D,T)
India Pavilion (T)
Isabella (D,T)
Jacob Wirth (D,T)
Jake's Boss BBQ (T)
Jasmine Bistro (D,T)
Joe's American B&G (D,T)
John Harvard's (T)
Johnny D's Uptown (T)
Julia's (T)

Karoun (T)
Kashmir (D,T)
Kebab-N-Kurry (D,T)
Kokopelli Chili Co. (T)
Lala Rokh (T)
La Paloma (T)
La Summa (T)
Legal C Bar (T)
Legal Sea Foods (D,T)
Lyceum B&G (T)
Maddie's Sail Loft (T)
Magnolias (T)
Maison Robert (T)
M&M Bar-B-Q (T)
Marcella's (T)
Marrakesh (T)
Mediterraneo (T)
Metropolis Cafe (T)
Michael Sherlock's (D,T)
Middle East (T)
Midwest Grill (D,T)
Mildred's (D,T)
Milk St. Cafe (D,T)
Moon Woman Cafe (D,T)
Mr. & Mrs. Bartley's (T)
Mucho Gusto Cafe (T)
Nara (T)
Narita (D,T)
Neighborhood Rest. (T)
New Bridge Cafe (T)
New Mother India (T)
Noble House (D,T)
No Name (T)
North East Brewing (T)
Norumbega Park (T)
Oasis Cafe (D,T)
Omonia (T)
On The Park (T)
Other Side Cosmic (T)
Pagliuca's (T)
Palenque (T)
Pandan Leaf (D,T)
Pandorga's (T)
Parrish Cafe (T)
Passage to India (T)
Pete's B&G (D,T)
Phoenicia (D)
Pit Stop Bar-B-Q (T)
Plaza III (T)
Poppa & Goose (T)
Pot au Feu/RI (T)
Purple Cactus (T)
Purple Cactus/C (D,T)
Rangoli (D,T)
Raphael Bar-Risto/RI (T)
Rasol (D,T)
Rebecca's (D,T)
Redbones (T)
Rhythm & Spice (T)

Ritz Cafe (T)
Road Trip (T)
Roggie's (D,T)
Roka (T)
R Place (T)
Rudy's Cafe (T)
Ruggieri's (D,T)
Rustica (T)
R. Wesley's (T)
Sablone's (T)
Salamander (T)
Salty Dog (T)
Samuel Adams (T)
S&S Rest. (D,T)
Shalimar of India (D,T)
Sherborn Inn (T)
Shilla (T)
Sindibad (D,T)
Siros (T)
Skewers (T)
Skipjack's (D,T)
Small Planet (D,T)
Sol Azteca (T)
Sonsie (T)
Sorrela's (D,T)
Sound Bites (T)
Stars (T)
Stephanie's (T)
Sultan's Kitchen (D,T)
Sunset Cafe (T)
Sunset Grill (D,T)
Tables of Content (T)
Tacos El Charro (T)
Tacqueria Mexicana (T)
Tallulahs (T)
Tam O'Shanter (T)
Tandoor House (D,T)
Taqueria la Mexicana (T)
Tasca (T)
Taste of India (T)
Tavern on Water (T)
Thyme's on Square (T)
Tim's Tavern (T)
Tullio's (T)
29 Newbury (T)
224 Boston St. (T)
Uncle Pete's (D,T)
Union Sq. Bistro (T)
Union Street (T)
Victoria (T)
Vidalia's (D,T)
Village Fish (T)
Village Smokehse. (T)
Vinny's at Night (D,T)
Warren Tavern (T)
Wayside Inn (T)
Willow Pond Kit. (T)
Woodman's (T)
Woody's (T)

Wrap Culture (T)
Ye Olde Union (T)
Yerardi's (T)
Zaatar's Oven (D,T)
Zaftigs Eatery (D,T)
Zuma Tex-Mex (T)

Dessert/Ice Cream

Baker's Best
Bristol
Cafe de Paris
Cafe Fleuri
Cafe Paradiso
Caffe Vittoria
Cheesecake Factory
Claremont Cafe
Elephant Walk
Fava
Hi-Rise Bread Co.
Hi-Rise Pie Co.
Metropolis Cafe
Salamander

Dining Alone

(Other than hotels, coffee
shops, sushi bars and places
with counter service)
Bok Choy
Claremont Cafe
Davio's/RI
eat
Five Seasons
Hamersley's Bistro
Harvard Gardens
Harvey's
Hungry i
Jae's Cafe
Le Languedoc/N
Locke-Ober Cafe
Maison Robert
Salamander
Sandrine's
Union Sq. Bistro
Veronique
Zaftigs Eatery

Fireplaces

Al Forno/RI
Amelia's
Barker Tavern
Barking Crab
Barnacle Billy's/ME
Black Dog Tavern/M
Bristol
Chanticleer/N
Chillingsworth/C
Clarke Cooke Hse./RI
Colonial Inn
Dalya's
Dancing Lobster/C

Donatello Rist.
Finally Michael's
Florentine Grille/RI
Flume/C
Gatehouse/RI
Grand Canal
Grendel's
Hampshire House
Harraseeket Inn/ME
Helmand
High Brewster/C
Hooch & Holly's/ME
Hungry i
Jimmy's Steer Hse.
Julien
Ken's Steak Hse.
L'Etoile/M
Library Grill
Lyceum B&G
Martin House/C
Mediterraneo
Mistral
Nauset Beach Club/C
North East Brewing
Piccolo Nido
Sherborn Inn
Silks
Spain/RI
Stockyard
Summer House/N
Tapeo
Ten Center St.
Toppers/N
Towne Lyne Hse.
Trattoria A Scalinatella
Tullio's
Upstairs at Pudding
Warren Tavern
West St. Grille
White Barn Inn/ME
White Horse Tavern/RI
Yerardi's

Game In Season

Al Dente
Al Forno/RI
American Seasons/N
Aujourd'hui
Aurora
Bay Tower Rm.
Black Pearl/RI
Blue Room
Boarding House/N
Cafe Fleuri
Cafe Louis
Cafe Soho
Cafe Suisse
Chanticleer/N
Colonial Inn
Cornwall's
Cottonwood Cafe

Cranebrook Tea Rm.
Dakota's
Dali
Dalya's
Donatello Rist.
Du Barry
Enzo's on Charles
Flume/C
Fore Street/ME
Fraser's on Ave.
Gargoyles
Glenn's Rest./Cool Bar
Grafton St. Pub
Hamersley's Bistro
Harraseeket Inn/ME
Hartwell House
High Brewster/C
Icarus
Il Capriccio
Iruna
Julien
Le Bocage
Le Lyonnaise
L'Espalier
Les Zygomates
L'Etoile/M
Lucia's Rist.
Lyceum B&G
Martin House/C
Mass Bay Rest.
Mistral
Moon Woman Cafe
Oak Room
Olives
Penguins/C
Piccolo Nido
Red Raven's Havana
Regatta of Cotuit/C
Regatta of Falmouth/C
Road Trip
R Place
Scandia
Seasons
Trattoria Pulcinella
Tuscan Grill
Upstairs at Pudding
Vin & Eddie's
White Barn Inn/ME
White Horse Tavern/RI

Health/Spa Menus

(Most places cook to order to
meet any dietary request;
call in advance to check;
almost all Chinese, Indian
and other ethnics have
health-conscious meals,
as do the following)
Bubala's by Bay/C
Five Seasons

Hampshire House
Red Raven's Havana
Red Raven's Love
Ritz Cafe
Rowes Wharf
Scandia
Silks

Historic Interest

(Year Opened; * Building)
1702 Wayside Inn*
1745 Chillingsworth/C*
1758 Sherborn Inn*
1760 Colonial Inn
1780 Warren Tavern*
1797 Plaza III*
1826 Ye Olde Union
1827 Durgin Park*
1833 Andover Inn*
1840 Hungry i
1847 21 Federal/N
1855 Cranebrook Tea Rm.*
1865 Cafe Louis*
1865 Maison Robert*
1868 Jacob Wirth*
1875 Locke-Ober Cafe
1876 L'Espalier*
1882 Cafe Marliave
1887 Upstairs at Pudding*
1889 Casablanca*
1902 Vault*
1910 Hampshire House*
1910 Library Grill
1912 Copley's
1914 Woodman's
1917 No Name
1918 Grill 23 & Bar*
1922 Julien*
1927 Charlie's Sandwich
1930 Santarpio's Pizza
1933 Sevens Ale Hse.
1943 Joe Tecce's
1963 Mill Falls

Hotel Dining

Back Bay Hilton Hotel
  Boodle's
Biltmore Hotel
  Davio's/RI
Boston Harbor Hotel
  Rowes Wharf
Cambridge Hyatt Regency
  Spinnaker Italia
Charles Hotel
  Henrietta's Table
  Rialto
Charlotte Inn
  L'Etoile/M

Colonnade Hotel
  Cafe Promenade
Comfort Inn
  Vinny Testa's
Copley Square Hotel
  Cafe Budapest
  Original Sports Saloon
Days Inn
  Enzo's on Charles
Doubletree Guest Suites
  Grille at Hobbs Brook
  Scullers Grille
Eliot Hotel
  Restaurant Clio
Fairmont Copley Plaza
  Copley's
  Oak Room
Four Seasons Hotel
  Aujourd'hui
  Bristol
Hampshire House
  Library Grill
Harraseeket Inn
  Harraseeket Inn/ME
High Brewster Inn
  High Brewster/C
Howard Johnson Hotel
  Bisuteki
  Pranzare
Hyatt Regency Hotel
  Jonah's
Le Meridien Hotel
  Cafe Fleuri
  Julien
Lenox Hotel
  Anago
  Samuel Adams
Midtown Hotel
  Tables of Content
Omni Parker House
  Last Hurrah
  Parker's
Outer Reach Motel
  Adrian's/C
Park Plaza Hotel
  Legal C Bar
  Legal Sea Foods
Radisson Hotel
  57 Rest.
Regal Bostonian Hotel
  Seasons
Ritz-Carlton Hotel
  Ritz Cafe
  Ritz Carlton Din. Rm.
Royal Sonesta Hotel
  Davio's
Sheraton Boston Hotel
  Mass Bay Rest.

Stonehedge Inn
  Silks
Swissôtel Boston
  Cafe Suisse
Tremont House Hotel
  La Famiglia Giorgio
Wauwinet Inn
  Toppers/N
Wayside Inn
  Wayside Inn
Westin Hotel
  Palm
  Turner Fisheries
Westin Providence
  Agora/RI
White Barn Inn
  White Barn Inn/ME

"In" Places

Al Forno/RI
Ambrosia
Appetito
Armani Cafe
Black Crow Caffe
Blue Room
Bok Choy
Bristol
Casablanca
Chez Henri
Claremont Cafe
Daddy-O's
Davio's
East Coast Grill
eat
Figs
Flora
Franklin Cafe
Ginza
Good Life
Grillfish
Grill 23 & Bar
Hamersley's Bistro
Harvey's
Hill Tavern
Hooch & Holly's/ME
Iguana Cantina
Jae's Cafe
Locke-Ober Cafe
Maddie's Sail Loft
Maison Robert
Matt Murphy's
Metropolis Cafe
Mistral
Papa Razzi
Pomodoro
Pot au Feu/RI
Red Raven's Havana
Restaurant Zinc
Salamander

Small Planet
Sonsie
Stephanie's
Tremont 647
29 Newbury
21 Federal/N
Vadopazzo

Jacket Required

Andover Inn
Bay Tower Rm.
Black Pearl/RI
Cafe Budapest
Chanticleer/N
Chillingsworth/C
Clarke Cooke Hse./RI
Exchange
Hampshire House
Julien
Locke-Ober Cafe
Oak Room
Promises To Keep/NH
Rowes Wharf
Silks
Summer House/N
Toppers/N
White Barn Inn/ME
White Horse Tavern/RI

Late Late – After 12:30
(All hours are AM)
Aku-Aku (1)
Anchovies (2)
Blue Diner (24 hrs.)
Boston Beer Works (12:45)
Cafe Paradiso (2)
Casablanca (1)
Chau Chow (2)
Club Cafe (1)
Coolidge Corner (1:15)
Cornwall's (1)
Division Sixteen (2)
East Ocean City (3:30)
Franklin Cafe (1:30)
Ginza (2)
Golden Temple (1)
Good Life (2)
Grand Chau Chow (3)
Gyuhama (2)
Harry's (1)
Harry's Too (1)
Kaya (1:30)
Kowloon (1:30)
Lei Jing (2)
Moon Villa (3:45)
Ocean Wealth (4)
Oskar's (1)
Peach Farm (3)
Rattlesnake Bar (1)

Restaurant Zinc (1:30)
Roggie's (4)
Savoy (1)
Sonsie (1)
Sunset Grill (1)
Tacqueria Mexicana (24 hrs.)
Tallulahs (1)

Noteworthy Newcomers (37)
(* not open yet, but looks promising)
Angelo's (Downtown)
Apollo Grill*
Bok Choy
Cafe Japonaise
Cena*
Chau Chow City
Ducky Wok
eat
Exchange
Fava
Franklin Cafe
Ginza (Brookline)
Good Life
Harvey's
Jae's Cafe (Stuart St.)
JP Seafood Cafe
Kokopelli Chili Co.
La Bettola
La Campania*
Legal C Bar
Marcuccio's
Mistral
Oak Room
Pandan Leaf
Penang
Pho Republique
Red Herring
Restaurant Clio
Restaurant Zinc
Ristorante Euno
Salts*
Sushinoya*
Tremont 647
Truc
Vadopazzo
Vault
Zaftigs Eatery

Noteworthy Closings (21)
Amigos del Norte
Angkor Wat
Ayers Rock
Azita
Bentonwood Bakery
Cafe Mojo
Cornucopia
East Wind

Eliot Cafe
Felucca
Grill & Cue
Ha Long
Harvest
Indochine
Noodle Bar
Pacifico
Pampas
Pomme Frites
St. Botolph
Wild Ginger
Zuxuz Cafe

Offbeat
Atlas B&G
Aurora
Barking Crab
Billy Tse
Blue Diner
Bob the Chef
Charlie's Sandwich
Chau Chow
Club Cafe
Daily Catch
Dixie Kitchen
eat
Fire & Ice
Franklin Cafe
Galleria Umberto
Helmand
House of Blues
Jake's Boss BBQ
Johnny D's Uptown
L St. Diner
M&M Bar-B-Q
M&M Station II
Matt Murphy's
Neighborhood Rest.
New Bridge Cafe
New Yorker Diner
No Name
Pit Stop Bar-B-Q
Redbones
Regina Pizzeria
R. Wesley's
Santarpio's Pizza
Savoy
Shilla
1369 Coffee Hse.
Tim's Tavern
224 Boston St.
Uncle Pete's
Victoria
Viet Hong
Vinny's at Night

Outdoor Dining

(G=garden; P=patio;
S=sidewalk; T=terrace;
W=waterside; best of many)

Andale! (S)
Armani Cafe (P,S)
Atlantic Fish Co. (S)
Back Bay (P,S)
Bangkok Blue (P)
Barking Crab (P,W)
Barrett's (P,W)
Bennigan's (S)
Bini Vini (S)
Black Pearl/RI (P)
Blue Ribbon BBQ (S)
Blue Room (P)
Boston Sail Loft (P,T,W)
Brown Sugar (T)
Bubala's by Bay/C (P,W)
Cactus Club (P,S)
Cafe Louis (T)
Cafe Promenade (P,S)
Cambridge Brewing Co. (P)
Carla's (S)
Casa Romero (P)
Chanticleer/N (G,P)
Charley's Saloon (P)
Chart House (P,W)
Chillingsworth/C (P)
Ciao Bella (S)
Claremont Cafe (P,S)
Clarke Cooke Hse./RI (W)
Colonial Inn (P)
Cottonwood Cafe (P)
Cranebrook Tea Rm. (G)
Daddy-O's (G)
Dalya's (T)
David's (P)
Davio's (P)
DiMillo's/ME (T,W)
Du Barry (G)
Duckworth Lane (P)
Fire & Ice (P)
Fishery (S)
Gardner Museum Cafe (G,P)
Gatehouse/RI (G,W)
Giannino's (P)
Grapevine (G)
Grendel's (P)
Grillfish (T)
Hamersley's Bistro (P,S)
Harraseeket Inn/ME (T)
Harvey's (P)
Henrietta's Table (P)
Homeport/M (P)
Houlihan's (P)
Hungry i (P)
Iguana Cantina (P)

Il Baccio (S)
Iruna (P)
Jacob Wirth (S)
Jimmy's Harborside (W)
Jonah's (S)
La Bettola (P)
Landing (P,W)
Le Languedoc/N (P)
L'Etoile/M (P)
Maison Robert (G)
Mamma Maria (T)
Manhattan Sammy's (P)
Michael's Waterfront (P)
Mill Falls (P,S)
Miyako (P,S)
Mucho Gusto Cafe (P)
Museum of Fine Arts Rest. (T)
Neighborhood Rest. (T)
New Rivers/RI (S)
Other Side Cosmic (S)
Pentimento (G)
Pete's B&G (P)
Pho Republique (S)
Pizzeria Uno (T)
Plaza III (P)
Rattlesnake Bar (T)
Rebecca's (S)
Regatta of Falmouth/C (W)
Ristorante Marcellino (T)
Ropewalk/N (P,W)
Sal's Place/C (P,W)
Savoir Fare/M (P)
Sazarac Grove (P)
Sherborn Inn (P)
Silks (T)
Skipjack's (P)
Small Planet (S)
Sol Azteca (S)
Sonsie (S)
Sorento's (P)
Sound Bites (S)
Spasso (P)
Stellina (G)
Stephanie's (S)
Street & Company/ME (P,S)
Summer House/N (P)
Tapeo (P,S)
Tavern on Water (P)
Ten Center St. (P)
Tom Shea's (W)
Toppers/N (P)
Trattoria Pulcinella (P)
29 Newbury (S)
21 Federal/N (P)
224 Boston St. (G)
Union Sq. Bistro (P)
Union Street (P)
Upstairs at Pudding (G,P)
Vidalia's (P,S)

White Rainbow (G)
Woodman's (G,W)
Yerardi's (P)

Outstanding Views

Amelia's
Anthony's Pier 4
Aurora
Bay Tower Rm.
Biba
Bristol
Chart House
Davio's
Gardner Museum Cafe
Hampshire House
Jimmy's Harborside
Mill Falls
Ropewalk/N
Rowes Wharf
Siros
Spinnaker Italia
Straight Wharf/N
Tavern on Water
Top of the Hub

Parking/Valet

(L=parking lot;
V=valet parking;
*=validated parking)
Abbicci/C (L,V)
Adesso/RI (L)
Aesop's Tables/C (L)
Aigo Bistro (L)
Aku-Aku (L)
Al Dente (V)
Al Forno/RI (L)
Amarin/Thailand (L)
Ambrosia (V)
Amrheins (L)
Anago (L,V)
Andover Inn (L)
Angelo's (L,V)
Angelo's Seafood (L)
Antico Forno*
Appetito (V)
Armani Cafe (V)
Armida's*
Arrows/ME (L)
Artu*
Arturo's (L)
Aujourd'hui (V)*
Aurora (L)
Barker Tavern (L,V)
Barnacle Billy's/ME (L,V)
Barrett's (L,V)*
Bay Tower Rm.*
Bella's (L)
Bernard's (L)
Bertucci's (L)*

Biba (V)
Billy Tse (L)*
Bishop's (L)
Bison County BBQ (L)
Bisuteki (L)
Black Dog Tavern/M (L)
Black Goose (L)
Blue Ribbon BBQ (L)
Blue Room (L)*
Blue Wave (V)
Bob the Chef (L)
Boca Grande (L)
Bok Choy (V)
Bombay Club*
Boodle's (L)
Border Cafe (L)
Boston Sail Loft (L)*
Botolph's (V)
Brew Moon (L,V)
Bristol (V)*
Brown Sugar (L)
Bubala's by Bay/C (L)
Buddha's Delight (L)
Bugaboo Creek (L)
Bull & Finch Pub (V)
Burren (L)
Cafe Escadrille (L)
Cafe Fleuri*
Cafe Louis (L,V)
Cafe Marliave (L)
Cafe Nuovo/RI (V)*
Cafe Promenade (L,V)*
Cafe Soho (L)
Caffe Bella (L)
Caffe Lampara (L)
Caffe Luna (L)
Caffe Vittoria (V)
California Pizza Kit.*
Callahan's (L)
Cambridge Brewing Co. (L)
Cambridge Common (L)
Cantina Italiana (V)
Cape Sea Grille/C (L)
Capital Grille (V)
Capital Grille/RI (L)
Captain's Wharf (L)
Carla's (V)
Casablanca*
Casa Mexico*
Caserta Pizzeria/RI (L)
Changsho (L)
Chanticleer/N (L)
Charley's Saloon (L)
Chart House (V)
Chau Chow*
Chau Chow City*
Cheesecake Factory (L,V)
Chillingsworth/C (L)
China Pearl*

Ciao Bella (V)
Claddagh*
Claremont Cafe (V)
Clarke's*
Colonial Inn (L)
Coolidge Corner (L)
Copley's (V)*
Cottonwood Cafe (L,V)*
Cranebrook Tea Rm. (L)
Dakota's (V)*
Dalya's (L)
Davide Rist. (L,V)*
David's (V)
Davio's (L,V)*
Demo's (L)
Dick's Last Resort*
DiMillo's/ME (L,V)
Dino's Sea Grille (L)
Dockside (L)
Dodge St. B&G (L)
Dom's*
Donatello Rist. (L,V)
Doyle's Cafe (L)
Du Barry*
Duckworth Lane (L)
Ducky Wok (V)
Eastern Pier (V)
East Ocean City*
eat (L)
Elephant Walk (L,V)
Enzo's on Charles (L)
Erawan of Siam (L)
Exchange (V)*
Fajitas & 'Ritas (L)
Fava (L)
Felicia's (L)
57 Rest. (V)*
Figs (L)
Filippo Rist. (V)
Finally Michael's (L)
Finnegans Wake (L)
Fire King Bistro (L)
Fishery (L)
575 (V)
Florence's*
Florentina (L)
Florentine Grille/RI (L,V)
Flume/C (L)
Forest Cafe (L)
Fore Street/ME (L)
Frank's Steak Hse. (L)
Gallerani's Cafe/C (L)
Galleria Italiana (L)
Gargoyles (L)
Gatehouse/RI (L)
Giacomo's (V)
Golden Palace*
Golden Temple (V)
Grand Chau Chow*

Grand China (L)
Grapevine (L)
Green Papaya (L)
Greg's (L)
Grendel's*
Grill 23 & Bar (V)
Halfway Cafe (L)
Hamersley's Bistro (V)
Hampshire House (V)*
Hanmiok (L)
Hard Rock Cafe (L)
Harraseeket Inn/ME (L)
Harry's (L)
Harry's Too (L)
Hartwell House (L)
Harvey's (V)
Hemenway's/RI (V)*
High Brewster/C (L)
Hilltop Steak Hse. (L)
Hi-Rise Bread Co. (L)
Homeport/M (L)
Hooch & Holly's/ME (L)
Houlihan's*
House of Blues*
House of Siam (L)
Icarus (V)
Iguana Cantina (L)
Il Capriccio (L)
Il Giardino Cafe (L)
Jacob Wirth (L)*
Jae's Cafe (L,V)*
Jasmine Bistro (L)
J.C. Hillary's Ltd. (L)
Jimbo's Fish Shanty (V)
Jimmy's Harborside (V)
Jimmy's Steer Hse. (L)
Joe's American B&G (V)
Joe Tecce's*
John Harvard's (L)*
Jonah's (L)
Jose's (L)
Joyce Chen (L)
JP Seafood Cafe (L)
Julia's (L)
Julien (V)
Kaya (L)
Ken's Steak Hse. (L)
King & I (L)
Kong Luh (L)
Korea House (V)
Kowloon (L)
La Bettola (V)
La Famiglia Giorgio*
La Groceria (L,V)
Lala Rokh (L)
Landing (L)
La Paloma (L)
Last Hurrah (V)
La Summa (L)

Le Bocage (L)
Legal C Bar (V)
Legal Sea Foods (L,V)*
Lei Jing*
Lè Lyonnaise (L)
L'Espalier (V)
Library Grill (V)*
Locke-Ober Cafe (V)
L'Osteria*
Lotus Blossom (L)
Lucia's Rist. (V)
Lucky Garden (L)
Lyceum B&G (L)*
Ma Glockner's (L)
Main St. Diner/M (L)
Maison Robert (V)
Mamma Maria (V)
M&M Bar-B-Q (L)
M&M Station II (L)
Manhattan Sammy's (L)
Marino Rist. (L)
Marquee (L,V)*
Mass Bay Rest.*
Massimino's*
Maurizio's*
Medieval Manor (L)
Mediterraneo (L)
Mercury Bar (V)
Metropolis Cafe (V)
Michael's Waterfront (V)
Midwest Grill (L)
Milk St. Cafe (L)
Mill Falls (L)
Ming Garden (L)
Mistral (V)
Moon Villa (L)
Moon Woman Cafe (L)
Morton's of Chicago (V)
Mother Anna's (L)*
Museum of Fine Arts Rest. (L)
Nauset Beach Club/C (L)
New Bridge Cafe (L)
New Shanghai*
Noodles (L)
North East Brewing (V)
Norumbega Park (L)
Oak Room (V)*
Omonia*
Oskar's (V)
Paddock/C (L,V)
Panda Palace (L)
Pandorga's (L)
Parrish Cafe (L)
Passage to India (L)
Pat's Pushcart*
Peach Farm (L)
Pentimento (L)
Pete's B&G*
Piccola Venezia*

Piccolo Nido (V)*
Pignoli (V)
Pillar House (L)
Pinardi's (L)
Pit Stop Bar-B-Q (L)
Plaza III (V)*
Pond View/NH (L)
Ponte Vecchio (L)
Pot au Feu/RI (L)
Pranzare (L)
Promises To Keep/NH (L)
Providence (V)
Raphael Bar-Risto/RI (L)
Rattlesnake Bar (L)
Rebecca's (V)
Red Herring*
Regatta of Cotuit/C (L)
Regatta of Falmouth/C (L,V)
Restaurant Clio (V)
Restaurant Zinc (V)
Ristorante Marcellino (L)
Ristorante Toscano (V)
Rita's Place (L)
Ritz Cafe (V)
Ritz Carlton Din. Rm. (V)
Road Trip (V)
Rowes Wharf (L,V)
Royal East (L)
Rubin's (L)
Ruggieri's (L)
Rustica (L)
R. Wesley's (L)
Sablone's (L)
Sakurabana*
Salamander*
Sami's (L)
Samuel Adams (L)
S&S Rest. (L)
Saporito's (L)
Savoir Fare/M (V)
Savoy (V)
Schroeder's (V)
Scullers Grille*
Seasons (L,V)
Shalimar of India (L)
Shalom Hunan (L)
Sherborn Inn (L)
Silks (L,V)
Siros (L)
Skipjack's*
Sonsie (V)
Sorento's*
Spain/RI (L)
Spasso (V)
Spinnaker Italia*
Sports Depot (L)
Stars (L)
Stellina (L)
Stockyard (L)

Straight Wharf/N (L)
Sultan's Kitchen (L)
Sunset Cafe (L)
Tallulahs (L)
Tandoor House (L)
Tapeo (V)
Tasca (V)
Taste of India (L)
Tatsukichi*
Tavern on Water (L)
Ten Center St. (L)
T.G.I. Friday's (L)
Thai Basil*
Tom Shea's (L)
Toppers/N (L)
Towne Lyne Hse. (L)
Trattoria A Scalinatella (V)*
Trattoria Il Panino (L,V)
Tremont 647 (V)
Truc (V)
Tullio's (L)
Turner Fisheries (L,V)*
Tuscan Grill (L)
Upstairs at Pudding*
Uva (V)
Vadopazzo*
Vault (V)
Verona (L)
Veronique (L)*
Victoria (L)
Vidalia's (L)
Vin & Eddie's (L)
Vinny Testa's (L)
Watch City (L)
Wayside Inn (L)
West St. Grille (V)
Weylu's (L)
White Barn Inn/ME (V)
Willow Pond Kit. (L)
Woodman's (L)
Ye Olde Union (V)
Yerardi's (L)

Parties & Private Rooms

(Any nightclub or restaurant
charges less at off-times;
* indicates private rooms
available; best of many)
Aigo Bistro*
Ambrosia*
Anago*
Andover Inn*
Anthony's Pier 4*
Antico Forno
Armani Cafe*
Artu*
Arturo's
Aujourd'hui*
Aurora

Back Bay*
Barker Tavern*
Barnacle Billy's/ME*
Bay Tower Rm.*
Bella's*
Billy Tse
Bishop's
Blue Room*
Bok Choy*
Bombay Club*
Botolph's
Brandy Pete's
Brew Moon*
Brown Sugar
Cafe Barada*
Cafe Budapest*
Cafe Celador
Cafe Escadrille
Cafe Marliave*
Cafe Soho*
Cafe St. Petersburg*
Capital Grille*
Capital Grille/RI*
Carla's*
Carlo's
Casa Romero*
Changsho
Chanticleer/N*
Chart House*
Christopher's
Claremont Cafe*
Club Cafe*
Colonial Inn*
Commonwealth Brew.*
Cottonwood Cafe*
Cranebrook Tea Rm.*
Dakota's*
Dalya's*
Davide Rist.*
David's*
Davio's*
Davio's/RI*
De Pasquale's*
DiMillo's/ME*
Dom's*
Donatello Rist.*
East Coast Grill*
Elephant Walk*
Enzo's on Charles*
Exchange*
Felicia's*
Filippo Rist.*
Finally Michael's*
Fire & Ice*
Fire King Bistro
Five North Sq.*
575
Flora*
Florentina*

171

Fore Street/ME*
Gardner Museum Cafe
Glenn's Rest./Cool Bar*
Good Life*
Grapevine*
Grille at Hobbs Brook
G'Vanni's
Gyuhama*
Hampshire House*
Hartwell House
Harvey's*
Helmand*
High Brewster/C*
Hilltop Steak Hse.*
House of Blues*
Hungry i*
Il Baccio
Il Capriccio*
Il Moro
Jacob Wirth
Jimmy's Harborside*
Johnny D's Uptown
Joyce Chen*
Julien*
Karoun
Kashmir*
Ken's Steak Hse.*
La Groceria*
Lala Rokh*
Landing
La Paloma*
La Summa*
Le Bocage*
Le Languedoc/N*
Le Lyonnaise*
L'Espalier*
Library Grill*
Locke-Ober Cafe*
Lucia's Rist.*
Lyceum B&G*
Maison Robert*
Maluken*
Mamma Maria*
Marcuccio's*
Marrakesh*
Maurizio's
Medieval Manor
Mediterraneo*
Mercury Bar*
Mill Falls*
Mistral*
Moon Woman Cafe*
Morton's of Chicago*
Mother Anna's*
Museum of Fine Arts Rest.
Narita*
New Shanghai*
Nicole Rist.*
Noble House*

North East Brewing*
Norumbega Park
Oak Room*
Oasis Cafe
Olives*
Pagliuca's*
Palm*
Pellino's
Pete's B&G
Phoenicia
Piccola Venezia*
Piccolo Nido*
Pignoli*
Pillar House*
Providence*
Rebecca's*
Rhythm & Spice
Rialto*
Ristorante Marcellino
Ristorante Olivio*
Road Trip*
Rowes Wharf*
R Place
R. Wesley's
Sablone's
Salamander*
Sandrine's*
Saraceno*
Savoy*
Scandia*
Scullers Grille*
Seasons*
Sherborn Inn*
Shilla*
Silks*
Sol Azteca*
Sonsie*
Sound Bites
Stellina*
Tallulahs*
Tam O'Shanter
Tapeo
Tavern on Water*
Ten Center St.*
Top of the Hub
Tosca
Towne Lyne Hse.*
Tremont 647
Tullio's*
Union Street*
Upstairs at Pudding*
Vadopazzo*
Verona*
Veronique*
Vidalia's*
Villa Francesca
Walden Grille*
Watch City
West St. Grille

172

White Barn Inn/ME*
White Rainbow*
Ye Olde Union*

People-Watching
Al Forno/RI
Ambrosia
Armani Cafe
Bay Tower Rm.
Biba
Bristol
Ciao Bella
Grill 23 & Bar
Hamersley's Bistro
Hooch & Holly's/ME
Il Baccio
L'Espalier
Locke-Ober Cafe
Maison Robert
Mistral
Restaurant Zinc
Rialto
Sonsie
Sorrela's
Stephanie's
Summer House/N
29 Newbury
21 Federal/N
Vadopazzo

Power Scenes
Ambrosia
Aujourd'hui
Exchange
Grill 23 & Bar
Hamersley's Bistro
Julien
L'Espalier
Locke-Ober Cafe
Maison Robert
Mistral
Plaza III
Ritz Cafe
Salamander
Seasons
21 Federal/N
Vault

Pre-Theater Dining
(Call to check prices,
days and times)
Aesop's Tables/C
Aigo Bistro
Arturo's
Barking Crab
Barrett's
Cafe Marliave
Cape Sea Grille/C
David's
DiMillo's/ME

Fishery
Galleria Italiana
Greg's
Grille at Hobbs Brook
Jae's Cafe
Johnny D's Uptown
Julia's
La Famiglia Giorgio
Marcuccio's
Mercury Bar
Montien
Museum of Fine Arts Rest.
Omonia
Paddock/C
Penguins/C
Red Herring
Regatta of Cotuit/C
Roggie's
Scandia
Skipjack's
Verona
Yerardi's

Post-Theater Dining
(Call to check prices,
days and times)
Aigo Bistro
Angelo's
Barrett's
Botolph's
Brew Moon
Buddha's Delight
Cafe Promenade
Chez Henri
Club Cafe
Coolidge Corner
Cottonwood Cafe
Davide Rist.
David's
Fajitas & 'Ritas
Fire & Ice
Golden Temple
Good Life
Grendel's
Harvey's
Jacob Wirth
Johnny D's Uptown
Julien
Kashmir
L'Etoile/M
Montien
Providence
Redbones
Restaurant Zinc
Ritz Cafe
Roggie's
Skewers
Sonsie
Union Street

173

Prix Fixe Menus

(Call to check prices, days and times)

Aigo Bistro
Appetito
Barrett's
Blue Room
Boston Sail Loft
Bristol
Cafe Budapest
Cafe Celador
Cafe Promenade
Casa Romero
Chanticleer/N
Chez Henri
Delhi Darbar
Fire & Ice
Grafton St. Pub
Harraseeket Inn/ME
High Brewster/C
India Quality
Julien
Kashmir
La Bettola
L'Espalier
Les Zygomates
L'Etoile/M
Maison Robert
Medieval Manor
Pho Pasteur
Pot au Feu/RI
Providence
Ritz Carlton Din. Rm.
Sandrine's
Scullers Grille
Silks
Spinnaker Italia
Toppers/N
Turner Fisheries
Verona
West St. Grille
White Barn Inn/ME

Pubs/Bars/ Microbreweries

Amrheins
Back Bay
Black Rose
Boston Beer Garden
Boston Beer Works
Brew Moon
Bull & Finch Pub
Burren
Cambridge Brewing Co.
Cambridge Common
Casablanca
Charley's Saloon
Claddagh

Clarke's
Commonwealth Brew.
Coolidge Corner
Cornwall's
Delux Cafe
Doyle's Cafe
Finnegans Wake
Grafton St. Pub
Grand Canal
Green Dragon
Hill Tavern
Jacob Wirth
John Harvard's
Le Languedoc/N
Maddie's Sail Loft
Matt Murphy's
North East Brewing
Original Sports Saloon
Pete's B&G
Rattlesnake Bar
Samuel Adams
Sevens Ale Hse.
Small Planet
Sports Depot
Sunset Grill
Tim's Tavern
Union Sq. Bistro
Union Street
Warren Tavern
Watch City
Whiskey's
Wonder Bar

Quiet Conversation

Bay Tower Rm.
Bok Choy
Bristol
Cafe Budapest
Cafe Celador
Casa Romero
Chanterelle
Chillingsworth/C
Cranebrook Tea Rm.
Davide Rist.
David's
Dom's
Du Barry
Elephant Walk
Gardner Museum Cafe
Hamersley's Bistro
Hampshire House
Harvey's
Icarus
Il Capriccio
Jasmine Bistro
La Bettola
Le Languedoc/N
L'Espalier
Locke-Ober Cafe

Maison Robert
New Rivers/RI
Providence
R Place
Salamander
Sandrine's
Seasons
Straight Wharf/N
Takeshima
Tatsukichi
Trattoria Il Panino
Union Sq. Bistro
Veronique

Reservations Essential

Abbondanza
Aigo Bistro
Ambrosia
American Seasons/N
Angelo's Seafood
Buteco
Cafe Budapest
Cafe Louis
Cafe St. Petersburg
Changsho
Chanticleer/N
Chillingsworth/C
Clarke Cooke Hse./RI
Club Car/N
Cranebrook Tea Rm.
Dakota's
Davide Rist.
Du Barry
Filippo Rist.
Galleria Italiana
Grapevine
Grill 23 & Bar
Hampshire House
Homeport/M
Johnny D's Uptown
Kashmir
La Bettola
Le Languedoc/N
L'Epicureo/RI
L'Espalier
L'Etoile/M
Library Grill
Locke-Ober Cafe
Maluken
Mamma Maria
Marrakesh
Martin House/C
Medieval Manor
Mistral
Morton's of Chicago
Pellino's
Ritz Carlton Din. Rm.
R Place
Siam Cuisine

Silks
Spinnaker Italia
Straight Wharf/N
Summer House/N
Thyme's on Square
Tokyo
Trattoria A Scalinatella
Uva
Walden Grille
White Barn Inn/ME
Yama

Romantic Spots

American Seasons/N
Arrows/ME
Bay Tower Rm.
Bok Choy
Bristol
Cafe Budapest
Casa Mexico
Casa Romero
Chanterelle
Chillingsworth/C
Cranebrook Tea Rm.
Dali
Davide Rist.
David's
Du Barry
Fava
Grapevine
Hampshire House
Homeport/M
Hungry i
Icarus
Iruna
Julien
La Bettola
Le Languedoc/N
L'Espalier
Locke-Ober Cafe
Maison Robert
Mamma Maria
Marcuccio's
Mill Falls
New Rivers/RI
Oak Room
Providence
Restaurant Clio
Salamander
Sandrine's
Seasons
Siam Cuisine
Sol Azteca
Straight Wharf/N
Tapeo
Tosca
Trattoria A Scalinatella
Trattoria Il Panino
Trattoria Pulcinella
Veronique

175

Saturday – Best Bets

(B=brunch; L=lunch)

Addis Red Sea (L)
Akbar India (L)
Amarin/Thailand (L)
Amarin II (L)
Amelia's (L)
Amrheins (L)
Andale! (L)
Angelo's (L)
Anthony's Pier 4 (L)
Antico Forno (L)
Armani Cafe (L)
Artu (L)
Arturo's (L)
Assaggio (L)
Atasca (L)
Atlantic Fish Co. (L)
Audubon Circle (L)
Back Bay (B,L)
Baja Mexican (B,L)
B & D Deli (B,L)
Barking Crab (L)
Bay Tower Rm. (L)
Bernard's (L)
Billy Tse (L)
Bison County BBQ (L)
Black Crow Caffe (L)
Black Rose (L)
Blue Ribbon BBQ (L)
Bluestone Bistro (B,L)
Blue Wave (B,L)
Bob the Chef (L)
Boca Grande (L)
Bombay Bistro (L)
Bombay Club (L)
Border Cafe (L)
Boston Beer Garden (L)
Boston Beer Works (L)
Boston Sail Loft (L)
Botolph's (B,L)
Brew Moon (L)
Brown Sugar (L)
Buddha's Delight (L)
Bugaboo Creek (L)
Bull & Finch Pub (L)
Café Brazil (L)
Cafe Budapest (L)
Cafe Jaffa (L)
Cafe Louis (L)
Cafe Marliave (L)
Cafe Promenade (L)
Cafe St. Petersburg (L)
Cafe Sushi (L)
Caffe Luna (L)
California Pizza Kit. (L)
Cambridge Brewing Co. (L)
Cambridge Common (L)
Carl's Pagoda (L)

Casablanca (L)
Casa Mexico (L)
Casa Portugal (L)
Centre St. Café (B)
Changsho (L)
Charley's Saloon (B,L)
Charlie's Sandwich (L)
Christopher's (L)
Ciao Bella (L)
Cityside at Circle (L)
Claddagh (L)
Claremont Cafe (B,L)
Clarke's (L)
Commonwealth Brew. (L)
Coolidge Corner (B,L)
Cottonwood Cafe (B,L)
Court Hse. Seafood (L)
Cybersmith (L)
Daily Catch (L)
Dakota's (L)
David's (L)
Davio's (B,L)
Delhi Darbar (B,L)
Demo's (L)
De Pasquale's (L)
Dick's Last Resort (L)
Dino's Sea Grille (L)
Dixie Kitchen (L)
Dockside (L)
Dodge St. B&G (L)
Dolphin (L)
Donatello Rist. (L)
Dong Khanh (L)
Doyle's Cafe (B,L)
Du Barry (L)
Ducky Wok (L)
Durgin Park (L)
Eastern Pier (L)
East Ocean City (L)
El Cafetal (L)
Elephant Walk (L)
Fajitas & 'Ritas (L)
Figs (L)
Fire King Bistro (L)
Five Seasons (L)
Florence's (L)
Florentine Cafe (L)
Forest Cafe (L)
Fuddruckers (L)
Galleria Umberto (L)
Gardner Museum Cafe (L)
Geoffrey's Cafe (B,L)
Giannino's (L)
Ginger Tree (L)
Ginza (L)
Goemon (L)
Golden Temple (L)
Good Life (L)
Green Dragon (L)

Green Papaya (L)
Greg's (L)
Grendel's (L)
G'Vanni's (L)
Gyuhama (L)
Hard Rock Cafe (L)
Harvard Gardens (L)
Henrietta's Table (L)
Hill Tavern (L)
Houlihan's (L)
House of Blues (L)
House of Siam (L)
Iguana Cantina (L)
Il Baccio (L)
Imperial Seafood (L)
Indian Cafe (B,L)
India Pavilion (L)
Iruna (L)
Jacob Wirth (L)
Jae's Cafe (L)
Jake's Boss BBQ (L)
Jimmy's Harborside (L)
Joe's American B&G (L)
Joe Tecce's (L)
John Harvard's (B,L)
Johnny D's Uptown (B)
Johnny's Luncheonette (B,L)
Julia's (B,L)
Kashmir (B,L)
Kaya (L)
King & I (L)
Kong Luh (L)
Korea House (L)
La Famiglia Giorgio (B,L)
La Groceria (L)
La Paloma (L)
Last Hurrah (L)
Legal C Bar (L)
Lei Jing (L)
Le Lyonnaise (L)
Lemon Grass (L)
L'Osteria (L)
Lotus Blossom (L)
L St. Diner (L)
Lucky Garden (L)
Maddie's Sail Loft (L)
Maluken (L)
M&M Bar-B-Q (L)
M&M Station II (L)
Manhattan Sammy's (L)
Marcella's (B,L)
Marcuccio's (B)
Marino Rist. (L)
Mary Chung (L)
Massimino's (L)
Matt Murphy's (L)
Maurizio's (L)
Metropolis Cafe (B)
Michael Sherlock's (L)

Michael's Waterfront (L)
Middle East (B,L)
Milano's (L)
Mildred's (L)
Mill Falls (L)
Ming Garden (B,L)
Miracle of Science (L)
Miyako (L)
Montien (L)
Moon Villa (B,L)
Mr. & Mrs. Bartley's (L)
Mucho Gusto Cafe (L)
Museum of Fine Arts Rest. (L)
Narita (L)
Neighborhood Rest. (L)
New Asia (L)
New Bridge Cafe (L)
New Mother India (L)
New Shanghai (L)
Nicole Rist. (L)
Noble House (B,L)
No Name (L)
North East Brewing (L)
Oasis Cafe (B,L)
Oceanic Chinese (L)
Ocean Wealth (L)
On The Park (B)
Other Side Cosmic (L)
Pagliuca's (L)
Pandorga's (L)
Papa Razzi (L)
Parrish Cafe (L)
Passage to India (L)
Penang (L)
Pentimento (B,L)
Phoenicia (L)
Pho Pasteur (L)
Piccola Venezia (L)
Pignoli (L)
Pit Stop Bar-B-Q (L)
Polcari's (L)
Pomodoro (L)
Rangoli (L)
Rattlesnake Bar (B,L)
Rebecca's (L)
Redbones (L)
Regina Pizzeria (L)
Ristorante Marcellino (L)
Ristorante Toscano (L)
Rod Dee (L)
Roggie's (B,L)
Roka (L)
Rosebud Diner (B,L)
Royal East (L)
Ruby's (L)
Rudy's Cafe (L)
Rustica (L)
Sabra (L)
Saigon Vietnamese (L)

Salty Dog (L)
Sami's (L)
Samuel Adams (L)
Sandrine's (L)
Santarpio's Pizza (L)
Saraceno (L)
Scullers Grille (L)
Seaside (L)
Sevens Ale Hse. (L)
Shalimar of India (L)
Shilla (L)
Silks (L)
Sindibad (L)
Skewers (L)
Small Planet (L)
Sonsie (B,L)
Sorento's (L)
Sorrela's (B,L)
Sound Bites (L)
Sunset Cafe (L)
Sunset Grill (L)
Tables of Content (L)
Tacos El Charro (L)
Tacqueria Mexicana (L)
Takeshima (L)
Tallulahs (B,L)
Tam O'Shanter (L)
Tandoor House (L)
Tapeo (L)
Taqueria la Mexicana (L)
Taste of India (L)
Tavern on Water (L)
Ten Center St. (L)
T.G.I. Friday's (B,L)
Thai House (L)
Thai's (L)
Top of the Hub (L)
Tosca (L)
Trattoria Il Panino (L)
29 Newbury (L)
Uncle Pete's (L)
Union Street (L)
Upstairs at Pudding (B,L)
Verona (L)
Victoria (L)
Vidalia's (L)
Viet Hong (L)
Villa Francesca (L)
Village Fish (L)
Village Smokehse. (B,L)
Vin & Eddie's (L)
Vinny Testa's (L)
Warren Tavern (B,L)
Watch City (L)
Weylu's (L)
White Horse Tavern/RI (L)
Woody's (L)
Wrap Culture (L)
Yenching Palace (L)

Ye Olde Union (L)
Zaatar's Oven (L)
Zuma Tex-Mex (L)

Sunday – Best Bets

(B=brunch; L=lunch;
D=dinner; plus most hotels
and Asians)
Abbicci/C (B,D)
Akbar India (L,D)
Al Dente (D)
Alloro (D)
Ambrosia (D)
Anago (L,D)
Anchovies (D)
Andale! (L,D)
Andover Inn (B)
Angelo's (D)
Angelo's Seafood (D)
Anthony's Pier 4 (L,D)
Antico Forno (D)
Appetito (B,D)
Armani Cafe (L,D)
Arrows/ME (D)
Artu (L,D)
Arturo's (L)
Atlantic Fish Co. (L,D)
Audubon Circle (L,D)
Aujourd'hui (B,D)
Baja Mexican (L,D)
Barker Tavern (D)
Bernard's (L,D)
Biba (B,D)
Billy Tse (L,D)
Bini Vini (L,D)
Bishop's (L,D)
Bisuteki (D)
Black Crow Caffe (B,L)
Black Rose (L,D)
Blue Room (B,D)
Blue Wave (L,D)
Bob the Chef (B,L,D)
Boca Grande (L,D)
Bombay Club (L,D)
Boodle's (L,D)
Brown Sugar (L,D)
Bull & Finch Pub (L,D)
Buteco (D)
Café Brazil (L,D)
Cafe Budapest (D)
Cafe Jaffa (L,D)
Cafe St. Petersburg (L,D)
Cafe Sushi (D)
Caffe Luna (B,L,D)
Cambridge Brewing Co. (L,D)
Capital Grille (D)
Captain's Wharf (L)
Carla's (D)
Carlo's (L,D)

Carl's Pagoda (L,D)
Casablanca (L,D)
Casa Elena (D)
Casa Mexico (L,D)
Casa Portugal (L,D)
Casa Romero (D)
Chanterelle (D)
Chart House (D)
Chau Chow (L,D)
Cheesecake Factory (L,D)
Chef Chang's Hse. (L,D)
Chez Henri (B,D)
Ciao Bella (B,L,D)
Club Cafe (B,D)
Colonial Inn (L,D)
Commonwealth Brew. (L,D)
Cottonwood Cafe (L,D)
Cybersmith (L,D)
Daddy-O's (B,D)
Daily Catch (L,D)
Dali (D)
Davide Rist. (D)
David's (B,D)
Davio's (B,L,D)
De Pasquale's (D)
Dino's Sea Grille (L,D)
Division Sixteen (D)
Donatello Rist. (D)
Duckworth Lane (D)
Ducky Wok (L,D)
East Coast Grill (B,D)
Eastern Pier (L,D)
East Ocean City (L,D)
eat (D)
El Cafetal (L,D)
Elephant Walk (D)
Enzo's on Charles (L,D)
Felicia's (D)
57 Rest. (D)
Figs (B,L,D)
Fire King Bistro (L,D)
Five Seasons (B,D)
575 (D)
Flora (B,D)
Florentine Cafe (L,D)
Forest Cafe (D)
Franklin Cafe (D)
Frank's Steak Hse. (B,D)
Galleria Italiana (D)
Gardner Museum Cafe (L)
Gargoyles (B,D)
Geoffrey's Cafe (L,D)
Giacomo's (D)
Giannino's (B,D)
Ginger Tree (L,D)
Ginza (L,D)
Goemon (L,D)
Golden Temple (L,D)
Grapevine (D)

Green Papaya (L,D)
Grillfish (D)
Grill 23 & Bar (D)
G'Vanni's (L,D)
Gyuhama (L,D)
Hamersley's Bistro (D)
Hampshire House (B,D)
Helmand (D)
Henrietta's Table (B,D)
Hilltop Steak Hse. (L,D)
House of Blues (B,L,D)
Hungry i (B,D)
Icarus (B,D)
Iguana Cantina (B,L,D)
Imperial Seafood (L,D)
Isabella (D)
Jae's Cafe (L,D)
Jake's Boss BBQ (L,D)
Jasmine Bistro (D)
Jimmy's Harborside (D)
Joe's American B&G (L,D)
Johnny D's Uptown (D)
Joyce Chen (L,D)
JP Seafood Cafe (D)
Kashmir (L,D)
Kaya (L,D)
Kebab-N-Kurry (L,D)
King & I (L,D)
La Groceria (L,D)
Lala Rokh (D)
Landing (B,D)
La Paloma (D)
La Summa (D)
Le Bocage (D)
Legal C Bar (D)
Legal Sea Foods (L,D)
Lemon Grass (L,D)
Les Zygomates (D)
Library Grill (B,D)
L'Osteria (L,D)
Lotus Blossom (D)
L St. Diner (L,D)
Lucia's Rist. (L,D)
Lucky Garden (L,D)
Lyceum B&G (B,D)
Maddie's Sail Loft (B,L)
Main St. Diner/M (L,D)
Maluken (L,D)
Mamma Maria (D)
Marcuccio's (D)
Marino Rist. (L,D)
Martin House/C (D)
Mass Bay Rest. (D)
Matt Murphy's (B,L,D)
Maurizio's (D)
Metropolis Cafe (D)
Michael Sherlock's (L,D)
Michael's Waterfront (L,D)
Middle East (L,D)

Midwest Grill (L,D)
Milano's (L,D)
Miracle of Science (L,D)
Mistral (D)
Miyako (L,D)
Morton's of Chicago (L,D)
Mother Anna's (D)
Mucho Gusto Cafe (B)
New Bridge Cafe (L,D)
New Mother India (D)
New Shanghai (L,D)
Nicole Rist. (D)
Noble House (L,D)
No Name (L,D)
Norumbega Park (D)
Oak Room (D)
Omonia (D)
Pagliuca's (L,D)
Palm (D)
Panda Palace (L,D)
Papa Razzi (L,D)
Penang (L,D)
Pho Pasteur (L,D)
Piccola Venezia (L,D)
Pignoli (D)
Plaza III (L,D)
Polcari's (L,D)
Pomodoro (L,D)
Ponte Vecchio (L,D)
Pranzare (D)
Providence (B,D)
Rangoli (L,D)
Rasol (L,D)
Rattlesnake Bar (L,D)
Rebecca's (B,D)
Redbones (L,D)
Regatta of Cotuit/C (D)
Restaurant Clio (B,D)
Restaurant Zinc (D)
Rhythm & Spice (D)
Rialto (D)
Ristorante Euno (D)
Ristorante Olivio (D)
Ristorante Toscano (D)
Ritz Cafe (D)
Ritz Carlton Din. Rm. (B,D)
Rod Dee (L,D)
Roggie's (L,D)
Roka (L,D)
Rosebud Diner (L,D)
Rowes Wharf (B,L,D)
Rubin's (B,L,D)
Ruby's (L,D)
Rudy's Cafe (L,D)
Rustica (B,L,D)
R. Wesley's (D)
Sabra (L,D)
Sage (D)
Saigon Vietnamese (D)

Salty Dog (B,L,D)
Sami's (L,D)
Samuel Adams (L,D)
Saporito's (D)
Saraceno (L,D)
Sawasdee Thai (L,D)
Sazarac Grove (L,D)
Scandia (L,D)
Scullers Grille (L,D)
Seaside (L,D)
Seasons (D)
Shalimar of India (L,D)
Shalom Hunan (D)
Sherborn Inn (B,D)
Shilla (L,D)
Shogun (D)
Sichuan Garden (L,D)
Silks (B,D)
Siros (L,D)
Skipjack's (B,L,D)
Small Planet (B,L,D)
Sol Azteca (D)
Sonsie (D)
Sorento's (L,D)
Sorrela's (L)
Spasso (B)
Stars (L,D)
Stellina (D)
Sunset Cafe (L,D)
Takeshima (D)
Tallulahs (L,D)
Tam O'Shanter (B,D)
Tandoor House (L,D)
Tapeo (L,D)
Taqueria la Mexicana (L,D)
Tasca (D)
Taste of India (L,D)
Tatsukichi (D)
Tavern on Water (L,D)
Ten Center St. (B,L,D)
Terramia (L,D)
Tokyo (D)
Top of the Hub (D)
Toppers/N (B,D)
Tosca (L,D)
Towne Lyne Hse. (L,D)
Trattoria A Scalinatella (D)
Trattoria Il Panino (L,D)
Trattoria Pulcinella (D)
Tremont 647 (B,D)
Tullio's (D)
Turner Fisheries (B,D)
Tuscan Grill (D)
29 Newbury (B,D)
224 Boston St. (D)
Uncle Pete's (D)
Union Street (B,D)
Upstairs at Pudding (L,D)
Vadopazzo (D)

Veronique (B,L,D)
Village Fish (D)
Village Smokehse. (D)
Vin & Eddie's (L,D)
Vinny Testa's (L,D)
Walden Grille (B,L,D)
Warren Tavern (L,D)
White Rainbow (D)
Woodman's (L,D)
Woody's (L,D)
Ye Olde Union (B,D)
Yerardi's (D)
Yokohama (D)
Zuma Tex-Mex (L,D)

Senior Appeal
Andover Inn
Capital Grille
Captain's Wharf
Cheesecake Factory
Colonial Inn
Copley's
Cranebrook Tea Rm.
Dolphin
Fishery
Grille at Hobbs Brook
Hampshire House
Hartwell House
Henrietta's Table
Jimmy's Steer Hse.
Ken's Steak Hse.
La Famiglia Giorgio
Legal Sea Foods
Ma Glockner's
Maison Robert
Mill Falls
Parker's
Pillar House
Schroeder's
Sherborn Inn
Stockyard
Towne Lyne Hse.
Turner Fisheries
Veronique
Vinny Testa's
Wayside Inn
White Rainbow
Zaftigs Eatery

Singles Scenes
Armani Cafe
Atlas B&G
Bennigan's
Black Rose
Border Cafe
Boston Beer Garden
Boston Beer Works
Botolph's
Brew Moon

Bull & Finch Pub
Cactus Club
Cambridge Brewing Co.
Cambridge Common
Charley's Saloon
Cityside at Circle
Clarke's
Commonwealth Brew.
Fire & Ice
575
Fuddruckers
Good Life
Gyuhama
Hard Rock Cafe
Hill Tavern
Joe's American B&G
John Harvard's
Kokopelli Chili Co.
Maddie's Sail Loft
Michael's Waterfront
New Bridge Cafe
Pete's B&G
Pho Republique
Purple Cactus
Rattlesnake Bar
Savoy
Sunset Grill
T.G.I. Friday's
Watch City
West St. Grille
Wonder Bar
Wrap Culture

Sleepers
(Good to excellent food,
but little known)
Andale!
Angelo's Seafood
Assaggio
Cape Sea Grille/C
Court Hse. Seafood
Dong Khanh
Glenn's Rest./Cool Bar
Hanmiok
Hooch & Holly's/ME
Il Giardino Cafe
Kong Luh
Le Grenier/M
Library Grill
L St. Diner
Main St. Diner/M
O'Fado
Pandorga's
Pit Stop Bar-B-Q
Pizzico/RI
Raphael Bar-Risto/RI
Restaurant Clio
Ristorante Euno
Ristorante Olivio

Sorrela's
Taqueria la Mexicana
Thyme's on Square
Uncle Pete's
Viet Hong
Woo Chun

Teflons
(Get lots of business, despite
so-so food, i.e. they have
other attractions that prevent
criticism from sticking)
Anthony's Pier 4
Atlantic Fish Co.
Barking Crab
Barrett's
Bennigan's
Blue Diner
Bugaboo Creek
Cactus Club
Cambridge Brewing Co.
Charley's Saloon
Cityside at Circle
Colonial Inn
Commonwealth Brew.
Coolidge Corner
Dick's Last Resort
Durgin Park
Fajitas & 'Ritas
Fuddruckers
Grendel's
Hard Rock Cafe
Houlihan's
Jacob Wirth
J.C. Hillary's Ltd.
La Famiglia Giorgio
Pizzeria Uno
Rattlesnake Bar
Road Trip
Sports Depot
T.G.I. Friday's
Vinny Testa's

Smoking Prohibited
(May be permissible
at bar or outdoors)
Abbicci/C
Al Forno/RI
Alloro
Amarin/Thailand
Amarin II
Anna's Taqueria
Baja Betty's
B & D Deli
Bangkok Basil
Bangkok Blue
Bangkok Seafood
Barker Tavern

Barnacle Billy's/ME
Bernard's
Bertucci's
Bini Vini
Bisuteki
Black Crow Caffe
Black Dog Tavern/M
Black Eyed Susan's/N
Black Pearl/RI
Blossoms Cafe
Blue Ribbon BBQ
Blue Room
Boca Grande
Bok Choy
Bombay Bistro
Bombay Club
Buddha's Delight
Cafe Celador
Cafe China
Cafe Edwige/C
Cafe Louis
Cafe St. Petersburg
Cafe 300
Caffe Lampara
Caffe Luna
California Pizza Kit.
Cape Sea Grille/C
Carlo's
Casa Mexico
Casa Romero
Centre St. Café
Changsho
Charlie's Sandwich
Cheesecake Factory
Chef Chow's Hse.
Chillingsworth/C
Claremont Cafe
Coolidge Corner
Country Life
Court Hse. Seafood
Cybersmith
Daddy-O's
Dalya's
Delhi Darbar
Dolphin
Duckworth Lane
Fava
Figs
Five North Sq.
Five Seasons
Flora
Fore Street/ME
Front Street/C
Gardner Museum Cafe
Geoffrey's Cafe
Goemon
Golden Temple
Green Papaya
Grille at Hobbs Brook

Hamersley's Bistro
Harraseeket Inn/ME
Harry's Too
Hartwell House
Helmand
Henrietta's Table
High Brewster/C
Hi-Rise Bread Co.
Hi-Rise Pie Co.
Homeport/M
Il Capriccio
Indian Club
India Pavilion
Jasmine Bistro
Johnny's Luncheonette
Joyce Chen
JP Seafood Cafe
Kareem's
King & I
Kokopelli Chili Co.
Kong Luh
Le Bocage
Le Grenier/M
Lemon Grass
L'Espalier
L'Etoile/M
Lucia's Rist.
Lucky Garden
Main St. Diner/M
Mamma Maria
Marino Rist.
Marrakesh
Mary Chung
Matt Murphy's
Maurizio's
Metropolis Cafe
Milk St. Cafe
Ming Garden
Moon Woman Cafe
Museum of Fine Arts Rest.
Nara
Nauset Beach Club/C
New Asia
New Mother India
Noble House
Noodles
Norumbega Park
O'Fado
Palenque
Pandan Leaf
Pandorga's
Pentimento
Pete's B&G
Pho Republique
Piccola Venezia
Pillar House
Pomodoro
Pranzare
Providence

Purple Cactus
Purple Cactus/C
Rangoli
Red Herring
Regatta of Falmouth/C
Ristorante Euno
Ritz Carlton Din. Rm.
Rod Dee
R Place
Rubin's
R. Wesley's
Sage
Saigon Vietnamese
Sakurabana
Salamander
Sal's Place/C
Sami's
Sandrine's
Santa Barbara Cafe
Savoir Fare/M
Scandia
Shalimar of India
Shalom Hunan
Sichuan Garden
Skewers
Skipjack's
Sol Azteca
Sorrela's
Sound Bites
Spinnaker Italia
Stellina
Street & Company/ME
Sultan's Kitchen
Tables of Content
Takeshima
Tam O'Shanter
Tandoor House
Taqueria la Mexicana
Thai Basil
Thai House
1369 Coffee Hse.
Toppers/N
Tuscan Grill
Upstairs at Pudding
Uva
Veronique
Vidalia's
Village Fish
Village Smokehse.
Vinny Testa's
Walter's Cafe/ME
Warren Tavern
Wayside Inn
Yangtze River
Yokohama
Zaatar's Oven
Zaftigs Eatery

Teenagers & Other Youthful Spirits

Bertucci's
Bishop's
Blue Ribbon BBQ
Bugaboo Creek
California Pizza Kit.
Cheesecake Factory
Figs
Fire & Ice
Galleria Umberto
Hard Rock Cafe
Jimbo's Fish Shanty
Johnny's Luncheonette
Kokopelli Chili Co.
Pizzeria Uno
Purple Cactus
T.G.I. Friday's
Vinny Testa's
Wrap Culture

Visitors on Expense Accounts

Ambrosia
Capital Grille/RI
Chillingsworth/C
Exchange
Grill 23 & Bar
Hamersley's Bistro
Il Capriccio
L'Espalier
Locke-Ober Cafe
Maison Robert
Mistral
Morton's of Chicago
Plaza III
Restaurant Clio
Salamander
Seasons
Tatsukichi
Vault

Wheelchair Access

(Most places now have wheelchair access; call in advance to check)

Wine/Beer Only

Abbondanza
Addis Red Sea
Al Dente
Alloro
Amarin/Thailand
Amarin II
Angelo's
Angelo's Seafood
Antico Forno
Antonio's
Armida's

Artu
Back Bay
Baker's Best
Bangkok Basil
Bangkok Blue
Bangkok House
Bangkok Seafood
Barking Crab
Bini Vini
Bisuteki
Black Crow Caffe
Blossoms Cafe
Bluestone Bistro
Bob the Chef
Bombay Cafe
Boston Beer Works
Botolph's
Brew Moon
Brown Sugar
Buddha's Delight
Buteco
Cafe Barada
Café Brazil
Cafe Celador
Cafe China
Cafe Jaffa
Cafe Louis
Cafe Shiraz
Cafe St. Petersburg
Cafe Sushi
Cafe 300
Cambridge Brewing Co.
Carlo's
Casa Elena
Caserta Pizzeria/RI
Chanterelle
Chau Chow
Chef Chow's Hse.
Circle Pizza
Claremont Cafe
Commonwealth Brew.
Daddy-O's
Daily Catch
Dali
Demo's
Dolphin
Duckworth Lane
Felicia's
Figs
Five North Sq.
Five Seasons
Flora
Florence's
Fuddruckers
Galleria Italiana
Galleria Umberto
Gardner Museum Cafe
Geoffrey's Cafe
Giacomo's

Ginza
Goemon
Grand Chau Chow
Green Papaya
G'Vanni's
Hanmiok
Harry's
Harry's Too
High Brewster/C
House of Siam
Ho Yuen Ting
Hsin-Hsin
Hungry i
Il Giardino Cafe
Il Moro
Imperial Seafood
India Pavilion
India Quality
India Samraat
Iruna
Isabella
Jasmine Bistro
John Harvard's
Johnny's Luncheonette
Jose's
JP Seafood Cafe
Kashmir
Kaya
Kebab-N-Kurry
King & I
Kong Luh
Korea House
La Bettola
La Famiglia Giorgio
Lala Rokh
La Summa
Lemon Grass
L'Osteria
L St. Diner
Magnolias
Main St. Diner/M
Maluken
Marcella's
Marcuccio's
Marino Rist.
Mary Chung
Maurizio's
Mediterraneo
Metropolis Cafe
Midwest Grill
Mike's City Diner
Moon Villa
Mucho Gusto Cafe
Nara
New Asia
New Mother India
Nicole Rist.
North East Brewing
Oasis Cafe

Omonia
On The Park
Pat's Pushcart
Peach Farm
Phoenicia
Pho Pasteur
Pho Republique
Piccola Venezia
Piccolo Nido
Pinardi's
Pomodoro
Ponte Vecchio
Poppa & Goose
Purple Cactus
Rangoli
Rasol
Rebecca's
Red Herring
Regatta of Falmouth/C
Regina Pizzeria
Ristorante Euno
Ristorante Olivio
Roggie's
Roka
Royal East
R Place
Rubin's
R. Wesley's
Sage
Sakurabana
Sal's Place/C
Sami's
Sandrine's
Savoir Fare/M
Sawasdee Thai
Sevens Ale Hse.
Shilla
Siam Cuisine
Sindibad
Sorento's
Street & Company/ME
Sultan's Kitchen
Sunset Grill
Tacos El Charro
Takeshima
Tallulahs
Tandoor House
Tasca
Taste of India
Terramia
Thai Basil
Thai House
Trattoria A Scalinatella
Trattoria Il Panino
Trattoria Pulcinella
Uncle Pete's
Union Sq. Bistro
Uva
Vadopazzo

Vidalia's
Villa Francesca
Watch City
Willow Pond Kit.
Woody's
Yenching Palace
Zaftigs Eatery

Winning Wine Lists

Al Forno/RI
Anthony's Pier 4
Boarding House/N
Cafe Louis
Chillingsworth/C
Galleria Italiana
Grapevine
Hamersley's Bistro
Il Capriccio
Maison Robert
Mamma Maria
New Rivers/RI
Plaza III
Salamander
Silks
Tosca
Uva
Vadopazzo
Veronique
White Barn Inn/ME

Worth a Trip

MAINE
Freeport
   Harraseeket Inn
Kennebunkport
   White Barn Inn
Ogunquit
   Arrows
MASSACHUSETTS
Bedford
   Dalya's
Cape Cod
   Bubala's by Bay
   Cafe Edwige
   Chillingsworth
   Paddock
   Regatta of Falmouth
   Regatta of Cotuit
Concord
   Colonial Inn
Essex
   Woodman's
Hingham
   Tosca
Hull
   Saporito's
Lawrence
   Bishop's

Martha's Vineyard
   L'Etoile
Nantucket
   Boarding House
   Chanticleer
   Summer House
   Toppers
   21 Federal
Newburyport
   Glenn's Rest./Cool Bar
Randolph
   Caffe Bella
Salem
   Grapevine
Scituate
   Barker Tavern
Tyngsboro
   Silks
RHODE ISLAND
Providence
   Agora
   Al Forno
   Capital Grille
   Florentine Grille
   Gatehouse
   New Rivers
   Pot au Feu
   Raphael Bar-Risto

Young Children

(Besides the normal fast-food
places; * indicates children's
menu available)
Aesop's Tables/C*
Amarin/Thailand
Amarin II
Amrheins*
Appetito*
Back Bay*
Baja Betty's*
B & D Deli*
Barking Crab*
Barrett's*
Bertucci's*
Bishop's
Black Dog Tavern/M*
Blue Ribbon BBQ
Blue Wave*
Boodle's*
Border Cafe*
Boston Sail Loft*
Brew Moon*
Bristol*
Bubala's by Bay/C*
Bugaboo Creek*
Bull & Finch Pub*
Cafe de Paris
Cafe Marliave*
Cafe Promenade*

Cafe Shiraz*
Caffe Lampara*
California Pizza Kit.
Cambridge Common*
Carla's*
Charley's Saloon*
Chart House*
Chau Chow
Chau Chow City
Cheesecake Factory
Cityside at Circle*
Clarke Cooke Hse./RI*
Clarke's*
Colonial Inn*
Commonwealth Brew.*
Coolidge Corner*
Copley's*
Daddy-O's*
Davio's*
DiMillo's/ME*
Dockside*
Fajitas & 'Ritas
Finnegans Wake*
Fire & Ice
Fore Street/ME*
Frank's Steak Hse.*
Galleria Umberto
Goemon*
Grand Canal*
Grille at Hobbs Brook*
Halfway Cafe*
Hampshire House*
Hard Rock Cafe
Harry's*
Harry's Too*
Hemenway's/RI*
Henrietta's Table*
Hilltop Steak Hse.*
Iguana Cantina*
Jacob Wirth*
J.C. Hillary's Ltd.*
Jimbo's Fish Shanty*
Jimmy's Harborside*
Joe's American B&G*
John Harvard's*
Johnny's Luncheonette*
Jose's*
Julia's*
Kokopelli Chili Co.*
La Groceria*
La Paloma*
Last Hurrah*

Legal Sea Foods*
Maddie's Sail Loft*
Marino Rist.*
Mass Bay Rest.
Mr. & Mrs. Bartley's*
Museum of Fine Arts Rest.*
New Bridge Cafe*
Norumbega Park*
Paddock/C*
Pat's Pushcart*
Penguins/C*
Pete's B&G*
Pizzeria Uno*
Purple Cactus
Rhythm & Spice*
Ristorante Olivio*
Ritz Cafe*
Road Trip*
Rowes Wharf*
Rubin's*
Rudy's Cafe*
Ruggieri's*
Rustica*
Sal's Place/C*
Scullers Grille*
Sherborn Inn*
Siros*
Skewers*
Skipjack's*
Sol Azteca*
Sound Bites*
Stars
Sunset Grill*
Tallulahs*
Tam O'Shanter*
Tavern on Water*
T.G.I. Friday's*
Tom Shea's*
Towne Lyne Hse.*
Turner Fisheries*
Union Street*
Vidalia's*
Village Smokehse.
Vinny's at Night*
Vinny Testa's
Warren Tavern*
Watch City*
Woodman's*
Wrap Culture
Yerardi's*
Zaftigs Eatery*
Zuma Tex-Mex*

Wine Vintage Chart 1985-1996

This chart is designed to help you select wine to go with your meal. It is based on the same 0 to 30 scale used throughout this *Survey*. The ratings (prepared by our friend Howard Stravitz, a law professor at the University of South Carolina) reflect both the quality of the vintage and the wine's readiness for present consumption. Thus, if a wine is not fully mature or is over the hill, its rating has been reduced. We do not include 1987 because, with the exception of '87 cabernets, those vintages are not recommended.

	'85	'86	'88	'89	'90	'91	'92	'93	'94	'95	'96
WHITES											
French:											
Burgundy	27	28	20	29	24	18	26	19	25	25	26
Loire Valley	–	–	–	25	24	15	19	22	23	24	24
Champagne	28	25	24	26	28	–	–	24	–	25	26
Sauternes	22	28	29	25	26	–	–	–	18	22	24
California:											
Chardonnay	–	–	–	–	23	21	26	25	22	23	22
REDS											
French:											
Bordeaux	27	26	25	28	28	–	19	23	24	25	24
Burgundy	24	–	26	27	29	21	23	25	22	23	24
Rhône	26	20	26	28	27	26*	16	23*	23	24	22
Beaujolais	–	–	–	–	–	22	13	21	22	24	21
California:											
Cab./Merlot	27	26	16	22	28	26	25	24	24	23	22
Zinfandel	–	–	–	–	–	20	20	20	22	20	21
Italian:											
Tuscany	27	16	25	–	26	19	–	20	19	24	19
Piedmont	26	–	24	27	27	–	–	19	–	25	25

*Rating and recommendation is only for Northern Rhône wine in 1991 and Southern Rhône wine in 1993.

Bargain sippers take note: Some wines are reliable year in, year out, and are reasonably priced as well. These wines are best bought in the most recent vintages. They include: Alsatian Pinot Blancs, Côtes du Rhône, Muscadet, Bardolino, Valpolicella and inexpensive Spanish Rioja and California Zinfandel.